KUNSTHISTORISCHES MUSEUM VIENNA

The Secular and Ecclesiastical Treasuries

ILLUSTRATED GUIDE

RESIDENZ VERLAG

Authors:
Rotraud Bauer
Rudolf Distelberger
Stefan Krenn †
Manfred Leithe-Jasper
Karl Schütz
Helmut Trnek

Translators:
Sophie Kidd
Peter Waugh

Guide to the Collections of the Kunsthistorische Museum No. 35

Kunsthistorisches Museum
Treasury
Hofburg, Schweizerhof
1010 Wien
Postal address
Burgring 5, 1010 Wien

Opening hours:
Wed — Mon 10 a.m. — 6 p.m.
Closed Tuesdays

Photographs: Kunsthistorisches Museum

The guide contains 354 illustrations,
207 in colour

Published by the
Kunsthistorisches Museum Vienna
© 1991 Kunsthistorisches Museum Vienna

Production: Residenz Verlag, Salzburg and Vienna
Printed and bound by F. Sochor, Zell am See
ISBN 3-7017-0686-7

CONTENTS

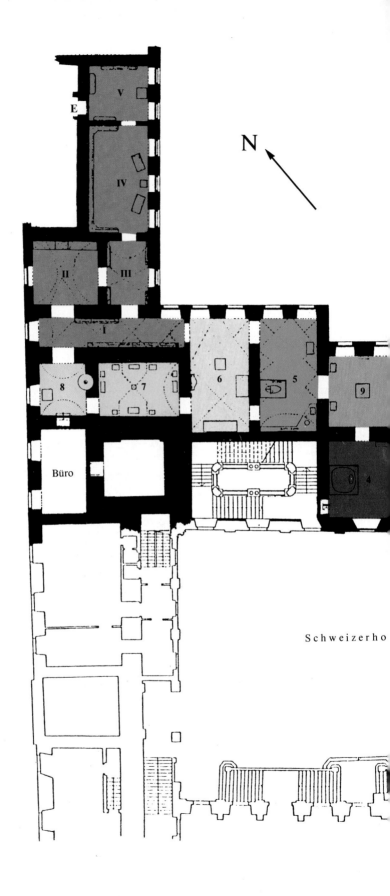

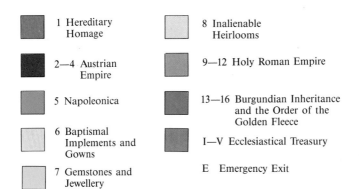

1 Hereditary Homage

2—4 Austrian Empire

5 Napoleonica

6 Baptismal Implements and Gowns

7 Gemstones and Jewellery

8 Inalienable Heirlooms

9—12 Holy Roman Empire

13—16 Burgundian Inheritance and the Order of the Golden Fleece

I—V Ecclesiastical Treasury

E Emergency Exit

Burggraben

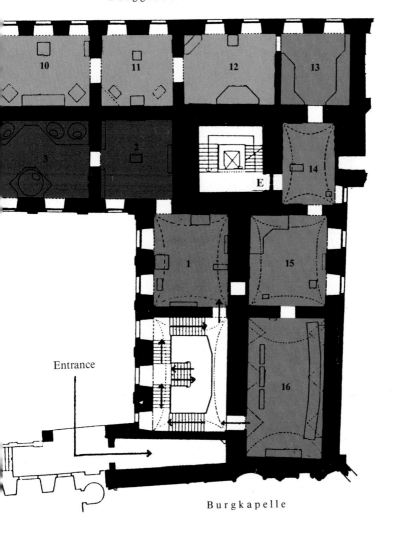

Entrance

Burgkapelle

Translators' Acknowledgements
The translators would like to express their gratitude to the authors of the guide for their unfailing support and assistance during all stages of the translation, which has greatly benefited not only from their helpful criticisms and advice, but above all from the learning they so generously placed at our disposal.

Sophie Kidd and Peter Waugh

FOREWORD

The reorganisation of the Treasury has a long history. In fact, it goes back to the Collection's official opening after the Second World War, on 3rd July 1954. Austria was at that time still occupied by the Allied Powers and nobody had any idea that the State Treaty would bring our country its long hoped-for freedom and independence only one year later. Nor could anybody at that time have even suspected what great interest the newly organised Collection would arouse. However, due to the financial limitations of that difficult time, only slight improvements on the last reorganisation of 1928 could be made, so that the facilities provided in 1954 were soon no longer able to meet the public's needs. It was for this reason that I began negotiations, in my capacity as Director of the Collection, to obtain additional space for us, in order to improve the entrance area. In 1962 an agreement was concluded with the Direction of the Vienna Hofburg and the Federal Office for the Preservation of Historical Monuments which made it possible to undertake the planning of the appropriate reorganisation. My thanks go to Hofrat Dipl.-Ing. Paul Neumann, at that time Director of the Hofburg, and Univ.-Prof. Dr. Walter Frodl, President of the Federal Office for the Preservation of Historical Monuments, for all their sympathetic help. I never once thought, when I left my job at the Kunsthistorische Museum for offices abroad, that I would find the reorganisation of the Treasury still unfinished upon my return to the Museum twenty years later. In the meantime, more rooms had been acquired for the Treasury, affording more space for the exhibition, making it not only more suitable for large numbers of visitors, but also better adapted to present-day knowledge of the conservation of textiles, especially with regard to appropriate light conditions for the various objects. Thanks for this are due to Dipl.-Ing. Karl Bayer, the Director of the Vienna Hofburg. I would like to add my own special thanks to him for having spontaneously approved the lowering of the corridor from the Swiss Court to the Chapel Court, something which had not been possible in 1954. This facilitated access to the Treasury for handicapped people, something which will hopefully soon be possible in all the other collections of the Kunsthistorische Museum as well. The Federal Office for the Preservation of Historical Monuments gave us their consent immediately. For this, as for their help in many other ways, sincere thanks are due to its President, Dr. Gerhard Sailer, its Curator-General, Univ.-Doz. Dr. Ernst Bacher, and its Regional Curator, Hofrat Dr. Peter Pötschner.

When I took office as First Director of the Kunsthistorische Museum, the architects had already been nominated: Prof. Dipl.-Ing. Rudolf Pamlitschka of the Federal Ministry for Building and Construction for all civil engineering matters, and Prof. Dipl.-Ing. Karl Mang and Dipl.-Ing. Eva Mang-Frimmel for the interior decoration. Building supervision was undertaken by Arch. Dipl.-Ing. Engelbert Eder and his colleagues. Thus the basic outlines of the design of the Collection began to take shape.

The Museum owes a debt of gratitude to many: to the Federal Ministries of Building and Technology, and of Science and Research, who were extremely sympathetic towards our wishes and demands, although there were many problems of a technical and financial nature which were not easy to solve; to Min.-Rat. Dipl.-Ing. Karl Jaschke and his colleague Dipl.-Ing. Karl Fritsch from the Ministry of

Building and Construction, who deserve especial mention, as do Dipl.-Ing. Herbert Schiff from the Management of Federal Buildings; and, on the other hand, to the Section Heads Dr. Wilhelm Schlag and Dr. Johann Marte, Min.-Rat. Dr. Carl Blaha, Min.-Rat. Dipl.-Ing. Georg Hanreich and Section Councillor Dr. Georg Freund. Dipl.-Ing. Wolfgang Beer from the Direction of the Vienna Hofburg has taken care of the construction and the many questions relating to it for many years. Heartfelt thanks are due to him, as also to the Director of the Vienna Hofburg Oberrat Dipl.-Ing. Dr. techn. Richard Kastner. The many firms involved have contributed outstanding work.

Many people at the Kunsthistorische Museum also participated in the design of the Treasury, first and foremost the members of the Kunstkammer: its Director, Dr. Manfred Leithe-Jasper, Dr. Rudolf Distelberger, Dr. Rotraud Bauer and Dr. Helmut Trnek. The late Dr. Stefan Krenn worked on the catalogue and on scientific research into the objects belonging Ecclesiastical Treasury. The financial basis for this last task was provided by the Getty Foundation in Los Angeles, for which I express my sincere thanks, above all to Harold Williams, the President and Chief Executive Officer of the Foundation.

In particular, I wish to thank Dr. Rudolf Distelberger, who judiciously supervised the construction work on behalf of the Museum and greatly contributed to the detailed planning. In accordance with the Museum's official regulations, its First Director certainly participated in the design as a whole, although the exhibition itself, as well as the choice of objects, was wholly the work of the Kunstkammer. The same applies in the case of the present guide. Residenz Verlag has accepted the challenge of designing a guide for the general public with typical circumspection and good taste, and my heartfelt thanks are also due to all who work there.

Univ. Prof. Dr. Hermann Fillitz
First Director of the
Kunsthistorische Museum

PREFACE

This guide to the Secular and Ecclesiastical Treasuries is based on an entirely new approach. It includes all the objects which have been displayed in the Treasury since its reorganisation; nearly all of the items are illustrated, most of them in colour. Emphasis has been laid on the description and explanation of the objects, in view of the fact that it is sometimes difficult to understand the significance of many of them today. The aim was to serve the needs both of visitors with little time to spare and of those who seek more profound knowledge and understanding. Each item in the catalogue thus has a short description in key words followed, if necessary, by a more detailed commentary which attempts to guide the visitor's eye over the object, on the principle that one only perceives what one is already aware of.

The guide is thus intended for use while visiting the Treasury, for further study, and also for repeated, more intensive visits. The individual introductory chapters on the history of the Treasury, frequently recurring historical titles and on the various groups of objects themselves are intended as supplementary information to elucidate the respective context. To this end, we have included genealogies of the House of Habsburg together with lists of the kings and emperors of the Holy Roman Empire, the dates of their reigns and their places of coronation. References to specialist literature on individual objects or groups of objects are only given if they are of fundamental importance. They are supplemented by a compilation in chronological order of the most important general literature on the Viennese Treasury. The existence of the guide in its present form is primarily due to the efforts of the First Director of the Kunsthistorische Museum, Hermann Fillitz, who expressed an unfailing interest in its publication. He allowed the authors complete freedom in all respects, for which they would like to express their sincere gratitude.

The authors received valuable support from many sources. Thanks are owed to Ferdinand Anders, Dorothea Duda, Matthias Eichinger, Harold W. Glidden, Susanne Gneisz, Eva Irblich, Otto Pächt, Gerhard Schmidt and Christiane Thomas for ideas and clarification. Thanks are also due to the Verein der Museumsfreunde in Wien, in particular to Rudolf Bazil. Our colleagues at the Kunsthistorische Museum, Christian Beaufort-Spontin, Alfred Bernhard-Walcher, Herbert Haupt, Georg J. Kugler, Wolfgang Prohaska, Gudrun Rotter and Helmut Satzinger, made valuable contributions within their various disciplines. Daniel De Jonghe, Manfred Grasserbauer, Gero Kurat, Liliane Masschelein, Gerhard Niedermayr, Annemarie Nikiforov, Erich Pucher, Manfred Schreiner and Helmut Schweppe provided support in technical matters and in the identification of materials. Grateful thanks to Saskia Durian-Ress, Dora Heinz, Ingeborg Petraschek, Anne Wardwell and Leonie von Wilckens for their helpful advice on matters relating to textiles, and to Father Gottfried Undesser for his assistance at the Provincial Archives in the Capuchin Monastery in Vienna. Collaboration with the metal restorers Christa Angermann, Elisabeth Krebs and Verena Krehon led to many new insights. The textile restorers Gabriele Bachl, Susanne Biedermann, Gisela Illek, Ulrike Messner, Brigitta Pfeifer and Hertha Zajic contributed to the solving of hitherto unanswered questions with their identification of textile techniques and fabric analyses. The visual opulence of the guide is primarily due to the photographs of Marianne Haller, who was ably supported by Michaela Gregor as coordinator. Especial thanks are due to Sieglinde Ochnitzberger: her critical attention to detail and untiring commitment during the typing of the extensive manuscript set a shining example for us all.

Thanks are also due to the Residenz Verlag for their interest and support in the publication of the guide.

The Authors

Authors

Rotraud Bauer	**R. B.**
Rudolf Distelberger	**R. D.**
Stefan Krenn	**S. K.**
Manfred Leithe-Jasper	**M. L.-J.**
Karl Schütz	**K. S.**
Helmut Trnek	**H. T.**

INTRODUCTION

LOCATION AND DEVELOPMENT OF THE TREASURY IN THE HOFBURG.

The Vienna Hofburg has housed at least part of the Habsburg treasures ever since the early 14th century. It is first mentioned in 1337, by Johannes von Viktring. He records that the treasure was kept in the precincts of the Chapel in the Hofburg; to be more precise, in the Sacristy, known as the *Sagrer.* In the treaty of partition concluded on 29. 5. 1458 between Emperor Friedrich III, his brother, Archduke Albrecht VI, and his cousin Duke Siegmund of Tyrol, establishing the possessory rights to the Vienna Burg, the individual rooms and their function and location in the Burg are described in detail. Among those rooms which were supposed to belong to all three of the Habsburgs jointly were the Chapel and: *"the two sagrers next to the chapel, in the lower of which are the jewels,"* (treasures) *"in the other sagrer, above, the letters"* (documents). The two rooms can be located on the southern side of the Chapel, either in or near the Burg's south-east tower. The significance of this treasury must have diminished somewhat under Friedrich III, who preferred Wiener Neustadt and Graz as his places of residence, and even more so under Maximilian I, who was seldom in Vienna at all. It was only when Ferdinand I, the grandson of Maximilian, chose Vienna as his place of residence, and deposited there that part of the inheritance which his grandfather had left to him in Innsbruck, Graz and Wiener Neustadt, that the Viennese Treasury began to regain its importance. It was Ferdinand who had it transferred from the area of the Burg Chapel to that of the west wing, inside the Schweizer Tor, which was restored between 1551 and 1554. As early as 1555 there is mention of a treasure vault under the supervision of a treasurer, Leopold Heyperger. In 1558 it was decided to construct a new *Kunstkammer* in the area of the north-west tower. This seems to have consisted of two rooms, one above the other, on the upper floors, directly above the chambers of Archduke Ernst. By 1578 they were already in need of restoration. There is evidence that between 1566 and 1587 there was also another *Kunstkammer* — perhaps an auxiliary depot — in the rear tract of the Mint in the Wollzeile.

Of particular significance in the history of the Vienna Treasury is the report that between 1583 and 1585, under the governorship of Archduke Ernst — apparently as a commission of Emperor Rudolf II — a new tract was built, at first known as the *Kunsthaus,* later as the *Treasury,* the north side of which was connected to the north-west tower. This was a 12-windowed, three-storied gallery, whose windows looked out on to the old Burggarten (today the Summer Riding School). Its rear wall backed onto the *Spanish Kitchen* and the old *Tennis Courts (Ballhaus),* which had been erected in 1540. Both buildings were situated in the Kohlmarkt, which once extended over the Michaelerplatz as far as the inner square of the Hofburg. This gallery tract could be reached from the Burg itself, which had retained an annex built over the Burggraben, as well as from the Burggarten and the street, through an entrance situated between the Kitchen and the Tennis Courts. On the uppermost floor of the gallery tract was the Treasury. It is first mentioned in 1608, as the treasury of King Matthias, and then in 1637 as that of Emperor Ferdinand II. In the middle of the lower floor, open towards the garden, there was a grotto. The actual use of the ground floor and the second upper floor has still to be clarified. By 1640 the whole building complex was already so desperately in need of restoration, that the Treasury had to be partly moved elsewhere in order to implement the necessary safety measures. Plans and sketches from this time have survived, and contain exact information as to the location of the individual rooms and their uses. The *Treasury* of Emperor Ferdinand III, for example, was on the first floor of the gallery tract facing the Burggarten, while the *Ecclesiastical Treasury* was installed above the *Spanish Kitchen.* Above the *Ecclesiastical Treasury,* in a room accessible from the gallery on the second floor, was the famous silver fountain of Wenzel Jamnitzer, which had been commissioned by Emperor Maximilian II around 1570, probably for display in the Fasangarten (Neugebäude Palace), and delivered to Rudolf II in 1578. Next to it was another room, intended for an enlargement of the Treasury, should it become necessary. The proposal to renovate the *Tennis Courts,* which were also badly in need of restoration, by installing columns and fitting false ceilings, and to use them as a new Treasury, was rejected by Ferdinand III. This part of the buildings continued to be used as the *Tennis Courts* until rebuilt as the *Hofburgtheater* between 1743 and 1760. The Treasury gallery, which runs from south to north, began in the whereabouts of what is today Room IV of the Ecclesiastical Treasury, although it was probably only as wide as the present-day Room III, situated above the Burggraben. The increased width of the present-day Rooms IV and V almost certainly derives from the fact that the staircase once situated behind the gallery was demolished during construction of the tract for the Imperial Chancellery, built between 1720—1730, under Emperor Karl VI. The alterations undertaken at this time also seem to have signified the end of at least part of the gallery tract. This was perhaps connected with the installation of a new picture gallery in the Stallburg. The Treasury was temporarily accomodated in the old Burg tract, which was connected to the old gallery rooms, and received a new, additional entrance which opened on to the newly-constructed *Säulenstiege,* although this does not seem to have been intended for the general public. Its beautiful iron door displaying the monogramme of Karl VI — two interlocking C's — can today be seen in Room 1 of the Secular Treasury.

It was in these rooms that between 1747 and 1750 Karl's daughter, the Empress Maria Theresia, ordered her Treasurer, Joseph Angelo de France, to rehouse the objects of the Secular Treasury in the magnificent glass cases which have been preserved to the present day. In order to cover, at least in part, the resulting high costs of this reorganisation, Joseph Angelo de France had the above mentioned silver fountain of Wenzel Jamnitzer melted down. Of this once much-admired work of art, which nevertheless no longer appealed to the taste of the 18th century, only the figures of the four seasons in gilded bronze still survive; they can today be seen in the Kunsthistorische Museum.

It must also have been during this period — if not already under Emperor Karl VI — that the *Secular Treasury* was installed. According to a description by Christoph Gottlieb Murr, dating from 1771, it was at that time situated in a room of the old Burg, with a view of the Summer Riding School. Its *"nine cabinets, exquisitely fashioned from oak and with glass doors",* still exist today and can be identified as the cabinets of the so-called *Old Ecclesiastical Treasury,* a room near the Burg Chapel. They were probably placed there when Emperor Joseph II transferred the custody of the Ecclesiastical Treasury to the court priest at the Hofburg. During the reign of Emperor Franz Joseph, the interior decoration of the Secular Treasury, dating from the time of Maria Theresia, was renovated. Its entrance was at that time situated in Room V of the present-day Secular Treasury. No further large-scale alterations to the Treasury were then carried out until after the Second World War, with the reunification of the *Ecclesiastical* with the *Secular Treasury.* From 1952 onwards, the objects of the *Ecclesiastical Treasury* were exhibited in the rooms and cases dating from the time of Maria Theresia, which had previously been reserved for the *Secular Treasury.* The *Secular Treasury* itself was then extended as far as the north wall of the Burg Chapel and refurnished. Yet even this enlarged Treasury, which was reopened in 1954, was soon unable to cope with the constantly increasing stream of visitors. Above all it lacked a spacious entrance hall and the requisite facilities. The recent alterations, which were carried out between 1983 and 1987, brought some very necessary improvements in this respect, quite apart from additional exhibition rooms. The installation of a lift and the levelling out of differences in floor levels then made it accessible for people in wheelchairs as well. Furthermore, everything was done to improve the presentation of the exhibits for the public and in particular to create the best possible conservation conditions for the fragile, extremely precious textiles (such as air conditioning or protection from the light) and to preserve them for future generations.

HISTORY OF THE COLLECTION

The Vienna Treasury has, with justification, been described as the cradle of the Imperial Collections. As we shall subsequently see in more detail, its roots go back to the medieval family treasures of the House of Habsburg. Time and again, however, important pieces belonging to the Treasury have been removed and placed in the special collections which began to develop in the 18th century. During the great reform of the Imperial Collections around 1870, exhibits from the Treasury found their way primarily into the Kunsthistorische Museum, but also into the Natural History Museum. Although we have only scant knowledge of the *Family or House Treasure* of the individual branches of the House of Habsburg in the Middle Ages, some sources do nevertheless inform us about what once existed; however, the history of some of the individual objects still preserved today in the Kunsthistorische Museum can be traced back at least as far as the early 15th century. Although recognisable efforts were made from quite early on to keep the whole treasure of the House together in one place throughout the generations, it was in fact subject to far more frequent changes during the Middle Ages than in later times. The store of ecclesiastical relics must have been considerable from the very beginning and the treasure vault must have contained not only insignia, a wealth of profane jewels and valuable tableware made of precious metals, but also minted and unminted silver, gold and also documents. These documents primarily concerned rights of possession and thus legal justification of earthly power, since the possession of the greatest possible number of holy relics was regarded as a spiritual pledge of the same. Basically, princely treasure at that time constituted a moveable private fortune which could either be used to publicly display princely power, or, in the case of gifts, princely largesse; it was also, however, a fortune which could be quickly lucred in times of necessity.

In Vienna the *treasure* and the *archive* seem to have been separated relatively early on. As already mentioned, we learn from the partition treaty of 1458 that, in the Vienna Burg, the jewels were kept in the *lower sagrer,* beside the Burg Chapel, while the documents were kept in the *upper sagrer* above it. On the other hand, it is only in post-medieval times that one can speak of a systematic classification of the treasure in Vienna, such as occurred in France from the late 14th century onwards for the collections of King Charles V or his younger brother Jean, Duke of Berry, or later still for the collection of the Dukes of Burgundy. Nevertheless, even here some documents survive which indicate the existence of a different attitude in earlier times.

On 18. 11. 1364 the brothers Rudolf IV, Albrecht III and Leopold III, acting in compliance with the will of their deceased father, Duke Albrecht II of Austria, drew up in Vienna a set of 'House Ordinances' in which, among other things, it was stated that the treasure of jewels, minted and unminted silver and gold, stones and pearls, as well as the documents of the archive, should belong to the three brothers jointly, although they should be kept and preserved by the eldest. Here, for the first time, there is talk of a communal *House treasure;* moreover, it was to be administered in accordance with the *principle of seniority.* This is a concept which Emperor Rudolf II and Emperor Matthew also later attempted to put into practice. No less interesting are two passages in the will of Duke Albrecht III dated 27. 8. 1395, which ordained that all the monstrances and *Hailtum* (relics) preserved in the Vienna Burg should be taken to Laxenburg and kept there for all time; on the other hand, three especially valuable gemstones which had been in his Duchy of Austria since ancient times, as well as two golden vessels, were not to be removed from the land. These objects did in fact continue to be kept in the *Sagrer* of the Vienna Burg. After the death of King Albrecht II and the extinction, with Ladislaus Postumus, in 1457, of the Albertinian line of the House of Habsburg, acts of pawning the treasure become more frequent. As early as 1440, the widow of Albrecht II, Elisabeth of Luxemburg, pawned the royal crown to Friedrich III. As the guardian of Ladislaus Postumus, Friedrich III was still in possession of the *Holy Hungarian Crown,* the Crown of St. Stephen, in 1463, well after his former ward's early death. In 1467, Friedrich III also redeemed the jewels which had been pawned by Ladislaus Postumus to Duke Ludwig of Bavaria for 40,000 gulden, among them a cross set with several large diamonds, 45 balases, a large ruby, 33 sapphires, 2 emeralds and 307 pearls, for which he pledged the Duke the duty from the wine and merchandise toll at Spitz an der Donau until he could repay his debt.

Some idea of the considerable amount of jewellery owned by this ruler can be gained from the report that in 1445 he transferred precious stones, as well as some silver and gold tableware which had probably become unfashionable, to Lucas Kemnater in Nuremberg, out of which several crosses and pieces of jewellery were to be made. Time and again, report is also made of ducal and royal crowns. According to all accounts, Archduke Albrecht VI was the first to make an appearance in the archducal vestments: in Rome in 1452, at the marriage of his brother Friedrich III to Eleonora of Portugal. He wore a scarlet robe and mantle, both lined with ermine, and a many-pointed coronet, braced with a golden arch and set with a cross at the front. Friedrich's private Imperial crown, which he took with him to Rome at that time, must also have been particularly splendid. However, for his actual coronation as Emperor the *Reichskrone* (Imperial Crown) was used, having been brought for him from Nuremberg. On the head of the Empress, the Pope placed a crown which derived from the estate of the widow of Emperor Sigismund. These late-Gothic Imperial crowns can be seen in two pictures of Friedrich III and Eleonora in the Kunsthistorische Museum. If Friedrich III was responsible for redeeming jewels that had been pawned, his son Maximilian I, who had to fight for his Burgundian inheritance and was thus constantly in need of money, was frequently forced to pawn parts of the once immeasurable Burgundian treasure which had passed to his House after the death of Charles the Bold. In 1488 alone, jewels and fine tableware to the value of 801,000 gulden were pawned to a consortium of creditors in the Netherlands, which was chiefly composed of Italian bankers. One or other of the pieces did later return to the Habsburg treasure, such as the *Court Goblet of Philip the Good* (Cat. No. 206), the *Ainkhürn Sword* (Cat. No. 204) and other precious objects, among them a set of imperial and several sets of archducal vestments, were placed by Emperor Maximilian I — who had no fixed residence himself — in his father's castles at Wiener Neustadt, Graz or Innsbruck for safe-keeping. His grandsons Karl V and Ferdinand I divided this property between them. Karl took his portion to Spain, while Ferdinand placed his in the Vienna Burg.

We have hardly any detailed knowledge of the contents of the treasure of Ferdinand I. Nevertheless, it seems feasible to suggest that this ruler put into practice in Vienna those principles which had been cultivated in Italy ever since the Renaissance: namely, that collecting should be determined by artistic and aesthetic as well as dynastic considerations. This finds its expression in the frequently alternating adoption of the names *Schatzkammer* and *Kunstkammer* ('Treasury' and 'Art Cabinet') for one and the same collection.

From the estate of Emperor Ferdinand I derive two objects which, have maintained their places of honour in the Imperial Treasury right up to the present day: the large *Agate Bowl* (Cat. No. 137) and the *Ainkhürn* (Cat. No. 138). Their ideal value was regarded as being so great that, after the death of Ferdinand I in 1564, his sons agreed to declare them *inalienable heirlooms of the House of Austria,* to be entrusted to the safe-keeping of the eldest member of the family, that is, according to the seniority principle once more. In his testament, Ferdinand I left the royal insignia and his important collection of coins and antiques to his eldest son, Maximilian II. The jewels and treasures, on the other hand, were divided up between his younger sons, the Archdukes Ferdinand II of Tyrol and Karl of Inner Austria, and this laid the foundations of the Habsburg *Kunstkammer* in Innsbruck, at Castle Ambras and in Graz. The inventories for the collections of Maximilian II are missing today, but one may assume with some certainty that the most important part of their contents passed to his eldest son, Rudolf II, and that he took it with him to Prague, when he chose that city as his place of residence. Nonetheless, considerable parts of the collections also passed to his brothers Ernst, Matthias, Maximilian, Albrecht and Wenzel.

Although, due to the still-extant inventory, we are extremely well informed about this Emperor's *Kunstkammer,* information with regard to his *Schatzkammer* is nevertheless meagre. The showpiece of this was certainly the *Imperial Crown of the House of Habsburg* (Cat. No. 56), which was made for him in 1602. Emperor Rudolf, whose collections were based on a certain systemisation of their internal organisation, pursued with characteristic tenacity the ideal of a combined *Kunst* and *Schatzkammer* of the House of Austria, an ideal which had already been realised once in 1364, although it had later been abandoned. Indicative of this are Rudolf's constant efforts to concentrate in his own hands the treasure which had belonged to his father, which had been dispersed as far afield as Spain, or his purchase of the *Ambras Collection* from the inheritance of Ferdinand II in Tyrol. His brother and successor, Emperor Matthias, pursued the same goal. The decisive step, however, was then taken by Emperor Ferdinand II, with the so-called *Majorat Dedication* of 1621 and 1635, which decreed that all the House relics and art treasures — both existent ones and those to be acquired — should belong by right of primogenitor *"to the House as its inalienable property"* and should no longer be bound to the "land and its people".

Emperor Matthias not only had the *Rudolphine House Crown* complemented by an *Orb* (Cat. No. 57) and a *Sceptre* (Cat. No. 58) but also began, soon after the death of Rudolf II in 1612, to bring the most precious pieces of the Prague Treasury and *Kunstkammer* to Vienna, which preserved them from falling into the hands of the invading Swedish army in 1648. Matthias reactivated the above-mentioned *Treasury Gallery* and in doing so seems — like Rudolf II before him — to have organised his collections into a separate *Treasury* and *Kunstkammer,* although the exact location of the latter is purely a matter of speculation. It may have been housed on the uppermost floor of the *Gallery Tract,* although after Archduke Leopold Willhelm returned to Vienna in 1657, his collections were installed in the *Stallburg.*

The first detailed descriptions of the Imperial Treasury that have survived were made during the reign of Emperor Leopold I. From them we can also draw some conclusions about the Treasury of Ferdinand III. This was always housed in the *Treasury Gallery;* or, to be more precise, in 13 black cabinets standing opposite the windows and crowned with gilded eagles bearing the monogramme of Ferdinand III, the doors decorated with costly paintings — presumably pictures set into frames. The pieces were arranged according to the principle of the unity of the material. In the first two cabinets were works of ivory, among which were pieces turned by some of the Habsburg princes themselves. The next two cases contained watches and automatons, some of which derived from the Rudolphine collection. The fifth case contained silver work, the sixth cameos, among them such famous pieces as the *Gemma Augustea* and the *Ptolemy Cameo.* In the seventh case were further silver objects, while the eighth contained objects made of gold, among which were also Turkish weapons decorated with precious stones. In the ninth and tenth cases were vessels made of precious stones, while in the eleventh and twelfth was housed the large collection of vessels made of rock crystal, among which was also to be found the famous five-tier *Pyramid* by Dionysio

Miseroni, today preserved in the Kunsthistorische Museum, a piece which was valued at 20,000 Imperial talers alone. Finally, the thirteenth case held the most precious objects of this Treasury: the *Rudolphine Imperial House Crown;* the *Imperial Orb* and *Sceptre* (Cat. No. 57, 58) made under Matthias; a copy of the Imperial Crown richly set with diamonds, which had first been worn by Ferdinand III; and the Bohemian insignia and the *Crown of Stephan Bocskay* (Cat. No. 105). Beside these were still other treasures, prominent among them the 2,680 carat Columbian *Emerald* which Dionysio Miseroni had carved into a vessel (Cat. No. 104).

Opposite the cases, placed against the pilasters along the row of windows, were tables inlaid with costly intarsia plates. Upon these usually stood cabinets with drawers which contained those precious stones which were of smaller dimensions. The board game made for Ferdinand I by Hans Kels in 1537, today in the Kunsthistorische Museum, was also kept here. On the last table lay a very special treasure: the large *Agate Bowl* (Cat. No. 137), dating from late antiquity, one of the *Inalienable Heirlooms of the House of Austria.* Even at that time the *Keys to the Coffins of the Members of the House of Habsburg* were also preserved in the Treasury (Cat. No. 103). According to descriptions from the 17th century, the inventory of the Treasury, bound in red velvet, also lay on one of these tables; it has since disappeared. Its loss is particularly regrettable, for the next complete inventory only goes back to 1750.

The Treasury also housed the bronze portrait bust of Ferdinand II by Georg Schweigger; beside it were bronze monuments of other members of the Habsburg family, and presumably the equestrian statuettes by Caspar Gras. To these were later added the ivory statuettes of the Emperors Leopold I, Joseph I and Karl VI, made by Matthias Steinl. In this way, the Treasury came to acquire an accentuated dynastic and stately character during the Baroque period, designed to impress upon the spectator the greatness and import of the House of Habsburg. The concept of the Treasury as *Kunstkammer,* which had determined its character during the Renaissance, now began to take second place to this new aspect.

At the time of the Counter-Reformation, after the reign of Emperor Matthias and under the influence of his wife, Empress Anna, the Treasury's collection of relics were accorded increased significance. In all probability it was at this time that the *Ecclesiastical Treasury* was newly installed, next to the Treasury Gallery and above the *Spanish Kitchen.* Apart from the *Reliquary of the Nail from the Cross of Christ* (Cat. No. 155), the records also mention reliquaries with a thorn from Christ's crown, or with a piece of wood from the cross, as well as numerous costly reliquaries adorned with precious stones, valuable altar implements, pearl-covered vestments for mass and sundry curiosities.

Little is known about the Treasury at the time of Emperor Karl VI, for whose large-scale renovation of the Hofburg the Treasury Gallery was, at least in part, sacrificed. During his reign, in addition to the *Secular Treasury,* there was also a second Treasury, the so-called *Privy Treasury,* of which an inventory dating from 1731 has survived. Some of the objects in this *Privy Treasury* were transferred to the Maria-Theresian Treasury and the Ecclesiastical Treasury. Many of these were expensive pieces of jewellery, perhaps belonging to the jewels sold by Maria-Theresia in order to be able to finance the Austrian War of Succession. There is, namely, a conspicuous lack of jewellery in the inventory compiled by her Treasurer, Joseph Angelo de France, in 1750. However, this Treasury, which had been newly set up under Maria Theresia, obviously included numerous objects from the *Kunstkammer* which had not been mentioned as being in the *Treasury Gallery* of Ferdinand III and Leopold I. For the first time we find here numerous bronze statuettes, arranged purely as decoration on the 13 cases and on the wall-shelving, some of which are already familiar from the *Kunstkammer* inventories of Emperor Rudolf II and Emperor Matthias. It also seems that, with the exception of the Insignia of the Imperial House, the insignia were accorded less significance in the age of Maria Theresia than had formerly been the case. Under the directorship of Joseph Angelo de France, the Treasury had once again assumed the character of a *Kunstkammer.* The first change came with the creation of a separate jewellery room; after the death of her husband Franz Stephan of Lorraine in 1765, the Empress deposited the crown of Lorraine there, together with her late spouse's valuable collection of diamonds and other precious stones (including the famous Florence Diamond, of which, curiously enough, a copy — albeit made of quartz — had been in the possession of the Treasury ever since the Baroque age). The golden toilet and breakfast service were added to the collection after the Empress' death.

The administrative separation of the Ecclesiastical from the Secular Treasury occurred during the reign of Emperor Joseph II. The former was placed in the care of the clergy at the Hofburg and combined with the reliquaries and paraments of the individual court chapels. The crown insignia of Bohemia, and for a short while that of Hungary, were also kept in Vienna at this time. Leopold II had them sent back to Prague and Budapest respectively. Otherwise, little changed as far as the character of the Treasury was concerned, except that a considerable number of paintings which, until then, had formed part of its collection, were gradually incorporated into the Imperial paintings gallery.

The upheavals of the era of Napoleon subsequently brought significant changes for the Treasury. As early as 1794, the treasure of the Order of the Golden Fleece was transferred from Brussels to Vienna, where it was provisionally deposited in the Treasury. In 1796, the Imperial treasures in Aix-la-Chapelle and Nuremberg were rescued from the encroaching French troops under General Jourdan and entrusted to the Imperial Commissary, Baron von Hügel, in Regensburg. They were finally deposited in the Vienna Treasury on the instructions of Emperor Franz II. When, in 1804, he then elevated the Austrian Hereditary Lands into a new hereditary Empire of Austria and made the private Imperial insignia the official insignia of this new Empire, the Treasury possessed a wealth of emblems of sovereignty unequalled anywhere in Europe. Although the insignia of the Holy Roman Empire did indeed lose their official character with the dissolution of the Empire in 1806, only then — having become, as it were, historical monuments — was their true value appreciated. These official and historic insignia finally became the centrepiece of the Treasury, overshadowing its traditional role as *Kunstkammer,* which it had enjoyed ever since the time of Maria Theresia, to such an extent that internal reoganisation appeared to be necessary. Ever since the late 18th century, works of antiquity or with classical subjects had begun to be transferred to the Imperial Cabinet of Coins and Antiques; now, when the most important elements of the *Ambras Collection* had been brought from Tyrol to safety in Vienna during the Napoleonic age, nearly all the objects in the Treasury which were of a 'merely' *Kunstkammer* nature were incorporated into this collection, although the most valuable objects, those made of precious stones or metals, at first remained in the Treasury and were even complemented by similar pieces from the Ambras Collection. Once begun, the process of the deconcentration of the Imperial collections then continued. On the occasion of the reorganisation of the collections in 1871, which resulted in the construction of the Kunsthistorische Museum, all the art objects which still remained in the Treasury were finally removed, and in 1891 put on display in this new Museum. Since that time, the only objects preserved in the Treasury are those which, on account of their historical and symbolic nature or their great material value, serve as an expression of the power and historical status of the Imperial House, or as a reminder of its individual members. In 1898 the *Order of the Golden Fleece* placed the *Cross of Allegiance* (Cat. No. 215) and the *Potence* (Cat. No. 213) in the Treasury for safekeeping; otherwise, only the private collection of precious jewellery has been extended in any considerable way — primarily in the form of the parures which were newly-made or reworked for the Empress Elisabeth. However, only twenty years later, the Treasury suffered its worst loss, through the outcome — so disastrous for Austria — of the First World War. Emperor Karl and his family were forced to leave Austria in 1918 and took their private jewellery with them into exile. The peace treaty of St. Germain awarded the states of succession the right to demand various cultural objects as their patrimony. Thus the vestments and insignia of Napoleon as King of Italy had to be surrendered to Italy, and the vestments and gem-studded Cross of the Order of St. Stephen, which had been worn by Empress Maria Theresia, to Hungary.

The administration of the Treasury, which had formerly been under the jurisdiction of the Grand Chamberlain, was transferred to the Kunsthistorische Museum. Since then it has been administered by the directors of the Kunstkammer (formerly the Collection of Sculpture and the Decorative Arts). In 1921, the so-called *Capuchin Treasure* was incorporated into the *Ecclesiastical Treasury*. This can be traced back to an endowment of the Empress Anna (wife of Emperor Matthias and foundress of the Imperial tomb at the Capuchin Monastery) who died in 1618, although it always remained Imperial property. When, on Hitler's orders, the insignia and treasures of the Holy Roman Empire were taken to Nuremberg, the Treasury was closed. In 1946 the insignia returned to Vienna, having survived, like the other treasures, the Second World War intact. In 1954 the Treasury was reopened, and for the first time since Emperor Joseph II, the *Secular* and the *Ecclesiastical Treasuries* were united in the same building once again. This reunification of the Secular and Ecclesiastical Treasuries *"reflects the polarity of the secular and spiritual status of the Christian European sovereign, as it had continued up until the time of Karl VI."*

Today there is hardly any other place in Europe where a thousand years of western history can be so immediately and intensively experienced as in the Vienna Treasury.

M. L.-J.

Ref.: Schlager 1850, pp. 675—679; von Karajan 1863, pp. 139—141; Zimmermann 1883, pp. I-LXXVIII; Zimmermann 1889, Regesten 6241 and 6253; Luschin von Ebengreuth 1899, pp. CXC-CXCVI; Sitte 1901, pp. 14—17; Sitte 1909, pp. 100—108; Dreger 1914, pp. 34—50, 106, 171—174, 289; Lhotsky 1939, pp. 17—20, 35; Lhotsky 1941—1945; Kühnel 1956, pp. 258, 265—267; Kühnel 1964, pp. 11, 17, 19, 24, 31—37, 50—52; Bauer und Haupt 1976; Distelberger 1985, pp. 39—46.

HISTORICAL TITLES

With the election of Rudolf of Habsburg as Roman King in 1273, the House of Habsburg gained admission to the Collegium of the Imperial Princes. In the following centuries the numerous honours and titles which are so impressively represented by the insignia and heraldic vestments preserved in the Treasury began to accumulate. The dynasty later lost some of these titles again in the course of its history — for example, the title of King of Spain in 1713, that of Duke of Lorraine in 1737, that of Duke of Burgundy in 1797 and finally, in 1806, the title of King and Emperor of the Holy Roman Empire. However, in the form of honorary titles or memorial arms, most of the honours were retained for a very long time. Many of them are still mentioned in the great majestic title of Emperor Karl, the last Emperor of Austria: *"Emperor of Austria, Apostolic King of Hungary, King of Bohemia, Dalmatia, Croatia, Slavonia and Galicia, Lodomeria and Illyria. King of Jerusalem etc.; Archduke of Austria, Grand Duke of Tuscany and Cracow, Duke of Lorraine and of Salzburg, of Styria, of Carynthia, Carniola and Bukovina, Grand Prince of Transylvania; Margrave of Moravia; Duke of Upper and Lower Silesia, of Modena, Parma, Piacenza and Guastalla, of Auschwitz and Zator, of Teschen, Friuli, Ragusa and Zara; Prince-Count of Habsburg and Tyrol, of Kyburg, Görz and Gradisca; Prince of Trient and Brixen; Margrave of Upper and Lower Lausatia and in Istria; Count of Hohenembs, Feldkirch, Bregenz, Sonnenberg etc.; Lord of Trieste, of Cattaro , and on the Windische Mark; Grand Voivode of the Voivodeship of Serbia etc; Royal and Imperial Apostolic Majesty."*
If one compares this with, for instance, the great majestic title of Emperor Joseph II, one is struck not only by the fact that all reference to the Holy Roman Empire is entirely missing, but also that the titles Duke of Burgundy, of Brabrant, of Limburg, of Luxemburg and Guelders, that of Count of Flanders, of Hainault, of Namur, Duke of Württemberg, or the originally Lotharingian title of Count of Pont Mousson, Provins, Vaudemont, Blankenburg, Zutphen, Saarwerden, Salm and Falkenstein are all no longer included. This reflects the great transformations of the Napoleonic era. The political map of Europe was altered even more decisively by the First and Second World Wars, so that many of the names mentioned in the majestic title of Karl of Austria are thus unknown today because they no longer possess any political significance whatsoever. It might therefore be useful to examine, at least cursorily, the historical dimension of this assemblage of Habsburg titles and explain the most important of them.

1. ARCHDUKE OF AUSTRIA

Rudolf of Habsburg, a count with estates on the Upper Rhine and at Aare, was elected King of the Holy Roman Empire without the electoral vote of Bohemia. He had demanded from King Ottakar II of Bohemia the surrender of the Imperial fiefdoms of Austria and Styria, these having become vacant with the extinction of the Babenberg line. Ottakar, who was married to Margaret of Austria, of the House of Babenberg, refused to do so, invoking the priviledge which later became known as the *privilegium minus,* and which had been granted to the Babenbergs in 1156, together with the title of Duke, by Emperor Friedrich I Barbarossa; in the event of the extinction of their dynasty it granted them the right to dispose of their lands as they wished. The conflict was resolved with the death of Ottakar in 1278 at the battle of Dürnkrut am Marchfeld. King Rudolf subsequently invested his sons Albrecht and Rudolf with the Duchies of Austria and Styria, and in doing so laid the foundations for his family's rise to power.
In 1335 the Habsburgs succeeded in acquiring the Duchies of Carynthia and Carniola in the south, and in 1363 the County of Tyrol in the west. In 1382 Trieste placed itself under the protection of Austria. By the late fourteenth century, the

Habsburg possessions, later known as the Hereditary Lands, were already a relatively compact group of territories, reaching from the Hungarian border on the River Leitha in the east, to the Alsatian counties on the Upper Rhine in the west; from the Bohemian-Moravian border on the Mark and Thaya in the north, to the Adriatic in the south. Together with the Wittelsbachs, the Habsburgs became the most powerful rivals of the Luxemburg dynasty, which at that time ruled the Holy Roman Empire. When the ambitious Duke Rudolf IV of Austria, his eye on territorial expansion, was forced to realise that the provisions contained in the 'Golden Bull', which had been issued by his father-in-law, Emperor Karl IV of Luxemburg in 1356, excluded his house from all possibility of ruling the Empire in the future (see also p. 116), he attempted (albeit in vain) to circumvent this bolt shot across the door of his ambitions by forging the documents of the so-called *privilegium majus,* allegedly containing ancient priviledges for his house. Among other things, he claimed for himself and his descendants the title of Archduke, which was the rank above all the princes of the Empire immediately after the Prince Electors. This document, which was recognised as a forgery even by Karl IV, did not receive legitimation and therefore validity until the Habsburg Emperor Friedrich III ratified it in 1442 and 1453. From then on, every member of the House bore the title of Archduke or Archduchess of Austria, thus enjoying precedence over every duke. The insigne, a twelve-pointed crown with an arch which imitated that of the crown of the Roman Empire, goes back to Rudolf IV (Cat. No. 3). The archducal vestments were first worn on an official occasion by Archduke Albrecht IV, at the marriage of his brother King Friedrich III to Eleonora of Portugal in 1452.

Territorially, the term *archduchy* was associated with Austria below the Enns and Austria above the Enns, the present-day provinces of Lower and Upper Austria. Heraldically, the following arms of the Habsburgs were regarded as belonging to the archducal group: Styria, Carynthia, Carniola and Tyrol, and those of the territories known as the Austrian *Vorlande,* situated in Swabia and the Upper Rhine, which were eventually reduced to present-day Vorarlberg. The Prince-Archbishopric of Salzburg, which had formerly been directly subordinate to the Empire, was added as a new duchy in 1805.

2. EMPEROR AND KING OF THE HOLY ROMAN EMPIRE

The Holy Roman Empire began on Christmas Day of the year 800 A.D., when Charlemagne was crowned Emperor in Rome. As the 'new Constantine', the Emperor of western Europe continued the *imperium romanum;* as the representative of Christ on earth, he constituted the supreme authority even in spiritual matters. However, as a result of the constant division of the inheritances of the Carolingian dynasty, the new imperium was soon threatened with disintegration. The necessary renewal occurred with the election of Heinrich I, Stem-Duke of the Saxons, after the extinction of the East Frankish line. From this point onwards, the Holy Roman Empire more or less corresponded to the area under the rule of the German king. As a result, after the 15th century, the Empire came to be unofficially called the *Holy Roman Empire of the German Nation,* although possession of the *regnum italiae* was at first still a prerequisite for receiving the title of emperor. Nevertheless, frequent changes of dynasty, the strained relations caused by the investiture controversy, and the munificent bestowal of Imperial land, finally weakened the power of the Emperor to such an extent that over the course of the centuries the Empire became an electoral kingdom (see p. 116). The electoral princes, who, from 1356, were the only ones entitled to vote, gathered in Frankfurt for the election of the king, who was then crowned in Aix-la-Chapelle (after 1562 usually in Frankfurt), by the Archbishop of Mainz. Later, the king was crowned emperor with the Imperial Crown by the Pope in Rome. However, the journey to Rome was an undertaking which was expensive, time-consuming and involved numerous hazards. Those regions in Italy which were largely opposed to the Emperor, and were becoming increasingly independent, often refused him the right of passage. In addition, a lengthy absence from Germany could encourage the forces of opposition to open rebellion. For these reasons it was not unusual for the king to dispense with his coronation as emperor altogether. When, in 1505, the Republic of Venice refused Maximilian I passage through its territory, the Emperor had himself crowned in Trento, receiving from the Pope the title of *Elected Roman Emperor,* which from then on was borne by all his successors to the Imperial throne. Maximilian's grandson and successor, Karl V, was the last Roman king to be crowned Emperor by the Pope. This ceremony took place in 1530, although not in St. Peter's in Rome, but in St. Petronio's in Bologna. Beginning with Rudolf I, the House of Habsburg and the House of Habsburg-Lorraine provided 21 kings and emperors, although there were long periods, such as that between Friedrich the Fair and Albrecht II, when they did not succeed to the title for more than a century (see the list of kings and emperors on pp. 32). The House even seemed to have been excluded from rulership of the Empire for good in 1356, when Karl IV of Luxemburg definitively regulated — to the disadvantage of the Habsburgs and the Bavarian line of the Wittelsbachs — the formalities for the king's election and the rights of the electoral princes in the stipulations of the 'Golden Bull' (see p. 116)

The only way in which the Habsburgs could return to the throne of the Holy Roman Empire was by acquiring the kingdom of Bohemia and the electoral vote connected with it. This was finally achieved by Duke Albrecht V of Austria, who married Elisabeth of Luxemburg, the daughter of Sigismund, Emperor of the Holy Roman Empire and King of Hungary and Bohemia. As Albrecht II, he became Roman King in 1438. Hungary and Bohemia were once again lost by the Habsburgs in 1457, with the death of Albrecht's posthumous son Ladislaus Postumus. Nevertheless, the crown of the Holy Roman Empire remained with the House until the extinction of the dynasty in the male line of descent in 1740. In 1745, after a short intermezzo under Karl VII of Bavaria, Franz Stephan of Lorraine, who was married to Maria Theresia, the legal heiress of the Habsburg lands, came to the imperial throne, and with him once again the House of Habsburg-Lorraine, which then continued to occupy it until the Holy Roman Empire was dissolved by Emperor Franz II in 1806.

3. DUKE OF BURGUNDY

When, in 1477, Archduke Maximilian I of Austria married Maria of Burgundy, the daughter and heiress of Duke Charles the Bold of Burgundy, a large group of economically and culturally highly developed domains came into the possession of the House of Habsburg in the west of the Empire.

However, this inheritance also had to be defended, for it not only consisted of Imperial fiefdoms, but also of fiefdoms from the French crown. King Louis XI of France immediately repossessed the Duchy of Burgundy. The House of Habsburg retained, in the south, the Free County of Burgundy, and in the north, the Duchies of Brabant, Limburg, Luxemburg and Guelders, the Margrave of Antwerp, the Counties of Flanders, Hainault, Namur, Artois, Holland and Zeeland, and the territory of Mecheln. When, in 1529, Emperor Karl V definitively renounced his claim to the Duchy of Burgundy, which had in any case already been lost, he expressly retained the honorary title of Duke of Burgundy, in order to ensure sovereignty for himself and his House over the *Order of the Golden Fleece,* founded by Duke Philip the Good in 1430 (see p. 202). For this reason the title and arms of *Old Burgundy* always had its honorary place in the sequence of titles and arms of both the Habsburg lines: the older Spanish line, which took

The 'Grand State Arms of Austria', as borne until 1866.

over the Burgundian inheritance from Karl V, and the younger Austrian line, which acquired it in 1700, after the extinction of the older line.

4. KING OF SPAIN

Dynastic ties between the House of Habsburg and the kingdoms on the Iberian peninsula were established as early as 1316, when Friedrich the Handsome married Elisabeth of Aragon, and in 1452, when Emperor Friedrich III married Eleonora of Portugal. Their grandchildren, Philip the Fair and Margaret, the children of Maximilian I and Maria of Burgundy, were married to Joan and John of Castile and Aragon respectively, the children of the 'Catholic king' of Spain, Ferdinand of Aragon and Naples-Sicily and Isabella of Castile-Leon. John died in 1497, and Castile was inherited by Philip the Fair in 1504, after the death of Isabella. Eventually, following the death of Ferdinand of Aragon, the whole of Spain, including the American colonies of the West Indies and Naples-Sicily, passed to Philip's elder son, the future Emperor Karl V. Under the sceptre of this Habsburg, who had also come into possession of the Burgundian inheritance, so many dominions were united that one really could speak of an Empire which spanned the whole globe, one on which *"the sun never sets"*.

Karl V founded the older Spanish line of the Habsburgs, while his brother Ferdinand I became the primogenitor of the younger Austrian line. In 1526 Ferdinand inherited the crowns of Hungary and Bohemia, after Karl had ceded the Austrian patrimonial dominions to him in 1522. In 1531 he was crowned Roman King, and when Karl V abdicated in 1558 was proclaimed Emperor. After Ferdinand I, the right of sucession in the Empire remained with the younger Austrian line.

Although the crowns of the Empire and of Spain were only combined for a short period of time, it would be wrong to speak of this simply as an episode. It had lasting effects, because the Habsburgs ruled in both kingdoms. For more than two centuries there existed a decisive overlapping of their political power and interests, among the causes of which was not least the fact that both the Imperial fiefdom of the Netherlandish Provinces from the Burgundian inheritance, and the Imperial fiefdom of Milan were acquired by the Spanish line. The wealth of revenue from the colonies made it possible for the Spanish line, which saw itself as the protector of Catholicism, to exercise its influence on the younger line, which was threatened by the Turks, for a long time. This found expression in supportive payments, in a conspicuously large number of marriages between members of the two lines, and, finally, also in the fact that several Austrian princes were sent to Madrid for their education. After the death of King Charles II of Spain, who was the last Spanish Habsburg, his cousin, Emperor Leopold I, claimed the Spanish throne for his son Karl, even though the Spaniard had named his great-nephew Philip of Bourbon-Anjou as his successor in his testament. However, Karl of Austria was never able to consolidate his position in Spain: after the early death of his elder brother, Joseph I, he was elected in 1711 to succeed the latter on the throne of the Holy Roman Empire as Karl VI; a reunification of the two crowns never again occurred, although Karl continued to bear the title of King of Spain. Nevertheless, in the peace treaty of Utrecht in 1713, Karl VI was able to retain possession of Milan, Naples and the Netherlandish Provinces. Naples-Sicily was ceded to the House of the Spanish Bourbons again in 1735, in the peace treaty of Vienna, in exchange for Parma and Piacenza (kept until 1748). The great majestic titles of the House of Habsburg expressed, if no longer the legal claim, at least the memory of this one-time possession of Spain and Naples-Sicily, linked with the title of the King of Jersualem, which went back to the marriage of Friedrich II of Hohenstaufen with Jolante of Brienne. On the Grand State Arms of Austria, which remained in use until 1866, even the arms of the Spanish possessions in the West Indies still appear.

5. KING OF HUNGARY AND KING OF BOHEMIA

The possession of Hungary and Bohemia, which had been acquired by the House of Habsburg through the marriage of Albrecht II to Elisabeth of Luxemburg, was lost again with the early death of Albrecht's posthumous son Ladislaus Postumus in 1457 (see also p.116). After the significant intermezzo of Matthias Corvinus, a branch of the House of Jagiello came to the throne of Hungary and Bohemia, once more through Elisabeth of Luxemburg, who entered into a second marriage with Casimir IV of Poland. Emperor Maximilian I resolutely pursued a close alliance with this dynasty, and this was sealed with the *'double marriage at Vienna'* of 1515, when the Emperor's grandchildren, Maria and Ferdinand, were respectively married to Ludwig of the House of Jagiello, heir to Hungary and Bohemia, and his sister Anna, with Ferdinand represented by Maximilian. The two ruling houses then made an agreement of inheritance, according to which, in the event of the extinction of one dynasty, the right of succession should pass to the other. Only eleven years later, in 1526, Ludwig, who was childless, fell at Mohács in a battle against the Turks. The Habsburgs were thereafter Kings of Hungary and Bohemia, although at first it was only Bohemia that they were able to maintain in its entirety. The Turks, together with the usurpers favoured by them, contested the Habsburgs' right to Hungary. Since the Margraviate of Moravia and the Silesian Duchies also belonged to the Bohemian crown, this group of lands from now on became one of the most important bastions of Habsburg power. In 1529, the Turkish army reached the gates of Vienna for the first time. It took two hundred years of armed conflict before the House of Habsburg came into complete possession of the lands of the Hungarian crown, to which also belonged the kingdoms of Croatia and Dalmatia and the Principality of Transylvania. As Queen of Hungary, Maria Theresia, the last Habsburg, received from Pope Clemens XIII in 1758 a renewal of the title of *Apostolic Majesty* for herself and her descendants, and this was borne until the end of the monarchy.

From the time of Ferdinand I onwards, the position occupied by the arms of the two Kingdoms of Hungary and Bohemia in the arms of the Austrian line of the Habsburgs was next in importance only to the inescutcheon shield divided into Austria and Old Burgundy. The Hungarian Crown of St. Stephen and the Bohemian Crown of St. Wenceslas are preserved in Budapest and Prague respectively. During the reign of Joseph II they were kept for a short while in the Vienna Treasury.

6. DUKE OF LORRAINE, GRAND DUKE OF TUSCANY

When Franz Stephan of Lorraine, heir to the dynasty which maintained its ducal status longer than any other within the Holy Roman Empire, married the Habsburg heiress Maria Theresia in 1737, he was forced, under pressure from France, to renounce his claim to the lands of his forefathers. His father-in-law, Emperor Karl VI, recompensed him for this with the Grand Duchy of Tuscany, where the dynasty of the Medici were on the verge of extinction. The name of the Duchy of Lorraine goes back to the Carolingian *Middle Kingdom* of Emperor Lothar I, and to his son Lothar II's Kingdom of *Lotharingia,* which emerged as the Duchy of Upper Lorraine after the division of the former into two duchies. That of Lower Lorraine consequently disintegrated into even smaller duchies and counties, namely into the Netherlandish Provinces. The name of Lorraine only continued in the arms of the House of Habsburg, where it was supposed to evoke the memory of the claim of the Duke of Burgundy — and consequently the Habsburgs — to the *Middle Kingdom.* The meaning of its arms, which were divided twice horizontally into red, white and red, and sometimes confused with those of Austria, was deliberately left ambiguous.

In the dynastic marriage ties of the Houses of Lorraine and Habsburg, the genealogists of the time saw the reunification of two branches of a single family reaching back to the old Alsatian ducal house of the *Etichones.* From this time on, the family name was changed to Habsburg-Lorraine out of respect for the venerable but extinct Habsburg branch. Emperor Franz Stephan bore both his own Lotharingian crown, which was similar to that of a king, and the Tuscan fleur-de-lys crown of the House of Medici. Neither of these insignia have survived.

Having become the possession of the Habsburgs by *secundogeniture,* the Grand Duchy of Tuscany first of all passed to the Archduke Peter Leopold, the second son of Emperor Franz Stephan and Maria Theresia. When he came to the throne as Leopold II, after the death of his brother Joseph II, who had died without issue, Tuscany passed to the second-born son, Ferdinand, thus continuing the Habsburg *secundogeniture* of Austria-Tuscany. During the Napoleonic Wars he lost Tuscany for several years and was at first recompensed with the secularised Archbishopric of Salzburg, which had been raised to an Electoral Principality. The arms of Lorraine, Bar, Anjou-Naples, along with those of Jerusalem and Tuscany (actually those of the Medici) were retained, as arms designating claimancy and commemoration, in the Grand State Arms of Austria, which continued to be borne until 1866.

Through Archduke Ferdinand, who was the second-youngest son of Franz Stephan and Maria Theresia, and married to Maria Beatrix Riccarda d'Este, the heiress of the Duchy of Modena, this duchy, too, finally passed to the Habsburgs. Ferdinand founded the Habsburg *tertiogeniture* of Austria-Este.

7. EMPEROR OF AUSTRIA, AFTER 1867 EMPEROR OF AUSTRIA AND KING OF HUNGARY

In 1713, Emperor Karl VI, the last male Habsburg monarch, established, by means of hereditary laws of his own making (the so-called *Pragmatic Sanction*), the precedence of his own children's — even his daughters' — right to succession in the Habsburg Hereditary Lands over that of the daughters of his deceased elder brother and predecessor, Joseph I. For this he managed to obtain, after long years of difficult diplomatic negotiations, the consent of all the European powers and dynasties, with the exception of Bavaria. Nevertheless, after his death in 1740, his daughter and heiress, Maria Theresia, still had to fight to uphold the *Pragmatic Sanction* in a war of succession which lasted eight years.

The Prince Elector Karl Albrecht of Bavaria made a claim to succession, despite the fact that his wife, a daughter of Joseph I, had expressly renounced all claim to territorial inheritance by her marriage — as had all the archduchesses. Prussia and France rallied to his support. In the end, however, Maria Theresia proved quite capable of asserting herself and — with the exception of Silesia, which she lost to Prussia — was able to secure her inheritance.

In 1772, in the wake of the first partition of Poland, which Maria Theresia at first opposed, Austria recieved East Galicia and Lodomeria; after the third division, in 1795, she also received West Galicia and large parts of Lesser Poland, including Cracow. The Netherlandish territories and parts of the *Vorlande,* all of which derived from the Burgundian inheritance of 1477, were retained right up until the Napoleonic Wars, following which they were lost for ever. The possessions in Italy, on the other hand, such as Milan, Tuscany, Modena, Mantua and Guastalla, were only temporarily lost at this time.

On 11. 8. 1804, in order to preempt the imminent coronation of Napoleon as Emperor of the French and to offer him some resistance in the form of a political counterbalance, Emperor Franz II adopted the title of Emperor of Austria and elevated all the crown lands still in his possession to the status of a hereditary empire. However, the actual independence of the individual countries remained practically untouched by this decree. The *Imperial Crown* of the House of Habsburg, which had been worn by Rudolf II, became the State Crown of the new Empire. The double-headed black Imperial eagle, on a golden ground, was adopted as the new Austrian arms, and black and gold became the colours of the Emperor. In 1814, after the fall of Napoleon, the territories of Görz, Carniola, Carynthia, Istria and Croatia, which had been combined together into the Province of Illyria in 1809, were returned to Austria. They were raised to a new *Kingdom of Illyria,* which continued until 1849. At the *Congress of Vienna* in 1815, Austria not only regained all her Italian territories, but even obtained the territory of the former Republic of Venice as well; and yet another kingdom under Austrian dominion was also established: *Lombardy and Venetia.* Nonetheless, in the wake of the Italian War of Unification, Austria lost almost all its possessions in Italy to the House of Savoy, which was supported by Napoleon III. The additional weakening of the Habsburgs' position in 1866, after its defeat by Prussia at the Battle of Königgratz, led to the *Ausgleich* of 1867 and the governmental dualism demanded by Hungary. As a result, Hungary, together with the kingdoms of Croatia, Slovenia and Dalmatia and the Grand Principality of Transylvania, all of which belonged to the Hungarian crown, was granted its own Parliament in Budapest. With this event was born the double monarchy of the *Empire of Austria and the Kingdom of Hungary.* After 1867, two separate arms existed, even though the Empire continued — held together by symbolic union in the person of the Emperor and King, a common foreign policy, financial sovereignty and a joint army — until its final collapse at the end of the First World War. Those affairs which concerned both Austria and Hungary were designated 'kaiserlich und königlich' (k. u. k.), meaning 'Imperial and Royal'; those solely concerning Austria 'kaiserlich-königlich' (k.k.) or 'Imperial-Royal'; and those concerning Hungary 'königlich' or 'Royal'. M. L.-J.

GENEALOGY OF THE HOUSE OF HABSBURG AND HABSBURG-LORRAINE

K. RUDOLF (1218—1291) m. 1.) 1245 Gertrude of Hohenberg (1225—1281)

K. ALBRECHT I (1248—1308)
m. 1274 Elizabeth of Görz - Tyrol

D. RUDOLF II (1271—1290)
m. 1289 Agnes of Bohemia

Johann (murderer of Albrecht I)

K. FRIEDRICH III (I)
The Handsome (1286—1330)
m. 1315 Elizabeth of Aragon

D. LEOPOLD I (1290—1326)
m. 1315 Catherine of Savoy

D. ALBRECHT II (1298—1358)
m. 1324 Johanna of Pfirt

D. OTTO (1301—1339)
m. 1.) 1325 Elizabeth of Bavaria
2.) 1335 Anna of Bohemia

D. RUDOLF III (1282—1307)
K. of Bohemia
m. 1.) 1300, Blanche of France
m. 2.) 1306, Elizabeth of Poland

D. ALBRECHT III (1348—1395)
m. 1.) 1366 Elizabeth of Luxemburg
2.) 1375 Beatrix of Hohenzollern

D. LEOPOLD IV (1371—1411)
m. 1393 Catherine of Burgundy

D. LEOPOLD III (1357—1386)
m. 1365 Viridis Visconti

D. ERNST (1377—1424)
m. 1.) 1392 Margarete of Pomerania
2.) 1412 Zimburg of Masovia

D. FRIEDRICH IV (1382—1439)
m. 1.) 1406 Elizabeth of the Palatinate
2.) 1410 Anna of Brunswick

D. RUDOLF IV (1339—1365)
m. 1357 Catherine of Luxemburg

D. WILHELM (1370—1406)
m. 1401 Johanna of Naples

2nd E. FRIEDRICH III (V)
(1415—1493)
Roman King and Emperor
m. 1452 Eleonora of Portugal

A. ALBRECHT VI
(1418—1463)
m. 1452 Mathilde of the Palatinate

A. SIGMUND (1427—1498)
m. 1.) 1449 Eleanor of Scotland
2.) 1484 Katharina of Saxony

2nd D. ALBRECHT IV
(1377—1404)
m. 1390 Johanna of Bavaria

K. ALBRECHT II (V)
(1397—1439)
K. of Bohemia and Hungary
Roman King
m. 1421 Elizabeth of Luxemburg
(m. 2. Ladislaus III of Poland
and Hungary)

E. MAXIMILIAN I
(1459—1519)
m. 1.) 1477 Mary of Burgundy
2.) 1494 Bianca Maria Sforza

Elisabeth (1437—1505)
m. 1454 Casimir IV of Poland

LADISLAUS (Postumus)
(1440—1457)
K. of Hungary and Bohemia

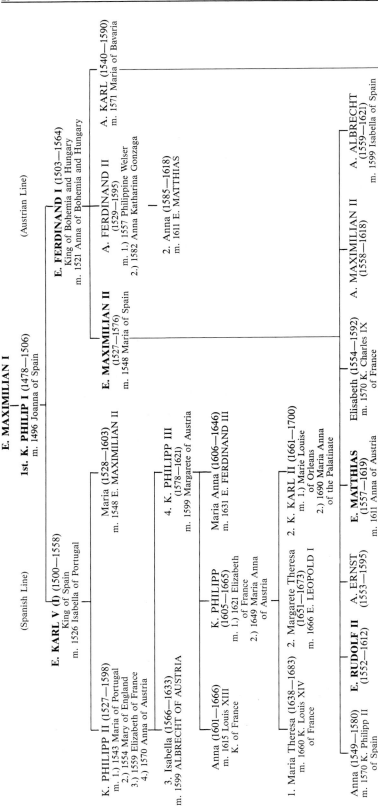

E. MAXIMILIAN I

1st. K. PHILIP I (1478—1506)
m. 1496 Joanna of Spain

(Spanish Line)

E. KARL V (I) (1500—1558)
King of Spain
m. 1526 Isabella of Portugal

K. PHILIPP II (1527—1598)
m. 1.) 1543 Maria of Portugal
2.) 1554 Mary of England
3.) 1559 Elizabeth of France
4.) 1570 Anna of Austria

3. Isabella (1566—1633)
m. 1599 ALBRECHT OF AUSTRIA

Anna (1601—1666)
m. 1615 Louis XIII
K. of France

K. PHILIPP
(1605—1665)
m. 1.) 1621 Elizabeth
of France
2.) 1649 Maria Anna
of Austria

1. Maria Theresa (1638—1683)
m. 1660 K. Louis XIV
of France

2. Margarete Theresa
(1651—1673)
m. 1666 E. LEOPOLD I

4. K. PHILIPP III
(1578—1621)
m. 1599 Margarete of Austria

Maria Anna (1606—1646)
m. 1631 E. FERDINAND III

2. K. KARL II (1661—1700)
m. 1.) Marie Louise
of Orleans
2.) 1690 Maria Anna
of the Palatinate

Maria (1528—1603)
m. 1548 E. MAXIMILIAN II

E. FERDINAND I (1503—1564)
King of Bohemia and Hungary
m. 1521 Anna of Bohemia and Hungary

(Austrian Line)

E. MAXIMILIAN II
(1527—1576)
m. 1548 Maria of Spain

A. FERDINAND II
(1529—1595)
m. 1.) 1557 Philippine Welser
2.) 1582 Anna Katharina Gonzaga

2. Anna (1585—1618)
m. 1611 E. MATTHIAS

A. KARL (1540—1590)
m. 1571 Maria of Bavaria

Anna (1549—1580)
m. 1570 K. Philipp II
of Spain

E. RUDOLF II
(1552—1612)

A. ERNST
(1553—1595)

E. MATTHIAS
(1557—1619)
m. 1611 Anna of Austria

Elisabeth (1554—1592)
m. 1570 K. Charles IX
of France

A. MAXIMILIAN II
(1558—1618)

A. ALBRECHT
(1559—1621)
m. 1599 Isabella of Spain

A. KARL

Anna (1573—1598)
m. 1592 K. Sigmund III
of Poland

E. FERDINAND II (1578—1637) Margarete (1584—1611)
m. 1.) 1600 Maria Anna of Bavaria   m. 1599 K. Philipp III
m. 2.) 1622 Eleonora Gonzaga   of Spain

Magdalena (1589—1631)
m. 1608 Cosimo II
de Medici
of Tuscany

Konstanze (1588—1631)
m. 1605 K. Sigmund III
of Poland

A. LEOPOLD V
(1586—1632)
m. 1626 Claudia de Medici

Maria Leopoldine
(1632—1649)
m. 1648
E. FERDINAND III

3. Marie Anna (1654—1689)
m. 1678 Johann Wilhelm
of the Neuburg Palatinate

A. SIGISMUND FRANZ
(1630—1665)

3. E. KARL VI (III) (1685—1740)
K. of Spain
m. 1708 Elizabeth Christine
of Braunschweig-Wolfenbüttel

I. E. FERDINAND III
(1608—1657)
m. 1.) 1631 Maria Anna of Spain
2.) 1648 Maria Leopoldine
of Austria
3.) 1651 Eleonora Gonzaga

I. Maria Anna
(1610—1665)
m. 1635 Maximilian I
of Bavaria

I. A. LEOPOLD
WILHELM
(1614—1662)

A. FERDINAND KARL
(1628—1662)
m. 1646 Anna de Medici

Claudia Felicitas (1653—1676)
m. 1673 E. LEOPOLD I

3. Eleonore Marie (1653—1697)
m. 1.) 1670 K. Michael of Poland
2.) 1678 D. Karl IV of Lorraine

3. Maria Anna (1683—1754)
m. 1708 K. John V of Portugal

Maria Anna (1718—1744)
m. 1744 D. Karl Alexander
of Lorraine

I. K. FERDINAND IV
(1633—1653)

I. E. LEOPOLD I (1640—1705)
m. 1.) 1666 Margarete Therese of Spain
2.) 1673 Claudia Felicitas of Austria
3.) 1676 Eleonore Magdalena
of the Palatinate

I. Maria Anna (1635—1695)
m. 1649 K. Philipp IV
of Spain

Maria Theresia (1717—1780)
Queen of Hungary and Bohemia
m. 1736 E. FRANZ I, Stephan, D.
of Lorraine

House of Habsburg-Lorraine

A. FERDINAND (1754—1806)
D. of Modena
m. 1771 Maria Beatrix d'Este

House of Austria-Este

Marie Antoinette
(1755—1793)
m. 1770
K. Louis XVI
of France

3. E. JOSEPH I (1678—1711)
m. 1685 Wilhelmine Amalie
of Braunschweig-Lüneburg

1. Maria Antonia (1669—1692)
m. 1685 Maximilian Emanuel II
of Bavaria

E. LEOPOLD II (1747—1792)
G. D. of Tuscany
m. 1765 Maria Ludovica
of Spain

Karoline
(1752—1814)
m. 1768
K. Ferdinand I
of Naples and Sicily

Maria Amalie
(1746—1804)
m. 1769 D. Ferdinand
of Bourbon-Parma

Maria Amalie (1701—1756)
m. 1722 K. Karl VII, Elector of Bavaria

Maria Josepha (1699—1757)
m. 1717 Friedrich August II (III)
K. of Poland, Elector of Saxony

E. JOSEPH II (1741—1790)
m. 1.) 1760 Isabella of Bourbon-
Parma
2.) 1765 Maria Josepha
of Bavaria

Marie Christine
(1742—1798)
m. 1766
D. Albrecht of
Saxony-Teschen

E. LEOPOLD II

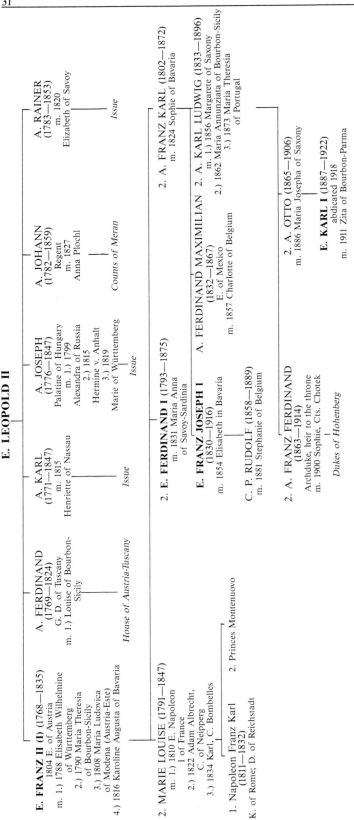

E. FRANZ II (I) (1768—1835)
1804 E. of Austria
m. 1.) 1788 Elisabeth Wilhelmine of Württemberg
2.) 1790 Maria Theresia of Bourbon-Sicily
3.) 1808 Maria Ludovica of Modena (Austria-Este)
4.) 1816 Karoline Augusta of Bavaria

A. FERDINAND (1769—1824)
G. D. of Tuscany
m. 1.) Louise of Bourbon-Sicily

House of Austria-Tuscany

A. KARL (1771—1847)
m. 1815 Henriette of Nassau

Issue

A. JOSEPH (1776—1847)
Palatine of Hungary
m. 1.) 1799 Alexandra of Russia
2.) 1815 Hermine v. Anhalt
3.) 1819 Marie of Württemberg

Issue

A. JOHANN (1782—1859)
Regent
m. 1827 Anna Plochl

Counts of Meran

A. RAINER (1783—1853)
m. 1820 Elizabeth of Savoy

Issue

2. MARIE LOUISE (1791—1847)
m. 1.) 1810 E. Napoleon I of France
2.) 1822 Adam Albrecht, C. of Neipperg
3.) 1834 Karl, C. Bombelles

1. Napoleon Franz Karl (1811—1832)
K. of Rome; D. of Reichstadt

2. Princes Montenuovo

2. E. FERDINAND I (1793—1875)
m. 1831 Maria Anna of Savoy-Sardinia

A. FERDINAND MAXIMILIAN (1832—1867)
E. of Mexico
m. 1857 Charlotte of Belgium

2. A. FRANZ KARL (1802—1872)
m. 1824 Sophie of Bavaria

2. A. KARL LUDWIG (1833—1896)
m. 1.) 1856 Margarete of Saxony
2.) 1862 Maria Annunziata of Bourbon-Sicily
3.) 1873 Maria Theresia of Portugal

E. FRANZ JOSEPH I (1830—1916)
m. 1854 Elisabeth in Bavaria

C. P. RUDOLF (1858—1889)
m. 1881 Stephanie of Belgium

2. A. FRANZ FERDINAND (1863—1914)
Archduke, heir to the throne
m. 1900 Sophie, Cts. Chotek

Dukes of Hohenberg

2. A. OTTO (1865—1906)
m. 1886 Maria Josepha of Saxony

E. KARL I (1887—1922)
abdicated 1918
m. 1911 Zita of Bourbon-Parma

Abbreviations: E. = Emperor; K. = King; C. P. = Crown Prince; A. = Archduke; G. D. = Grand Duke; D. = Duke; C. = Count; Cts. = Countess; m = married

THE EMPERORS AND KINGS OF THE HOLY ROMAN EMPIRE FROM HEINRICH I TO THE DISSOLUTION OF THE EMPIRE
(After Georg Johannes Kugler, Die Reichskrone)

	Ruled	Coronation as King			Coronation as Emperor		
The Saxon Dynasty							
Heinrich I	919— 936						
Otto I the Great	936— 973	Aix	7. 8.	936	Rome	2. 2.	962
Otto II	973— 983	Aix	26. 5.	961	Rome	25. 12.	967
Otto III	983—1002	Aix	25. 12.	983	Rome	21. 5.	996
Heinrich II the Saint,							
Duke of Bavaria	1002—1024	Mainz	7. 6.	1002	Rome	14. 2.	1014
The Franconian (Salian) Dynasty							
Konrad II, 1033							
King of Burgundy	1024—1039	Mainz	8. 9.	1024	Rome	26. 3.	1027
Heinrich III	1039—1056	Aix	14. 4.	1028	Rome	25. 12.	1046
Heinrich IV	1056—1105	Aix	17. 7.	1054	Rome	31. 3.	1084
Anti-kings:							
Rudolf of Swabia	1077—1080						
Hermann of Salm	1081—1088						
Konrad of Lower Lorraine,							
son of Heinrich IV († 1101)	1087—1098	Aix	30. 5.	1087			
Heinrich V	1106—1125	Aix	6. 1.	1099	Rome	13. 4.	1111
Lothar of Supplinburg,							
Duke of Saxony	1125—1137	Aix	13. 9.	1125	Rome	4. 6.	1133
The Dynasties of the Staufers, the Welfs and their anti-kings							
Konrad III	1138—1152	Aix	13. 3.	1138			
Friedrich I Barbarossa,							
Duke of Swabia	1152—1190	Aix	9. 3.	1152	Rome	18. 6.	1155
Heinrich VI, 1194 King							
of Sicily	1190—1197	Aix	15. 8.	1169	Rome	15. 4.	1191
Philip of Swabia	1198—1208	Mainz	8. 9.	1198			
		Aix	6. 1.	1205			
Otto IV of Brunswick	1198—1218	Aix	12. 7.	1198	Rome	4. 10.	1209
Friedrich II, 1198 King of Sicily,	1212—1250	Mainz	9. 12.	1212			
1225 King of Jerusalem		Aix	25. 7.	1215	Rome	22. 11.	1220
Heinrich VIII, 1212 King							
of Sicily, 1220 elected							
German King († 1242)	1222—1235	Aix	8. 5.	1222			
Konrad IV, 1250 King of							
Sicily, King of Jerusalem,							
1237 elected German King	1250—1254						
Anti-kings:							
Heinrich Raspe, Landgrave							
of Thuringia	1246—1247						
Wilhelm, Count of Holland	1247—1256	Aix	1. 11.	1248			
Interregnum							
Richard, Earl of Cornwall	1257—1272	Aix	17. 5.	1257			
Alfonso, King of Castile	1257, †1284						
Rudolf I, Count of Habsburg	1273—1291	Aix	24. 10.	1273			
Adolf, Count of Nassau	1292—1298	Aix	24. 6.	1292			
Albrecht I of Habsburg,							
Duke of Austria	1298—1308	Aix	24. 8.	1298			
Heinrich VII, Count of							
Luxemburg	1308—1313	Aix	6. 1.	1309	Rome	29. 6.	1312
Friedrich, Duke of Austria,							
'the Handsome' (as King							
Friedrich III), from 1325 co-regent	1314—1330	Bonn	25. 11.	1314			

	Ruled	Coronation as King		Coronation as Emperor	
Ludwig the Bavarian	1314—1347	Aix	25. 11. 1314	Rome	17. 1. 1328
Karl IV of Luxemburg, King of Bohemia	1346—1378	Bonn	26. 11. 1346		
		Aix	25. 7. 1349	Rome	6. 4. 1355
Wenceslas, King of Bohemia († 1419)	1376—1400	Aix	6. 7. 1376		
Ruprecht of the Palatine	1400—1410	Cologne	6. 1. 1401		
		Aix	14. 11. 1407		
Sigismund of Luxemburg 1387 King of Hungary, 1420 King of Bohemia	1410—1437	Aix	8. 11. 1414	Rome	25. 11. 1433

The House of Habsburg:
Dukes (Archdukes) of Austria, after Ferdinand I Kings of Bohemia and Hungary

	Ruled	Coronation as King		Coronation as Emperor	
Albrecht II, 1438 King of Bohemia and Hungary	1438—1439				
Friedrich III (King Friedrich IV)	1439—1493	Aix	17. 6. 1442	Rome	19. 3. 1452
Maximilian I, 1508 elected German King	1493—1519	Aix	9. 4. 1486	(Trento	6. 2. 1508)
Karl V, 1516 King of Spain, 1520 elected Roman Emperor, † 1558	1519—1556	Aix	23. 10. 1520	Bologna	24. 2. 1530
Ferdinand I, 1531 Roman King, 1558 proclaimed Emperor	1556—1564	Aix	11. 1. 1531		
Maximilian II	1564—1576	Frankfurt	30. 11. 1562		
Rudolf II	1576—1612	Regensbg.	27. 10. 1575		
Matthias	1612—1619			Frankfurt	13. 6. 1612
Ferdinand II	1619—1637			Frankfurt	28. 8. 1619
Ferdinand III	1637—1657	Regensbg.	22. 12. 1636		
Ferdinand IV, † 1654		Regensbg.	24. 5. 1653		
Leopold I	1658—1705			Frankfurt	1. 8. 1658
Joseph I	1705—1711	Augsburg	26. 1. 1690		
Karl VI, 1703 King of Spain	1711—1740			Frankfurt	22. 12. 1711
Karl VII Albrecht, Duke of Bavaria *(House of Wittelsbach)*	1742—1745			Frankfurt	12. 2. 1742

The House of Habsburg-Lorraine

	Ruled	Coronation as King		Coronation as Emperor	
Franz Stephan I, Duke of Lorraine, Grand Duke of Tuscany	1745—1765			Frankfurt	4. 10. 1745
Joseph II	1765—1790	Frankfurt	3. 4. 1764		
Leopold II Grand Duke of Tuscany	1790—1792			Frankfurt	9. 10. 1790
Franz II, after 1804 Emperor of Austria, † 1835	1792—1806 Dissolves the Holy Roman Empire			Frankfurt	14. 7. 1792

The Secular Treasury

THE HEREDITARY HOMAGE

During the course of the Middle Ages, numerous territories had broken away from the old German stem duchies and, under the rule of their own dynasties, had achieved a greater or lesser degree of political independence. However, the enfeoffment in 1282 of the brothers Albrecht and Rudolf of Habsburg with the Duchies of Austria below and above the Enns and Styria by their father, King Rudolf, initiated a process of concentration whereby over the following centuries the House of Habsburg succeeded in bringing most of the territories in the southeast of the Holy Roman Empire under its rule. Nevertheless, these territories succeeded — quite independently of each other — in preserving a considerable degree of political independence for themselves. This led to the development of provincial diets representing the free estates of the prelates, the nobles, knights and burghers. In Tyrol, the nobles and knights were united in one estate, with a fourth estate representing the free peasants. The so-called Hereditary Lands of the Habsburgs, however, were not kingdoms (with the exception of Bohemia), but rather duchies, principalities and counties, where a new ruler's formal accession to power was solemnized not by coronation, but by a state act of a contractual character, namely the Hereditary Homage *(Erbhuldigung)* of the provincial diets. Before the estates paid homage to the new ruler and swore allegiance to him, he was obliged to ratify their ancient chartered rights and privileges. For the constitutional act of the Hereditary Homage, a special ceremony evolved in which certain insignia were used. These were carried by the holders of the various Grand Offices of the Hereditary Lands. They belonged to the estate of the nobles and were members of the most distinguished families in the land. The ceremony of the Hereditary Homage of the estates of Lower Austria took place in the Hofburg at Vienna. The Archducal Coronet, the official insigne of the province, which was donated by Archduke Maximilian III in 1616, and is still preserved today in the monastery of the Augustinian canons at Klosterneuburg, was conveyed to the ceremony in Vienna in solemn procession on a litter (today in the Collection of Carriages in the Wagenburg) carried by two mules. It was the hereditary privilege of the Grand Cupbearer of this Hereditary Land to carry this insigne before the ruler. The sceptre, Imperial orb and sword, taken from the Treasury for this ceremony, were carried by the Grand Chamberlain, the Grand Steward and the Grand Marshal of this Hereditary Land respectively.

The last ceremonies of he Hereditary Homage took place under Emperor Ferdinand I: in 1835 for the Duchy of Austria below the Enns and in 1838 in Innsbruck for the Princely County of Tyrol.

Ref.: Castelli 1837; Zolger 1917; Puchl 1954; Thomas 1963, pp. 338—359; Catalogue, Uniform und Mode, pp. 91—121.

1, 2, 3

1 THE SCEPTRE

Prague, 3rd quarter of the 14th century
Silver-gilt; 79.6 cms long (Inv. No. XIV 44)

The slim, rounded shaft of the sceptre, tapering to a point, is divided into sections by clearly defined console-type bosses on the haft and on the crowning bi-part flower.

As Hermann Fillitz has shown, influences from architecture are reflected in these forms, mainly deriving from buildings executed by the Parlers in Bohemia. This translation of forms originally developed in architecture into the medium of metalwork would seem to point to the leading artistic personality of the age, i.e. Peter Parler himself. As artist to the Imperial Court, he had acted as adviser to Karl IV's court workshops at Prague since 1356. It is known that the architect and sculptor Peter Parler was also active in the field of the applied arts and that one of his sons was a goldsmith. Moreover, the form of this royal insigne closely reflects his specific artistic language. As a portrait of Emperor Matthias as King of Bohemia attests (Cat. No. 141), this sceptre and the Imperial orb belonging to it were still in use as the royal insignia of Bohemia in the early 17th century. These two Gothic insignia were superseded in this function by a pair of insignia from the second third of the 16th century. From that time on, they were used in the ceremony of the Austrian Hereditary Homage.

For a survey of the development and significance of sceptres in general, see Cat No. 163.   H. T.

Ref.: Fillitz 1969, p. 400 ff.; Schramm-Fillitz 1978, No. 28; Fritz 1982, p. 266.

2 THE IMPERIAL ORB

Prague (?), 3rd quarter of the 14th century (?)
Silver-gilt; 16 cms high (Inv. No. XIV 43)

With the exception of the engraved lines on its upper hemisphere, the globe of this orb is quite smooth and unadorned, so that it is to the heavy trefoil-shaped ends of the arms of the cross, and the latter's compact overall proportions, that we must look for clues to its origin. In all the above points of style the cross is almost identical to the one surmounting the reliquary containing the tooth of John the Baptist, which is with certainty Bohemian work from the third quarter of the 14th century (Cat. No. 169) — reason enough for redating this Gothic orb from the 15th century to the 14th century. Furthermore, the same proportions of the cross and the trefoil extremities are also to be found in major works of art from the Prague Court of Karl IV, as well as in the fields of monumental or panel painting. Extreme smoothness of form and a certain noble simplicity are distinguishing features of most of the goldsmiths' work done during this period at the Prague court.

Concerning the function and significance of orbs in general, see Cat. No. 161.   H. T.

Ref.: Fillitz 1969, p. 400

3 PAINTING OF THE BAROQUE COPY OF THE AUSTRIAN ARCHDUCAL CORONET

Austrian (Vienna?), c. 1765
Oil on canvas; 78.5 x 65 cms (Inv. No. XIV 144)

This painting shows the archducal coronet made for Joseph II's ceremonial entry into Frankfurt in 1764, on the occasion of his coronation as Roman-German King. With its twelve gables and simple arch, it is a conscious imitation of the original form of the 14th century, as this appears in the archducal coronet of Duke Rudolf IV, 'the Founder'. The official insigne donated by Archduke Maximilian III in 1616, however, has eight gables and two high arches intersecting at the crown of the head. This coronet had been placed with the reliquary skull of St. Leopold, the patron saint of Lower Austria, in Klosterneuburg and according to the dedication of its donor was only to be lent to the sovereign on the occasion of the Hereditary Homage or the Receipt of Fealty. Thus the sovereign — in this case Joseph II — was obliged to have a private archducal coronet made for other occasions. This coronet is today preserved in the Treasury (Inv. No. XIV 113), but without its precious stones: these were also used for other purposes and therefore interchangeable and were only borrowed from the House jewellery for this occasion.   M. L.-J.

**4 SHIELD OF THE ARCHDUCHY
OF AUSTRIA BELOW THE
ENNS**
Vienna, 1835
Silver, parcel-gilt, lustred and painted;
red velvet; 64 cms long, 51.5 cms wide
(Inv. No. XIV 35)

This targe-shaped shield displays five golden eagles on a blue ground. The priviledge of carrying it was reserved for the Grand Carver, Arbitrator and Shield-Bearer of this Hereditary Land, a hereditary office introduced — or, rather, revived — by Emperor Joseph I in 1705. Originally, the shield of the Archduchy was made of silver and displayed not only the eagles but also a silver fesse on a red ground, the so-called Austrian *Bindenschild.* When the Empire of Austria was created in 1804, the *Bindenschild* was adopted as the inescutcheon of the new Imperial arms, leaving only the five eagles as the arms of the Archduchy of Austria below the Enns. As a result, the old shield of the Archduchy was then altered to the five-eagled targe for the ceremony of the Hereditary Homage to Emperor Ferdinand in Vienna in 1835.   M. L.-J.

THE COURT HOUSEHOLD — COURT OFFICES — HEREDITARY OFFICES

A court is the household of a prince, and comprises the prince and his family on the one hand, and the court staff on the other. The latter includes all the people in the service of the prince: both those directly involved with the affairs of his household or the running of his court, and those with official court functions to perform. Ever since the early Middle Ages, the division of responsibility necessary for the organisation of the courts of European princes had led to the creation of different household staffs, leadership of which the prince entrusted as offices in their own right to meritorious dignitaries. Thus the office of Marshal, for example, entailed responsibility for all matters of equestrian nature, ranging from the court's travelling arrangements to warfare. The responsibilities of the office of Chamberlain included everything directly concerned with the prince's person, such as his accommodation, household and clothing, as well as all the expenses connected with them. Finally, there were the offices of Steward and Cupbearer, involving responsibility for the administration of the kitchen and cellar, and for the princely estates supplying these. However, with time, the significance of these court offices changed, because the princes also bestowed them as fiefs hereditary to certain families. They thus came to be more closely connected with particular Hereditary Lands than with the court itself. In the Holy Roman Empire they had been connected, as arch-offices, with certain territories ever since the 13th century: the office of Steward to the County of the Palatinate on the Rhine, the office of Marshal to Saxony, the office of Chamberlain to Brandenburg and that of Cupbearer to Bohemia. Since, however, the court required these services just as they had before, the result was that a division occurred between those offices which were hereditary, and primarily ceremonial *(Oberst Erbland-Ämter),* and those which were non-hereditary and involved duties at court *(Oberste Hofämter),* whose holders were only employed by the prince for a certain period of time. In the end, the holders of the hereditary offices (in the Archduchy of Austria below the Enns eighteen such offices had arisen in the course of the centuries) only used to appear in their functions at court when required for a state occasion concerning their respective lands — such as the ceremony of the Hereditary Homage known as the *Erbhuldigung.*

For this reason, on 1. 1. 1527, the future Emperor Ferdinand I reorganised his court household along his own lines, according to a scheme which was partly based on the Burgundian-Spanish model, and divided it into four different staffs each with their own areas of responsibility. At the head of these were the four highest court offices, those of Grand Comptroller, Grand Chamberlain, Grand Marshal and Grand Equerry (in that order). With only minor modifications, this arrangement was continued at the Imperial court in Vienna until 1918.

The Grand Comptroller's staff were supervised by the so-called Grand Attendants: the Grand Master of the Table, who was in charge of table protocol, the Grand Master of the Kitchen, the Grand Master of the Silver Treasury, the Grand Master of the Hunt and the Grand Master Falconer and, finally, the Grand Master of Ceremonies. The Grand Comptroller was therefore the highest dignitary and the foremost official at the court. Generally speaking, the most important of all his responsibilities was that of ensuring that life at the court ran smoothly. The Grand Chamberlain's staff was responsible for the internal service of the court and the administration of the private finances of the Imperial household and the Habsburg-Lorraine household treasure, but was also in charge of the Imperial collections and all their academic undertakings. The Grand Marshal was the custodian of court security, morals and order, and thus responsible for justice at court — the members of the court household being exempt from ordinary legal jurisdiction. Finally, the Grand Equerry was in charge of the court stables, riding schools, court carriage house and court stud farm, the armoury and arsenal and their personnel, as well as the pages, gun-chargers and lackeys.

Special importance at court was also attached to the bearers of various court honours, in particular to the large number of chamberlains. The title of chamberlain was an honorary one, open to male members of the nobility who could prove noble descent on each side for at least four generations. The title of chamberlain provided admission to the court and was therefore much coveted, although the bearer was also obliged to perform certain services at 'publicly proclaimed' court festivities.

All these court titles, court offices and hereditary offices had their own insignia, some of which are still preserved in the Treasury today.   M. L.-J.

5 THE INSIGNIA FOR THE HEREDITARY GRAND MASTER FALCONER
Vienna, 1835 (?)
Consisting of:

a) Falconer's pouch
Dark green leather; dark green velvet, trimmed with gold braid and embroidered in gold. In the centre the Imperial double-headed eagle with the arms of Austria-Habsburg-Lorraine on its breast and the monogramme of Emperor Ferdinand I, fringes of green silk and gold thread. Clasp of silver-gilt with a cord of gold thread interwoven with green silk. (Inv. No. XIV 36)

b) Two falcon's hoods
Slight differences in size and design. Red, black, dark green and beige leather with ornamentation and the monogramme of Emperor Ferdinand I embossed in gold; dark green velvet; black feathers. (Inv. No. XIV 37 and 38)

5, 6

c) Falcon lure
Red leather and red silk cord; the feathers originally belonging to it are missing; a cord of gold thread interwoven with green silk on the mounts. (Inv. No. XIV 39)

The bag at least was probably first made for the Hereditary Homage of the Estates of the Princely County of Tyrol to Emperor Ferdinand I in Innsbruck in 1838. At the Hereditary Homage of the Estates of Lower Austria in Vienna in 1835, black clothing was prescribed for the official period of court mourning following the death of Emperor Franz I.   M. L.-J.

6 THE DOG-COLLAR, INSIGNE OF THE HEREDITARY GRAND MASTER OF THE HUNT
Vienna, 1838 (?)
Dark green velvet, on dark green leather, decorated with gold braiding and gold embroidery. On the silver-gilt mounts with the monogramme of Emperor Ferdinand I is a cord of gold thread interwoven with green silk. (Inv. No. XIV 40)

The dog-collar was worn by the hunting dog led by the Hereditary Grand Master of the Hunt at the ceremony of Hereditary Homage *(Erbhuldigung)*. This one was probably made as late as 1838, for the Hereditary Homage paid by the provincial diet of the Princely County of Tyrol in Innsbruck to Emperor Ferdinand I. Black dress was prescribed for the Hereditary Homage of the Lower Austrian provincial diet in 1835, because the court was in mourning after the death of Emperor Franz I.
M. L.-J.

7 RIDING WHIP FOR THE HEREDITARY GRAND EQUERRY OF THE PRINCELY COUNTY OF TYROL
Vienna (?), 1838
Plaited cane, silver-gilt; 102 cms long (Inv. No. XIV 42)

On the boss of the whip are the arms of the Princely County of Tyrol and the date 1838. The whip was made for the Hereditary Homage of the Tyrolean Estates held on 12. 8. 1838 in Innsbruck. It was carried by the Hereditary Grand Master of the Horse, Ernst, Count Wolkenstein, and placed in the Treasury after the ceremony.
M. L.-J.

8 MAIN DE JUSTICE
Western German (?), 17th century
Gilded and silvered brass, the hand silver; 64.5 cms long (Inv. No. XIV 18)

The form of this sceptre, with its *main de justice* at the end, recalls French insignia. According to tradition used by the government of the Austrian *Vorlande* at investiture ceremonies, the insigne was entrusted to the safekeeping of the Treasury by the United Court Chancery of the Hereditary Lands on 2. 8. 1826.   M. L.-J.

9 STAFF OF THE IMPERIAL COURT OF CHANCERY
German, 16th/17th century
Rosewood, bone, silver; 91 cms long (Inv. No. XIV 17)

This staff was presented to Emperor Ferdinand I in 1837 as a gift of the Assembly of the German Diet, by its president, Count Münch-Bellinghausen. According to one tradition, the staff, which until then had been kept in the Imperial Court of Chancery at Wetzlar, was used by Emperor Maximilian I at the opening of the Imperial Court of Chancery on the Braunfels in Frankfurt on 13. 10. 1495, when he bestowed the rank of Judge of the Imperial Court of Chancery on his Privy Councillor and Grand Comptroller, Eitel Friedrich, Count of Zollern.

However, the form of the staff and the turning indicate that it was made at a later date.   M. L.-J.

10 THE HEREDITARY BANNER OF AUSTRIA

Austria, 1705

The banner: red silk damask embroidered with gold, silver and silk; fringes, cords and tassels: red silk and gold. The staff: wood, red, gold and silver, painted; the point: brass-gilt. The bandolier: red velvet and red silk, embroidered with gold, silver and silk; the mounts: brass-gilt; length of the staff 248 cms (Inv. No. XIV 34)

Among the oldest privileges of the rulers of Austria was that of having the hereditary banner carried before them. For this reason, the banner is regarded as one of the archducal insignia of Austria above and below the Enns, whose respective arms adorn the sides of this swallow-tailed banner. Emperor Leopold I bestowed the hereditary office of Grand Standard-Bearer of the Hereditary Banner of Austria above and below the Enns as a hereditary male fief upon the Counts of Abensperg and Traun; their arms are also embroidered on both sides of the banner. The first member of this house to hold the hereditary office was Otto Ehren-

reich Count of Abensberg and Traun, Knight of the Order of the Golden Fleece, whose arms and monogramme are engraved on the point of the banner. He performed the duties of the office of standard-bearer for the first time at the ceremony of Hereditary Homage to Emperor Joseph I on 22. 9. 1705. It appears that the banner was made for this occasion.

Attested to in 1731, in the inventory of the Small Privy Treasury of Emperor Karl VI, it was transferred from the Imperial-Royal Privy Revenue Office in 1779.   M. L.-J.

11 a) TABARD FOR THE HERALD OF THE LAND OF AUSTRIA BELOW THE ENNS

Vienna, 1740 (?)

Gold and silver lamé, gold, silver and silk embroidery; 107 cms long, 105 cms wide (Inv. No. XIV 67)

Front and back: arms divided vertically. On the left, a silver fesse on a red ground; on the right, five golden eagles on blue. At the ceremonies of the Hereditary Homage held in 1615, 1705 and 1712, the tabard bore only the Austrian *Bindenschild*. From 1740 onwards, it is described as bearing divided arms and in 1790 specifically as having ornamental embroidery on the fesse. The raised embroidery with grotesque forms, however, would belong stylistically to the first half of the 17th century. The fact that it does not quite correspond to the shape of the tabard probably indicates that it had been used elsewhere before. Lining of red silk.   R. B.

Ref.: Püchl 1954, p.46 f., note 10.

b) Herald's staff
Vienna, before 1790
Wood, painted and gilded; 97 cms long (Inv. No. XIV 68)

This turned, white staff ends in a golden knob surmounted by a single-headed gold eagle. First mentioned as having been used at the Hereditary Homage to Emperor Leopold II in 1790.

Ref.: Püchl 1954, p. 47, note 11.

12 a) TABARD FOR THE HERALD OF THE PRINCELY COUNTY OF TYROL
Vienna, 1838
Johann Fritz, civic master embroiderer
Silver lamé, velvet, foils, gold, silver and silk embroidery; 98 cms long, 114 cms wide (Inv. No. XIV 71)

Front and back: crowned, single-headed eagle in red on a silver ground with a green wreath of honour and silver clasps on the wings. The escutcheon surmounted by the princely crown. Appliqué work, raised and silk embroidery. Red silk lining. Made for the ceremony of Hereditary Homage to Emperor Ferdinand I in Tyrol in 1838.

b) Herald's Staff
Vienna, 1838
Wood, painted, gilded, lustred; 93.5 cms long (Inv. No. XIV 72)

On the top of the turned white staff are the arms of Tyrol, surmounted by a crown.   M. L.-J.

13 STAFF OF THE GRAND COMPTROLLER
Southern German, beginning of the 17th century
Cane, painted black, mounts of silver-gilt; 138 cms long (Inv. No. XIV 158)

On the pommel is the *Bindenschild* under the archducal coronet and the monogramme L.E. Z.O., which presumably stands for *Leopold Erzherzog zu Österreich* (Leopold, Archduke of Austria) and probably refers to Leopold V (1586—1632), Regent of Tyrol and the Austrian *Vorlande* (=the Swabian provinces of Austria).
Transferred from the Department of Court Ceremonial in 1922.   M. L.-J.

14 STAFF OF THE HEREDITARY GRAND STEWARD OF THE COUNTY OF GORIZIA
Southern German, c. 1660
Cane, painted black; the mounts: enamelled gold; 136 cms long (Inv. No. XIV 189)

On the mounts the enamelled inscription:
LEOPOLDVS   D(EI)   G(RATIA) ROM(ANORVM)   IMP(ERATOR) SEMP(ER) AVG(VSTVS) / ARCHI-DVX AVSTRIAE COMES GORI-TIAE // DVM RECIPIT HOMA-GIVM / COMITATVS GORITIAE ANNO 1660 // SVPREMO DAPIFE-RORVM / MAGISTRO HAEREDI-TARIO. (Leopold, by the Grace of God Roman Emperor, Archduke of Austria, Count of Gorizia, as he received the Hereditary Homage from the County of Gorizia [presented this] to the Hereditary Grand Steward). On the pommel are the Imperial arms.
Donated to the Treasury in 1947 by Baroness Clarisse von Rothschild in memory of Baron Alphons von Rothschild.   M. L.-J.

13, 14, 15, 17, 23

15 STAFF OF THE HUNGARIAN GRAND EQUERRY

Vienna, 1st quarter of the 18th century
Cane, painted black, mounts of silver-gilt; on the pommel a Viennese hall-mark for 171(9?) and an indistinct, unidentified maker's mark, together with remarks dating from 1806/07, also on the ferrule; 144.5 cms long (Inv. No. XIV 168)

The pommel bears the Imperial double-headed eagle with the monogramme F.M.T. on the breast-shield. This monogramme, which was former-ly assumed to stand for Franz Stephan of Lorraine and Maria Theresia, is more likely to refer to Emperor Franz II (I) and his second wife, Maria Theresia of Bourbon-Sicily and their coronation as King and Queen of Hungary in 1792: Franz Stephan was not King of Hungary. It is in any case an adapta-tion of an older staff.
Transferred from the Direction of the Vienna Hofburg in 1923.   M. L.-J.

16 CANE OF THE HEREDITARY GRAND EQUERRY

Vienna (?), end of the 18th century
Rattan reed; pommel, eye and ferrule

of silver; silver cord and tassels inter-woven with red silk; 95 cms long (Inv. No. XIV 41)

Engraved on the pommel is the mono-gramme F.I. The cane was altered for the ceremony of the Hereditary Hom-age paid to Emperor Ferdinand by the provincial diet of the Archduchy of Austria below the Enns in Vienna in 1835.   M. L.-J.

Ref.: Thomas 1963, p. 342, note 15.

17 STAFF OF A MASTER OF CEREMONIES

Vienna (?), 1st third of the 19th century
Cane, painted white; bronze-gilt; the cord with tassels is missing; 135 cms long (Inv. No. XIV 159)

Pommel surmounted by a pedestal bearing the arms of Austria, Hungary, Bohemia, and Moravia under the Im-perial double-headed eagle. Probably from the reign of Emperor Franz I of Austria. Transferred from the Depart-ment of Court Ceremonial in 1922.
                                           M. L.-J.

18 STAFF OF THE HEREDITARY GRAND COMPTROLLER

Vienna, 1835
Wood, painted black; silver mounts; 152.5 cms long (Inv. No. XIV 45)

On the pommel is the monogramme F.I. beneath the archducal coronet. Made in Vienna in 1835 for the ceremony of the Hereditary Homage paid to Emperor Ferdinand I by the provincial diet of the Archduchy of Austria below the Enns.   M. L.-J.

19 STAFF OF THE HEREDITARY GRAND MASTER OF THE TABLE

Vienna, 1835
Wood, painted black; silver mounts, 133.5 cms long (Inv. No. XIV 46)

The pommel bears the monogramme F.I. below the archducal coronet. Made for the Hereditary Homage of the provincial diet of the Archduchy of Austria below the Enns to Emperor Ferdinand, held in Vienna in 1835.
                                           M. L.-J.

20 STAFF OF A MASTER OF CEREMONIES

Vienna (?), late 19th century
Cane, painted white; bronze-gilt mounts; the cord with tassels is missing; 99.5 cms long (Inv. No. XIV 161)

On the pommel is engraved the Imperial double-eagle, on its breast the cross of the Grand Master of the Order of the Teutonic Knights, above it a shield with the monogramme F.I. It either refers to Emperor Franz I or to Emperor Ferdinand I of Austria. The cross of the Grand Master of the Teutonic Order may indicate the Emperor's suzerainty over the Order of the Teutonic Knights. The staff was probably used at the investiture of a new Grand Master of the Teutonic Order.

Transferred from the Department of Court Ceremonial in 1922.   M. L.-J.

21 STAFF OF A JUNIOR MASTER OF THE TABLE

Vienna (?), beginning of the 19th century
Wood, painted black; mounts of bronze-gilt; 80 cms long (Inv. No. XIV 156)

The pommel bears the monogramme F.I. beneath a royal crown with four arches. This monogramme possibly refers to Ferdinand I, who had been crowned King of Hungary in 1830 during his father's lifetime. On the other hand, this type of crown was also used for the coronets of rank of the Archdukes.

Transferred from the Department of Court Ceremonial in 1922.   M. L.-J.

22 STAFF OF A GRAND MASTER OF THE TABLE

Vienna, c. 1867
Wood, painted black; silver-gilt mounts; 148.5 cms long (Inv. No. XIV 167)

Engraved in lateral inversion on the pommel is the Imperial double-eagle with the arms of Hungary; above it, the Hungarian crown. Next to this is the monogramme F.J. and the date 1867. This staff is a copy of the one used by the Grand Comptroller (Cat. No. 13) and, as the monogramme and date suggest, was made for the coronation of Emperor Franz Joseph I as King of Hungary on 8. 6. 1867.

Transferred from the Direction of the Vienna Hofburg in 1923.   M. L.-J.

23 STAFF OF A GRAND MASTER OF CEREMONIES

Vienna (?), 2nd half of the 19th century
Cane, painted white; bronze-gilt; gold cord, interwoven with black silk, with tassels; 127.5 cms long (Inv. No. XIV 163)

The pommel with the Imperial double-headed eagle goes back to older models. However, since this staff was last carried by Count Eduard von Choloniewski (1846—1928), it probably originated during the reign of Emperor Franz Joseph I.

Transferred from the Department of Court Ceremonial in 1922.   M. L.-J.

CHAMBERLAINS' KEYS

The Chamberlain's Key was a symbol of the Power of the Keys and therefore of admission at court. From the 17th century onwards, the Chamberlain wore this attribute on a pocket of his court dress; later it was worn behind, on a small cushion below the waist seam at hip level and finally, from the 18th century onwards, was additionally covered by a large tassel. Most of the keys on display originally came from the Office of the Grand Chamberlain, and in 1939 they were transferred to the Treasury.   M. L.-J.

24 25 31 38 43

47 49 51 53

24 KEY OF A CHAMBERLAIN OF EMPEROR KARL VI

Austrian (Vienna ?), between 1711 and 1714

Gilded iron; 16 cms long (Inv. No. XIV 204)

Double-bitted key with a sliding bow. This bears Karl's monogramme as Holy Roman Emperor (C VI) on one side, and as King of Spain (C III) on the other. Karl was crowned Holy Roman Emperor in 1711 and bore the title of King of Spain until 1714.   M. L.-J.

25 KEY OF A CHAMBERLAIN OF EMPEROR KARL VI

Austrian (Vienna?), between 1711 and 1714

Gilded iron; 19.3 cms long (Inv. No. XIV 205)

The bow of the key bears the monogramme of Karl as Roman Emperor (C VI) and as King of Spain (C III).
M. L.-J.

26 KEY OF A CHAMBERLAIN OF EMPEROR KARL VI

Austrian (Vienna ?), after 1714
Gilded iron; 18.1 cms long (Inv. No. XIV 206)

On the key's bow is the monogramme of the Emperor, with two Cs dorsally entwined beneath the Imperial crown.
M. L.-J.

27 KEY OF A CHAMBERLAIN OF EMPEROR KARL VI

Austrian (Vienna?), after 1714
Gilded iron; 15.1 cms long (Inv. No. XIV 207)

The bow of the key bears the Emperor's monogramme: two addorsed, intertwining C's, surmounted by the Imperial crown.   M. L.-J.

28 KEY OF A CHAMBERLAIN OF EMPRESS ELISABETH CHRISTINE

Austrian (Vienna ?), after 1714
Iron, the bow gilded; 14.7 cms long (Inv. No. XIV 208)

On the key's bow is the monogramme of the wife of Emperor Karl VI, Elisabeth Christine von Braunschweig-Wolfenbüttel (the initials EC) beneath the Imperial crown.   M. L.-J.

29 KEY OF A CHAMBERLAIN OF ARCHDUCHESS MARIA THERESIA

Austrian (Vienna?), between 1740 and 1741

Gilded iron; 14.9 cms long (Inv. No. XIV 212)

The bow of the key bears the monogramme MT, the T having been sawn out at a later date. The archducal coronet indicates that it originated between the death of Karl VI on 20. 20. 1740 and the coronation of Maria Theresia as Queen of Hungary on 25. 6. 1741.   M. L.-J.

30 KEY OF A CHAMBERLAIN OF EMPEROR FRANZ I AND EMPRESS MARIA THERESIA

Austrian (Vienna ?), between 1745 and 1765

Gilded iron; 18.8 cms long (Inv. No. XIV 209)

On one side of the key's bow is the monogramme F I, on the other side, intertwined, MTR. Emperor Franz I was crowned Emperor in 1745 and died in 1765.   M. L.-J.

31 KEY OF A CHAMBERLAIN OF EMPEROR FRANZ I AND EMPRESS MARIA THERESIA

Austrian (Vienna?), between 1745 and 1765

Brass; 16.8 cms long (Inv. No. XIV 210)

Enclosed in the bow is the Imperial double-headed eagle. On one side the eagle bears a breast-shield surrounded by the neckchain of the Order of the Golden Fleece, with the arms of Lorraine on the right, those of Tuscany on the left and on the inescutcheon the monogramme FI. On the other side, a laurel wreath surrounds the escutcheon with the arms of New Hungary on the right, those of Bohemia on the left and, as the inescutcheon, the Austrian *Bindenschild* with the monogramme MT.   M. L.-J.

32 KEY OF A CHAMBERLAIN OF EMPRESS MARIA THERESIA

Austrian (Vienna ?), c. 1745

Gilded iron; 17.9 cms long (Inv. No. XIV 211)

In the bow is the monogramme MT beneath the Imperial crown (?). M.L.-J.

33 KEY OF A CHAMBERLAIN OF EMPRESS MARIA THERESIA AND EMPEROR JOSEPH II

Vienna (?), between 1765 and 1780

Brass, partially gilded and varnished black; 18.4 cms long (Inv. No. XIV 213)

On the bow is the Imperial double-headed eagle. The breast-shield, surmounted by the crown of Hungary and Bohemia, bears the monogramme MT on one side and J II on the other. Maria Theresia made her son, Emperor Joseph II, co-regent of all the Austrian hereditary kingdoms and dominions on 23. 9. 1765, following the death of her husband, Emperor Franz I. The key was probably varnished black for use during the period of official mourning.   M. L.-J.

34 KEY OF A CHAMBERLAIN OF EMPEROR LEOPOLD II

Vienna (?), between 1790 and 1792

Brass-gilt; 18.3 cms long (Inv. No. XIV 215)

In the bow the Imperial double-eagle. Above its breast-shield, which displays the monogramme L II, are the crowns of Hungary and Bohemia.   M. L.-J.

35 KEY OF A CHAMBERLAIN OF GRAND DUKE FERDINAND III OF TUSCANY

Austrian (?), beginning of the 19th century

Brass-gilt; 18.7 cms long (Inv. No. XIV 216)

The bow bears the cross of the Tuscan Order of St. Stephen, surmounted by a shield. This is divided into three, with the arms of Lorraine on the right, those of Austria in the centre and Tuscany (Medici) on the left; the obverse bears the monogramme F.III. The cross of the order is surmounted by the archducal coronet of Austria. M. L.-J.

36 KEY OF A CHAMBERLAIN OF THE ARCHDUKE AND LATER EMPEROR FRANZ II (?)

Austrian (?), 4th quarter of the 18th century

Brass-gilt; 17.6 cms long (Inv. No. XIV 217)

At the base of the bow is the monogramme F beneath a prince's coronet. The key has also been associated with Franz Stephan of Lorraine and Tuscany; before his election as Holy Roman Emperor in 1745 he too could have been intended by the monogramme.   M. L.-J.

Ref.: Pickl von Witkenberg, 1903, plate between pp. 204 and 205.

37 KEY OF A CHAMBERLAIN OF EMPEROR FRANZ II (I)

Vienna(?), between 1792 and 1806

Brass-gilt; 18.3 cms long (Inv. No. XIV 190)

The bow bears the Imperial double-headed eagle with a breast-shield dis-

playing the monogramme FII, and surmounted by the crowns of Hungary
and Bohemia. Engraved on the shaft is
the inscription: *"Dem Marschall Lefebvre Herzog von Danzig. Franz II."*
(To Marshal Lefebvre, Duke of Danzig.
Franz II.) It remains questionable
whether the inscription is genuine:
Lefebvre became Duke in 1808, but by
that time Franz II was already Franz I
of Austria!
Acquired from a private collection in
1949.   M. L.-J.

38 KEY OF A CHAMBERLAIN OF EMPEROR FRANZ I OF AUSTRIA

Vienna (?), between 1806 and 1835
Brass, partially gilded and varnished
black; 18.4 cms long (Inv. No. XIV
220)

In the bow is the Imperial eagle, and
above its breast shield, which bears the
monogramme F I, is the crown of Hungary and Bohemia. After the dissolution of the Holy Roman Empire in
1806, Franz II became Franz I of Austria. The black varnishing indicates
that the key was used at times of court
mourning.   M. L.-J.

39 KEY OF A CHAMBERLAIN OF EMPEROR FERDINAND I OF AUSTRIA

Vienna (?), 1835—1848
Silver-gilt; on the bit the hallmark of
the Imperial-Royal (k.k.) Office of the
Grand Chamberlain and the as yet unidentified maker's mark PSW; 18 cms
long (Inv. No. XIV 222)

The shield displays the Imperial eagle,
which bears a cross on its breast, surmounted by a shield with the
monogramme F I. It was rare for a
chamberlain's key to be made of silver.
                                                 M. L.-J.

40 KEY OF A CHAMBERLAIN OF EMPEROR FRANZ JOSEPH I

Vienna (?), after 1848
Brass-gilt; 16.6 cms long (Inv. No. XIV
227)

In the bow is the Imperial eagle. On its
breast is a cross, upon which is a shield,
charged with the monogramme F.J.I.
and surrounded by the neckchain of
the Order of the Golden Fleece.
                                                 M. L.-J.

41 KEY OF A CHAMBERLAIN OF EMPEROR FRANZ JOSEPH I

Vienna (?), after 1848
Brass, partially gilded and varnished
black; 16.6 cms long (Inv. No. XIV
228)

Identical in form to the previous key.
The black varnish, however, indicates
that it was used during a period of
court mourning.   M. L.-J.

42 KEY OF A CHAMBERLAIN OF EMPEROR FRANZ JOSEPH I

Vienna (?), 4th quarter of 19th century
Brass-gilt; 15.2 cms long (Inv. No. XIV
231)

The key belongs to the later type of
chamberlain's key in use under Emperor Franz Joseph I. In the bow is ornamentation and the intertwined
monogramme FJI in filigree work.
Above it is the Austrian Imperial
crown.   M. L.-J.

43 KEY OF A CHAMBERLAIN OF EMPEROR FRANZ JOSEPH I with accompanying tassel

Vienna (?), last quarter of the 19th
century
Brass-gilt; metal threads, bouillon,
mounted on a card covered with yellow
silk; 15.6 cms long (Inv. No. XIV 232)

The key itself is of the same type as
Cat. No. 42.   M. L.-J.

44 KEY OF A CHAMBERLAIN OF EMPEROR KARL I

Vienna (?), between 1916 and 1918
Brass-gilt; 15.6 cms long (Inv. No. XIV
262)

The design of the key follows in simplified form the later type of key of a
chamberlain of Emperor Franz Joseph
I. Within the bow is the initial K.

Gift of Baron Friedrich Leopold Popper von Podhrágy to Dr. Géza Baron Kövess von Kövessháza. The latter presented it to the Treasury in 1973.

M. L.-J.

45 KEY OF A CHAMBERLAIN OF THE PRINCE ARCHBISHOP OF SALZBURG, HIERONYMUS, COUNT COLLOREDO

Salzburg, between 1772 and 1803
Silver-gilt; 15.9 cms long (Inv. No. XIV 191)

The bow, in the form of a laurel wreath, encloses a pavilion. Above this is a prince's coronet resting on a crozier and sword, the emblems of ecclesiastical and secular power respectively.

Below this are the arms of the archbishopric, combined with those of the last reigning Prince Archbishop of Salzburg, Hieronymus, Count Colloredo, below the archbishop's coronet. Hieronymus, Count Colloredo, was elected on 14. 3. 1772, fled before the advancing French army on 3. 12. 1800, renounced his secular rule on 11. 2. 1803 and died on 20. 5. 1812. After its secularisation in 1803, Salzburg was granted to Ferdinand II of Tuscany as an electoral principality (in compensation for the titular domains which had been taken from him) and became part of Austria in 1805.

Acquired in 1955 with the support of the Verein der Museumsfreunde, Vienna.

M. L.-J.

STEWARDS' BADGES OF OFFICE

The Stewards were next in rank to the Chamberlains, belonging to the external Court household. The honorary duties of these court dignitaries consisted of attendance at table, and in particular at the 'Feeding of the Aged' which took place after the foot-washing ceremony on the Thursday before Easter. They were subordinate to the Junior Master of the Table and thus to the staff of the Grand Comptroller. Their badge of honour is similar in form to the bow of the chamberlains' keys, although it has merely a cleft shaft instead of a shaft and bit. It was also worn on the hip with a tassel.

M. L.-J.

46 BADGE OF HONOUR OF THE GRAND STEWARD OF EMPEROR FERDINAND I
with a tassel of Emperor Franz Joseph I

Vienna (?), c. 1848
Brass gilt; the edge of the bow perforated; the tassel of gold thread, bouillon and sequins on card covered with yellow silk; 11.8 cms long (Inv. No. XIV 236)

The bow of the clip-shaped badge of honour resembles, on a smaller scale, that of the key of a chamberlain of Ferdinand I. On the tassel below the double-eagle, however, is the monogramme of Emperor Franz Joseph I, formed from the intertwined initials FJI. It is thus possibly from the first years of this Emperor's reign. M. L.-J.

47 BADGE OF HONOUR OF A STEWARD OF EMPEROR FRANZ JOSEPH I
without tassel

Vienna (?), middle of the 19th century
Brass-gilt, partially varnished black; edge of the bow perforated; 11.8 cms long (Inv. No. XIV 238)

This badge of honour differs from that of Emperor Ferdinand I only in the monogramme; here: FJI.

M. L.-J.

48 BADGE OF HONOUR OF THE GRAND STEWARD OF EMPEROR FRANZ JOSEPH I
with tassel

Vienna (?), 2nd half of the 19th century
Brass-gilt; partially varnished black; the tassel: gold thread, bouillon and sequins on card covered with yellow silk; 13.1 cms long (Inv. No. XIV 239)

The bow repeats in simplified form, and on a smaller scale, the design of the earlier key of a chamberlain of Emperor Franz Joseph I. On the tassel below the double-eagle is the monogramme FJI.   M. L.-J.

49 BADGE OF HONOUR OF A STEWARD OF EMPEROR FRANZ JOSEPH I
with the tassel of Emperor Karl I
Vienna, beginning of the 20th century
Brass-gilt; tassel: gold thread, bouillon and sequins on leather covered with yellow silk; 14.9 cms long (Inv. No. XIV 192)

The bow follows, albeit in reduced form, those of the later Chamberlains' keys of Emperor Franz Joseph I. On the tassel, instead of the traditional double-headed eagle, are the Minor Imperial arms, created in 1915/16. A shield, surmounted by the neckchain of the Order of the Golden Fleece, bears the arms of Habsburg on the right, those of Austria in the centre and on the left those of Lorraine. It is surmounted by the Austrian Imperial Crown and the royal Hungarian crown; beneath it are two K's.
Donated to the Treasury in 1955 by Kommerzialrat Hans Maurer.   M. L.-J.

BADGES OF HONOUR OF THE JUNIOR TABLE MASTERS
The Junior Table Masters were subordinate to the Grand Master of the Table and thus to the Grand Comptroller's staff. They served as the connecting link between the stewards during service at table. Their badges of honour resembled the bow of the chamberlains' keys, although this is here combined with two black rods with gilded bosses. They were also worn at the hip with a tassel.   M. L.-J.

50 BADGE OF HONOUR OF THE JUNIOR TABLE MASTER OF EMPEROR FRANZ JOSEPH I
without tassel
Vienna (?), 3rd quarter of the 19th century
Brass-gilt; partially varnished black; 13.5 cms long (Inv. No. XIV 241)

The bow is a variation, in simplified form and on a smaller scale, of the design of the earlier type of chamberlain's key used under Emperor Franz Joseph I.   M. L.-J.

51 BADGE OF HONOUR OF A JUNIOR TABLE MASTER OF EMPEROR FRANZ JOSEPH I
with tassel
Vienna (?), 3rd quarter of the 19th century
Brass-gilt; tassel: gold thread, bouillon, sequins and coloured silk on card covered with yellow silk; 13.4 cms long (Inv. No. XIV 240)

On the tassel is the monogramme of Emperor Franz Joseph I surmounted by the Imperial Austrian Crown.
M. L.-J.

52 BADGE OF HONOUR OF THE JUNIOR TABLE MASTER OF EMPEROR FRANZ JOSEPH I
with tassel
Vienna (?), 4th quarter of the 19th century
Brass-gilt; partially lacquered black; the tassel: gold thread, bouillon, sequins and coloured silk on card covered with yellow silk; 16.2 cms long (Inv. No. XIV 248)

The top of this badge of honour presents a variation of the previous pieces, although this one exhibits heavy, neo-baroque forms.   M. L.-J.

53 BADGE OF HONOUR OF A JUNIOR TABLE MASTER OF EMPEROR FRANZ JOSEPH I
without tassel
Vienna (?), end of the 19th century
Brass-gilt, partially varnished black; 15.9 cms long (Inv. No. XIV 246)

A variation on the previous badge of honour, with more delicate, late neo-baroque forms. On one side of the double-headed eagle's breast-shield is

the monogramme of Emperor Franz
Joseph I: FJI; on the other side the
Austrian *Bindenschild.*   M. L.-J.

54 BADGE OF HONOUR OF THE JUNIOR TABLE MASTER OF EMPEROR FRANZ JOSEPH I
without tassel

Vienna, beginning of the 20th century
Brass-gilt; partially lacquered black;
14.3 cms long (Inv. No. XIV 249)

The design of the bow matches that of
the last type of chamberlain's key in
use under Emperor Franz Joseph I.
                                   M. L.-J.

55 THE ARCHDUCAL GOWN
Vienna, 1764

Red drugget-type silk weave, brocaded
with gold and silver, frisé and smooth;
front length 127 cms, back length 133
cms (Inv. No. XIV 116)

Of magnificent red silk, this narrow
robe widens slightly towards the hem
and has an asymmetrical opening at
the front with three buttons. The pattern consists of criss-crossing bands of
gold resulting in a lozenge-shaped pattern. Each lozenge contains a spray
composed of two rose blossoms and
one silver leaf (pattern repeat: H 10
cms, W 9 cms). The robe has long, narrow sleeves fastened with small buttons. Belonging to the robe is a belt of
the same material, 6.6 cms wide and
115.5 cms long, with a clasp of gilded
brass mesh and a baldric for a sword.
The robe was worn by Archduke
Joseph (later Emperor Joseph II) for
the processional entry into the Church

of St. Bartholomew in Frankfurt on
the occasion of his coronation as King
of Rome on 27. 3. 1764. For the same
occasion, copies of the coronation
robes of the Holy Roman Empire were
made for his father, Emperor Franz I
(Cat. No. 179a-k). In an addendum to
the Treasury inventory of 16. 12. 1750,
the *"new archducal habit, fashioned
for His Majesty the King's coronation"* is listed in all its parts. The red
velvet mantle trimmed with ermine has
not survived, but the archducal gown
can be identified in the description of
*"a brownish-coloured gown, rich with
gold and silver, sword baldric and belt
with a smooth clasp of the same gilt
brass without ornament."* With the
new robe, Joseph wore a new archducal
coronet, set with brilliants and pearls
(Cat. No. 3).   R. B.

Ref.: J. Petraschek-Heim, Teile eines Ornates
Kaiser Josephs II., in: Waffen- und Kostümkunde,
1977, p. 45—46.

THE AUSTRIAN EMPIRE

Napoleon's victories and the imminent danger of the disintegration of the Holy Roman Empire eventually forced Franz II, ruler of the Empire, King of Bohemia and Hungary and Archduke of Austria, to proclaim the Hereditary Empire of Austria on 11. 8. 1804. He thus became its first Emperor. Almost exactly two years later, on 6. 8. 1806, he dissolved the Holy Roman Empire, in compliance with one of Napoleon's demands. He was no longer able to count on the support of a number of German princes who had joined forces to form the *Rheinbund* (Confederation of the Rhine) under French protection and had proclaimed their secession from the Empire. The new Empire comprised all the territories belonging to the House of Habsburg, i.e. the Austrian hereditary lands and the kingdoms of Bohemia and Hungary, Galicia and Lodomeria. The constitution of the federation of these hereditary lands was unaffected by the assumption of the title of Emperor by the head of the House of Austria. The official insignia chosen for the Hereditary Austrian Empire were the crown of Emperor Rudolf II (Cat. No. 56), which had often been used as the dynastic crown of the *Casa de Austria,* and the orb and sceptre of his brother and successor, Emperor Matthias. However, despite the fact that it had been provided for, no coronation of a Hereditary Austrian Emperor ever took place.

In 1830, a suitable set of vestments had to be made for Emperor Franz I for the coronation of his son, Ferdinand, as younger King of Hungary. The commission was entrusted to the Director of Costumes at the Court Theater, Philipp von Stubenrauch. The Emperor was presented with two designs and decided on the one marked with a cross. An undergarment was not necessary, since Franz I decided to wear the uniform of a Hungarian general under the mantle. On this occasion the Emperor did not use the Rudolfine crown, wearing instead a specially made, much lighter crown, subsequently recorded in the Treasury inventories as the substitute Imperial crown. The carcass was made by the Viennese silver manufacturer Mayerhofer, and the gemstones were set by von Mack, jeweller to the Imperial Court. The carcass was melted down in 1871/72. The probable appearance of the crown can be reconstructed from Stubenrauch's designs.

Reward for civilian services to the state was provided for by the establishment of two secular orders: in 1808, Emperor Franz I created the Austrian Order of Leopold, in memory of his father, Emperor Leopold II. In 1816, he revived the Order of the Iron Cross, originally founded by Napoleon in 1805. Together with the Hungarian Order of St. Stephen, founded in 1764 by Maria Theresia on the occasion of her son Joseph's coronation as King of Rome, these three orders comprise the Orders of the House of Austria. The robes belonging to these orders are today kept in the Montur Depot in the Kunsthistorische Museum. In addition to the above-mentioned orders, there was the Military Order of Maria Theresia, founded by the Empress in 1757, to which only officers could belong.   R. B.

Ref.: Fillitz 1956, pp. 123—146; idem, Die österreichische Kaiserkrone, Vienna/Munich 1959; Catalogue, Uniform und Mode 1983.

56 THE CROWN OF RUDOLF II, LATER CROWN OF THE AUSTRIAN EMPIRE

Jan Vermeyen († 1606 Prague)
Prague, 1602
Gold, partially enamelled, diamonds, rubies, spinel rubies, sapphire, pearls, velvet; 28.3 cms high, circlet 22.4 cms diameter (with pearls), largest span (over the fleurs-de-lys on the brow and neck): 27.8 cms (Inv. No. XIa 1)
Inside the arch is the inscription: RVDOLPHVS · II · ROM (ANORVM) · IMP(ERATOR) · AVG (VSTVS) · HVNG(ARIAE) · ET BOH (EMIAE) · REX · CONSTRVXIT · MDCII (Made for Rudolf II, Roman Emperor, King of Hungary and Bohemia, in 1602).

In 1424, the insignia and jewels of the Holy Roman Empire were entrusted to the City of Nuremberg by Emperor Sigismund, and they were thereafter only used for the coronation ceremony. On all the other occasions when the Emperor had to appear in public wearing the crown, he had to have a personal crown made. The crown of Emperor Rudolf II is the only one of these personal crowns which has survived.

Emperor Matthias, Rudolf's brother and successor, commissioned an orb and sceptre to go with it. Emperor Ferdinand II declared the insignia to be treasures of the House of Austria, which ensured their preservation since they were no longer at the free disposition of any one individual. This crown was designated the crown of the House and, since it was a private possession of the Imperial family, had no state function. When Emperor Franz II adopted the title of Emperor of Austria on 11. 8. 1804 — in response to Napoleon's self-exaltion as 'Emperor of the French' — he chose it as the crown of the Austrian Empire. In this way something of the old tradition of the Holy Roman Empire, which came to an end two years later, was tacitly transferred to the new hereditary empire. The crown was never actually used for a coronation, since the right of succession to the new title of Emperor was not dependent upon an election or a coronation, but upon the legal right of succession.

The crown itself consists of three principal elements, each of them possessing great symbolic significance: the actual circlet with its fleur-de-lys mounts, which constitute a crown in their own right (cf. the crown of King Christian IV of Denmark, dating from 1596, in Copenhagen); the Imperial high arch from the brow to the neck (cf. the Imperial Crown, Cat. No. 153); and the mitre, which symbolises the Emperor's unique spiritual status as pontifex by divine right. This form of crown had a long tradition even at that time. As early as the 14th century, Karl IV is depicted wearing a similar mitre crown. This implies that personal crowns had existed even before 1424, as substitutes for the old Imperial crown, which had already attained the status of a relic. Time after time they were redesigned in accordance with the taste of the period. The crowns of Maximilian I and Karl V, also mitre crowns, were broken up and sold by Philip II in 1562. The predecessor of the Rudolfine crown was the crown of Ferdinand I, since no new insignia were made under Maximilian II.

Combining the extremely high expectations of the Emperor and the art of a goldsmith of genius, the Rudolfine crown represents the mitre crown at the height of its perfection. It bears no signature and, until now, no written sources concerning its manufacture have been discovered. Nevertheless, it can with certainty be concluded that it was made by Jan Vermeyen. The son of the painter Jan Cornelisz Vermeyen of Brussels, he moved from Antwerp to Frankfurt in 1589, evidently as a religious refugee, and thence to Vienna in 1597, from where he was summoned in the same year by Rudolf II to serve as court goldsmith in Prague. The most important arguments for his authorship of the crown are as follows: after October 1602, the year in which the crown was completed, the Emperor doubled his payments to Vermeyen, who had been receiving a supplementary 100 gulden per year, in addition to his monthly salary, ever since 1598; in the *Kunstkammer* inventory of Rudolf II, Vermeyen is described as a jeweller, and the crown is predominantly the work of a jeweller; in the Emperor's court household index there are no other goldsmiths who come into consideration; for this great task the master sent for assistants, whom he obviously knew from his time in Frankfurt: the Antwerp lapidaries Jan Moors and Jost Gelwe were brought from Frankfurt to Prague in 1598 and 1600 respectively *"for special work"*, the former returning there in 1602. In these years between 1598 and 1602 the Prague court workshop, which was responsible for so many outstanding achievements, produced its most important pieces of goldsmiths' work; among them this crown — in the opinion of many, the most beautiful crown in the world.

Vermeyen succeeded in creating a work of the greatest balance and clarity, in which he rounded the mitre crown into a classical form. The circlet, the wreath of fleurs-de-lys and the mitre are all differentiated in such a way that each element retains its significance. For each part of the crown the master has invented ornamental forms and decorative devices with their own particular character which are not repeated on any other part, although all of them are subordinate to the unity of the whole. Just as the torches once lit up the lines of the palaces in ceremonial illumination, so the shimmering rows of pearls accompany all of the crown's principal contours. Its richness encourages the capacity of heightened visual perception, such as the Emperor himself possessed. At the same time it is the perfect expression of Rudolf's elevated ideas of emperorship.

The circlet is dominated by the eight large and severe squares of the diamonds. They are set in the main axes and diagonals, the stone above the brow standing out in particular, on account of its greater size. Between the stones are two large pearls, one above the other, within white enamel rosettes and surrounded by scrollwork. In the circlet is a regular arrangement of drilled holes which have nothing to do with the existing stones. Two round holes, one vertically above the other, alternate with two square horizontal holes. It cannot, as was previously supposed, be a case of making provisions for another grouping of the existing stones and pearls, since there would be no room for them. Furthermore, a coloured drawing of the crown dating from 1610 conclusively proves that the existing arrangement is the original one. The most probable explanation is that Rudolf reused the circlet of the crown of Emperor Ferdinand I, so that the crown would bear a mark of tradition, and connect him with his predecessors. In the case of precious stones, such reuse often occurred, and there is evidence of it here too, among the larger rubies.

In the fleur-de-lys mounts, which incline outwards slightly, it is the ruby that dominates. Four large fleurs-de-lys in the main axes alternate with four smaller ones in the diagonals. In pictorial representations, the fleur-de-lys crown makes its first appearance in the 9th century with Charles the Bald. Throughout the whole of the Middle Ages it remained the most popular form of crown in the west, be

it as an insigne, or in one of the numerous depictions of the Madonna. Towards the end of the Middle Ages, on pictures of Friedrich III or Maximilian I, for instance, the fleurs-de-lys are often interwoven with a mass of intertwining late-Gothic foliate decoration, creating an almost complete wreath of leaves. Our master borrows from earlier medieval examples, such as the crown on the reliquary of Charlemagne in Aix-la-Chapelle or the crown of Wenceslas, because he is intent upon making a clear distinction of forms. The crab-like mounts on the outline of the fleur-de-lys are reminiscent of Gothic architecture. Black enamelled eagle claws in the centre of the principal fleur-de-lys hold a large ruby (the stones above the brow and left ear are spinel rubies which were mistaken for rubies). In front of the ajouré leaves are pointed diamonds, at each of the outwardly curving bases a table diamond, surrounded by the most exquisite bunches of fruit or by volutes. Large stones en cabochon exhibiting old drill holes decorate the fleurs-de-lys above the brow and the neck. Especially valuable pear-shaped pearls surmount the two fleurs-de-lys. The stones were obviously once set in earlier insignia.

A highly idiosyncratic design informs the smaller fleurs-de-lys. The way the stones are set does not follow any predetermined form and does not merely serve to ornament the fleurs-de-lys, but creates a separate pattern in its own right. The ten rubies en cabochon form a small obelisk with an extended base. The resulting stele, which is flanked by white enamel decoration, stands in front of an elongated triangle with concave sides and surfaces which have been delicately roughened, and whose long points penetrate beyond the filigree trefoil of the fleurs-de-lys. Behind the fleurs-de-lys, the elegant, sweeping curves of the mitre rise from the circlet. In contrast to ecclesiastical custom, it has been rotated through 90 degrees. Thus it has not been modelled on the infula of a bishop, but on that of an Old Testament high priest. In the 14th century an episcopal infula was still worn beneath the crown, but when the symbolism of the old imperial crown was adopted for personal crowns in the 15th century, it was turned parallel to the arch, just as the mitre of the high priest was depicted in paintings. Up until the time of Maximilian I it was still made of cloth, richly set with pearls and enamels and at most stiffened by a golden frame. In the crown of Rudolf, the mitre made of gold constitutes an essential part of the main body of the crown. It bears no precious stones. The mitre's golden surfaces, which are enlivened by bas-reliefs, are enclosed by the colourful enamel bands on a white ground as if by sumptuous embroidery. For technical reasons, each of these bands was made in several pieces. Cast and colourful enamel rosettes of fruits conceal the joins. The long bands to the brow and the neck, symmetrical from the side view, display admirably intricate grotesques of birds, butterflies, dragonflies, fruits and baldaquins, all made of translucent enamel. At the base of the mitre is another broad golden ornamental band with champlevé enamels, which is deliberately restrained, so as not to enter into competition with the circlet. Here again, Vermeyen has thought out new ornamental designs for the mitre which do not appear on any other part of the crown.

In the four golden spherical triangles Rudolf II is depicted in his four principal offices. The reliefs are exquisitely chased and chiselled and the details differentiated using matt and burnished gold. The sequence of the relief is neither to be read chronologically, nor from the side view, from where they can best be seen. Rather, in both the front and rear view of the crown, it follows the official sequence of titles inscribed in the arch: front left, Rudolf as *Imperator* (Commander), right as *Augustus* (Emperor), rear left as *Rex Hungariae* (King of Hungary), right as *Rex Bohemiae* (King of Bohemia). In the first relief, Rudolf is being celebrated for his victory over the Turks. He appears in full armour with the sceptre in his hand. The spirit of victory crowns him with the laurel wreath, which at the same time gleams like a sign from heaven above him. Rudolf here no longer stands solely for himself, but for the invincibility of the western Empire. From the right a winged genius of peace approaches him. The female figure behind him may represent the goddess of peace, or perhaps Hungaria, under the protection of the Emperor. In front of him lie the weapons of the enemy, the Turks, two of whose number crouch in chains in the bottom corners, hidden by the fleurs-de-lys. The second relief shows the coronation of Rudolf as Roman

Emperor in the Cathedral of Regensburg on 1. 11. 1575. He kneels on a cushion in front of the Archbishop of Mainz, who places the crown upon his head. The Archbishop is surrounded by six prince electors, the seventh being Rudolf himself. Since, as King of Bohemia, he was himself a prince elector, he had here to be represented in this office by another of those seated around him (see Cat. No. 140). At the right edge can be seen the altar, in the background the choir with the kettledrummers and fanfare players. To the left, below, again concealed by the fleur-de-lys, stands the herald of the Holy Roman Empire, displaying the double-headed eagle on his back. A score of knights surround the scene. On the third relief Rudolf can be seen riding up the coronation hill in Pressburg for his coronation as King of Hungary (on 26. 9. 1572). Sword in hand, he is in the act of performing the four sword-strokes towards the four regions of the world, a gesture symbolising that he will defend the kingdom against all foes. Here, the fleur-de-lys bottom left conceals the Hungarian coat-of-arms. The coronation took place in Pressburg, which at that time was still Hungarian, because Ofen was in the hands of the Turks. In the fourth relief we see Rudolf in procession at his coronation as King of Bohemia in Prague on 22. 1. 1575. As stipulated in the coronation regulations, two worthy old men carry before the procession the bast shoes and the tunic of the legendary ancestor of the Bohemian kings, the Ploughman Přemysl. Bottom right, the fleur-de-lys hides the shield with the Bohemian lion. On all four reliefs Rudolf is depicted as if in a portrait. This is probably the first and last time that a king and emperor has had himself portrayed on an insigne. This indicates, on the one hand, the personal nature of the crown, on the other, Rudolf's extreme self-identification with the offices he united in his person.

In the Imperial high arch, which rises above everything else, diamonds, rubies and pearls are combined in rhythmical alternation to produce the highest, densest and liveliest enhancement of the form. On the top, pointed diamonds alternate with pearls in groups of three, the middle one being slightly larger. On the sides, a pair of pearls lies below the respective diamonds, and below the pearls is a ruby en cabachon. All the pearls are underlaid with red enamel rosettes. The top is crowned with a small Greek cross with trefoil ends and a small diamond set in the centre. It supports an exceedingly large dark-blue sapphire, of a type which is only found in Kashmir. It is the only sapphire on the crown, and it is placed even higher than the cross.

In all pictorial representations of mitred crowns the cross is either above the fleur-de-lys on the brow (borrowing from the Imperial Crown) or on the top of the arch, usually above a small orb (the worldly globe). Here the cross supports a magnificent jewel. This uniqueness cannot be due to some act of caprice on the part of the goldsmith, but has some deeper significance, indicated in the shift of emphasis from the cross to the gem. If, however, this gem possesses some special significance, then we must also assume the same of all the other stones on the crown.

While the different gems form the greatest part of the decoration of the crown, they are at the same time its greatest secret. Thus, just as the form of the crown borrows from medieval models, its symbolic significance is influenced by older insignia, if it does indeed represent the venerated Imperial Crown. An emperor like Rudolf II would not have been satisfied with something which was simply a splendid ornament. That would not fit in with his distinct sense of rank, his exaggerated concept of emperorship, or with his love of jewels, in which he believed great powers resided. *"The emperor loves precious stones"*, wrote his physician Anselmus Boetius de Boot in his book 'Gemmarum et lapidum historia', printed in 1609 *"not in order*

with their help to increase his own honour and majesty, the greatness of which has no need of external support, but rather in order to behold in the precious stones the greatness and ineffable power of God, who in such minute bodies seems to have united the beauty of the whole world and enclosed the powers of all other things, and in order always to have there before his eyes a certain reflection and shimmer of godliness". Evidence of this is also to be found in the crown that he commissioned. Furthermore, Rudolf, who was always seeking a mystery behind ordinary things, was certainly familiar with the ancient symbolism of gemstones. Only diamonds, rubies, one sapphire and pearls were used in the crown. The emerald is missing. Nobody has yet ventured an elucidation of the meaning of the stone in this context. The area is too deep, for every gem has as many significations as it has properties, and for each property there are at least four possible interpretations. Although for this very reason we shall not arrive at any unequivocal conclusion, an attempt at interpretation ought to be made.

The one stone on the crown which actually shines is the pearl. Of this stone, Physiologus, who wrote somewhere around the year 200 A.D. and enjoyed great authority until well into the Enlightenment, says that it comes into being from mussels rising to the surface of the water, drinking the heavenly dust and imbibing the beams of the sun, moon and the stars. From these heavenly lights they bear pearls. The pearls in the crown are there as lights accompanying all the various forms. They require no further explanation.

The eight large diamonds of the circlet suggest the appearance of the number eight in the basic form of the Imperial Crown. The number eight has since time immemorial been used in monuments of imperial representation. It was not only associated with baptism but also signified the period of the rule of the risen Christ, the last period in the history of the salvation of the world (that of the present age), the time of mercy (in the Imperial Crown the brow-plate symbolises the New Testament, see Cat. No. 153). As double four — the number of the created world, with its four elements, four heavenly directions, four regions of the earth and so on — the number eight also signifies the perfect universe. This signification could contain the reason for only using diamonds in the circlet. Throughout the centuries, one meaning of the diamond has been retained, namely, that which can be derived from its Greek name: *Adamas,* meaning the invincible. The hardest stone conquers all and is itself not conquered by anything. Even in Physiologus these qualities are linked to Christ, who could not be conquered by evil, who judged all but cannot be judged by anyone. In the Imperial Crown, Christ was represented by the 'Waise' (orphan) stone (see Cat. No. 153) and in the enamel *Majestas Domini* plate he says: *"By me kings reign".* The empire becomes a reflection of the kingdom of heaven. The emperor does not derive his power from himself but from above, by the grace of God. He is Christ's representative on earth and ultimately responsible to him. The circlet accordingly symbolises the sacral dignity of the Empire in the age of salvation.

The symbolic structure which unfolds horizontally in the Imperial Crown is here developed in a vertical direction. The most salient characteristic of the ruby, which dominates the fleur-de-lys zone, is the fire of its deep red colour. For the Latin and Greek exegetes, this stone's colour made it a symbol of the state of being filled with the fire of the Holy Spirit. Red is also the ecclesiastical colour for Whitsun. It may well be that in this way the wisdom of the king is symbolised, to which reference is also made in one of the plates of the Imperial Crown. In the small fleurs-de-lys the red stones are built up in layers into obelisks, which were likewise regarded as symbols of wisdom. However, in the fleurs-de-lys and in the peculiar arrangement of the gems, numerological allegorism will also have played a role. The context and the whole pattern of meaning contained in this important zone has yet to be revealed.

The ruler's dignity as high priest, expressed by the mitre, has already been mentioned. *"As Vicar of Christ, the Emperor embodied sovereign dignity and sacral priesthood. When sovereign office is conceived as divine mission, the distinction between the office of ruler and that of priest dissappears."* (see Cat. No. 153).

In the blue sapphire one recognises the colour of the heavens. Even in the Bible it is associated with the heavens. The foundations of Jerusalem, both the future (Is. 54,11) and the heavenly city (Rev. 21,19), will be made of sapphire. It must have signified the goal of the earthly path, which is present to the eyes of all believers: heaven. Probably for that reason the jewel stands above the cross, which is the key to heaven. The path leads via the cross to glory.

Of necessity, this first attempt at an interpretation of the crown remains vague and incomplete. It is to be understood as an indication that there is another level of meaning of the crown which still has to be revealed, that the crown of Rudolf contains a pattern of meaning of the greatest significance, and that behind the scheme of its design, there was certainly, beside the Emperor himself, also a court humanist.   R. D.

Ref.: Weixlgärtner 1928, p. 279 ff; H. Fillitz, Studien zur Krone Kaiser Rudolfs II, in: Kunstmuseets Årsskrift, Copenhagen 1950, p. 79 ff; H. Fillitz, Die österreichische Kaiserkrone, Vienna/Munich 1959; Distelberger 1985, p. 278 ff.

57 THE IMPERIAL ORB

Andreas Osenbruck (dates unknown)
Prague, between 1612 and 1615
Gold, partially enamelled, diamonds, rubies, one sapphire, pearls; 26.9 cms high (Inv. No. XIa 3)

Emperor Mathias commissioned the Imperial orb and the sceptre as the accompanying insignia for the crown of Rudolf II. It is unsigned, and there is also no written source to prove that Andreas Osenbruck, goldsmith to the Imperial court, was its creator; never-

theless, his hand is unmistakeable. This piece, too, consciously imitates medieval models in its basic lines (cf. Cat. Nos. 2 and 161). The orb continues the formal concept of the crown, while simultaneously modifying it. As in the crown, only diamonds, rubies and pearls are used, and the cross is crowned by a sapphire. The broad equatorial band, like the circlet of the crown, is edged with rows of pearls, set with four large, square, table-cut diamonds, between which are pairs of pearls set on enamel rosettes.

The number four signified the created world in its entirety, the cosmos, which is also symbolised by the sphere of the Imperial orb itself (cf. Cat. No. 161). In contrast to Vermeyen, Osenbruck demands more than just nobility of form: he inlays the gold ground with delicate, wide-meshed ornamentation of black, blue and green champlevé enamel, which also covers the surfaces of the cross with fine tracery. Superimposed upon this are small bunches of fruit, as well as the large squares of the dia-

mond settings and volutes on either side of the pearls. This dense wealth of detail is effectively counterpointed by the smooth surfaces of the orb. These were in fact originally decorated in pointillé technique, although only traces of this can be seen today, and are too fine to reveal whether the decoration was ornamental or figural, the surfaces having been polished smooth at a later date. The narrow enamel bands are decorated with animals, flowers and fruits of similar design to those on the bands of the mitre on the crown, and are also attached with bunches of fruit. The pole is surrounded by a circle of diamonds around the base of the cross, and this is matched by another ring on which the orb stands.

The cross, with its heavy, massive proportions, stands directly on a square socle, from which rise four cleft volutes, forming the transition to the circular form of the pole ring. On the front of the cross, large table diamonds adorn the intersection and each trefoiled end. Powerful red volutes well out from under their rectangular settings. The prominence of these stones on the cross could confirm the symbolism of the diamonds in the crown, which purportedly relates to Christ. However, the significance of the four large rubies on the arms of the cross could be so multivalent that it is perhaps wiser to avoid any interpretation. The back of the cross is equally richly decorated: here again, the artist unreins a profusion of ornamental detail. Large, colourful bunches of fruit overlay the ornamental network of the ground at the extremities and on the intersection, the intervening surfaces being occupied by motifs in white ajouré enamel, with a red almond in the centre of each. The sides of the arms of the cross are also embellished with tiny bunches of fruit over delicate enamel bands. The tips of the cross and the angles formed by its arms are embellished with fine pearls. The surmounting uncut, polished sapphire is of outstanding colour and great age. It has been pierced, which points to it having been used in other pieces in the Middle Ages or possibly even in late antiquity. The close stylistic correspondence between orb and sceptre is self-evident. Osenbruck signed the sceptre, and his personal style can be illustrated by a few striking details. The sceptre displays the same small bunches of fruit and the delicate champlevé enamel network of the ground is repeated in a similar fashion on the barely visible undersides of the volutes on the bulb of the sceptre and on parts of the central gold tube. Osenbruck's authorship can be most clearly recognised in the multicoloured enamel bands of the orb, a motif which is repeated in identical detail on the enamelled capsule below the sapphire of the sceptre. The red volutes with their diagonally set diamonds flank the large, table-cut diamonds of both the cross and the sceptre in the same fashion.

Although Osenbruck took the crown as his model in terms of detail, it is likely that he was also inspired by the earlier orb of Emperor Ferdinand I, which Rudolf II carried with the crown, and which today lies beside the crown of Bohemia. The front of the cross on this orb is also closely set with large stones, while the other side is decorated with enamelled foliate decoration. Here, too, the angles and extremities of the cross are set with large pearls. Common to both orbs is the combination of richly decorative ornamentation with profound symbolic significance — a characteristic of such insignia (cf. Cat. No. 161). Osenbruck had been court goldsmith to Emperor Matthias since November 1612 (cf. Cat. No. 58). The orb was probably made at the same time as the sceptre, which is dated 1615.   R. D.

Ref.: Weixlgärtner 1928, p. 289 ff.; Distelberger 1985, p. 280.

58 THE SCEPTRE

Andreas Osenbruck (dates unknown)
Prague, 1615
Ainkhürn (narwhal tusk), gold, partially enamelled, diamonds, rubies, sapphire, pearls; 75.5 cms long (Inv. No. XIa 2)
In the capsule at the end of the handle, the signature: *Andreas Osenbruck fecitt Anno 1615,* on the outside of the capsule the monogramme MATTHIAS, surmounted by the Imperial Crown, crossed by sceptre and sword, and the date 1612 (year of accession to the throne).

The shaft of the sceptre has been turned from an *'Ainkhürn'.* By this is to be understood the 'horn' of the mythical unicorn, which became a symbol for Christ and thus a symbol for power and rulership legitimised by God (see Cat. No. 138). In order to prevent deformation of the delicate staff, a rod of iron with a diameter of 6 mm has been inserted into the bored-out core of the horn.

The choice of gemstones for the design of this extremely precious sceptre was determined by those on the Rudolfine crown. As with all these insignia, the emerald is missing. On the handle, the *Ainkhürn* shines through the decorative net of àjouré gold, which is enhanced by partial enamelling: surfaces in white and blue, elevations in green

grotesques. The middle of the rod is also marked by a ring of diamonds between two rows of pearls. The clasps themselves are extremely complex structures.

The principal clasps, which are set with diamonds, consist of numerous elements which have been worked separately. Beneath the rectangular settings of the table diamonds are six layers of ornamentation: the smallest white side-clasps, each with a red lens in the middle; the red volutes, set with diamonds; the bunches of fruit beneath them and the forcipate decorations above, set with little red spheres; the band with the white volutes sweeping out diagonally in both directions on the sides, continuing beneath the rows of diamonds and ending in split volutes, above in blue ones, below in large white ones; under them foliage turned inwards, set with enamelled leaves; and, finally, a detachable rosette as a large bunch of fruit.

All the elements are held together by a pin which is fixed to the settings of the stones. In the upper part a thick volute is also screwed to the rear side and coils inwards as far as the shaft, where it is fixed before returning, split in two, towards the clasp once again. Between the split volutes at the lower end are little diamonds in leaf-shaped settings, above them counter-volutes with minute bunches of fruit on the sides.

The ruby clasps are rather more simply designed. The large stone is surrounded by tendrils, upon which are four diamonds. Underneath is a scrollwork ornament, the sides of which are set with little red spheres. On the clasp there is a table diamond below, and a pointed diamond above, both of them on an enamelled leaf-staff, and beneath the ruby is a small bunch of fruit. Attached to the inner side are volutes, still rolled inwards. Below, the clasp ends in blue, rolled clubs and above bears diamonds with unusual cuts (naville) in triangular, leaf-shaped settings.

As with the other insignia, the crowning piece of the sceptre takes the form of a large sapphire. In this case, a small enamel sphere raises the sapphire above the volutes on its base. This

and red and accompanying lines in black. Thick rings of diamonds between two rows of pearls line both the handle and the pommel. The monogramme of the Emperor Matthias is visible in the àjouré capsule at the end of the shaft. Inside the detachable capsule is the artist's signature.

The pommel or 'sceptre flower' *"seems at first sight to be a confused tangle of the greatest and most perplexing artistry."* It consists of curved clasps, whose equator lies across the middle. Set into the largest projections of these are, alternately, large table diamonds and cabochon rubies. Although the eye can allow the overflowing wealth of forms and the abundance of lustre and colour to take their effect as a whole, the goldsmith's real achievement can only be comprehended if one takes the trouble to examine it in detail.

In the centre of the flower, the handle continues in the form of a gold tube into which the *Ainkhürn* is inserted and which is decorated with enamel

stone was also originally uncut but polished and was probably only facetted around 1600. On the flatter side are triangular facets in nine vertical bands, while the opposite side has a step cut with six steps above 18 facets, with the middle simply polished.

Osenbruck has transformed what for the Middle Ages was a plain motif into a virtuoso piece of goldsmith's work. His immediate model and artistic ideal was the sceptre which Rudolf II had carried with his crown, and which today lies beside the Bohemian crown in Prague. In the design of the handle direct influences can be perceived.

We have no biographical details of Osenbruck. As from 15. 11. 1612 he received a fixed salary in Prague, where he is mentioned for the last time in June 1622. The date 1612 on the capsule can therefore only refer to the succession of Emperor Matthias to the throne. The question remains as to whether the orb was made first and then the sceptre, or whether they were both made at the same time. At any rate, crown, orb and sceptre form a group of insignia which is unique of its kind.   R. D.

Ref.: Weixlgärtner 1928, p. 292 ff.; Distelberger 1985, p. 280.

orated with lions' masks and the allegorical figures of Victory and Fame. The bust is supported at the back by an eagle with a snake in its talons, symbolising the Emperor as victor over the Turks.

From the Kunstkammer of Emperor Rudolf II in Prague.   M. L.-J.

Ref.: Planiscig 1924, p. 210, no. 334; Larsson 1967, p. 47 f. and p. 123 f., no. 44; Bauer and Haupt 1976, no. 1920.

59 BUST OF EMPEROR RUDOLF II

(Vienna 1552—1612 Prague)
Adriaen de Vries (The Hague c. 1545—1626 Prague), Prague, 1607
Bronze; hollow cast, red-brown patina; signed on the back of the plinth: *ADRIANUS · FRIES · HAGIENSIS · FECIT · 1607;* 54.5 cms high (Inv. No. Pl. 5491)

The bust shows the Emperor in armour and bare-headed. On a ribbon round his neck he wears the Golden Fleece. The pauldrons of the armour are dec-

60 EMPEROR KARL VI
(1685—1740) IN THE ROBES OF
THE GOLDEN FLEECE

In the style of Johann Gottfried Auerbach (Mühlhausen 1697—1743 Vienna), c. 1730
Canvas; 297 x 196 cms (Inv. No. GG 2140)

Emperor Karl VI, wearing the robes of the Order of the Golden Fleece, indicates the table with the insignia of his titles as sovereign: the Austrian Archducal Coronet, the Bohemian Crown of Wenceslas, the Imperial Crown and the Hungarian Crown of Stephan; in the foreground is the *chaperon,* made of velvet and embroidered with gold, which formed part of the vestments of the Order of the Golden Fleece. The

picture goes back to a portrait which was repeated several times by the court painter Johann Gottfried Auerbach, from the period around 1730.   K. S.

61 TABARD FOR THE HERALD OF THE ROMAN-GERMAN KING

Vienna (?), 1st half of the 17th century (?)
Gold lamé, silk, gold and silk embroidery, glass; 94 cms long, 114 cms wide (Inv. No. XIV 102)

Back and front: black, single-headed eagle on gold. Appliqué work, mainly embroidered with gold thread. Eyes of glass. The eagle was probably appliquéd onto a more recent piece of gold lamé, since the shape of the tabard is not an exact match. Lining of yellow silk.   R. B.

62 TABARD FOR THE HERALD OF THE ROMAN EMPEROR

Vienna, 1613 and 1790
Gold lamé, silk, glass; 94 cms long, 116 cms wide (Inv. No. XIV 100)

Front and back: nimbused double-headed eagle on gold. On the breast-shield the grand arms of Emperor Leopold II, surrounded by the neckchain of the Order of the Golden Fleece and the Cross of the Tuscan Order of St. Stephen. Arms divided twice horizontally and twice vertically. Above: the Kingdoms of Galicia and Lodomeria between Hungary and Bohemia. Centre: inescutcheon with the Austrian Herediatary Lands between Transylvania and Württemberg. Below: the Italian possessions between the Netherlands and the titular arms of Lorraine. During a restoration in 1894/95 some slips of paper were found sewn in beneath the eagles' heads and proved to contain the name of two embroiderers: *"Matthias Helm Perlhöffter — apprentice, hath stitched this work and sewn on its ornament In the year of 1613"* and *"Christoff Rauch Perlhöffter — apprentice, hath worked on it In the yeare of 1613."* According to this testimony, the hereditary mantle and its complementary piece (Inv. No. XIV 101 — not exhibited) were made during the reign of Emperor Matthias. The arms of Emperor Leopold II were embroidered for his coronation in 1790. Appliqué work, gold, silver and silk embroidery, most of it in relief. Eyes of glass. Black silk lining.   R. B.

63 a) TABARD FOR THE HERALD OF THE KING OF HUNGARY

Vienna, 17th century
Red silver lamé, gold lamé, gold, silver and silk embroidery; 93 cms long, 112 cms wide (Inv. No. XIV 59)

Front and back: arms divided vertically into Old and New Hungary. Left: divided into seven, a silver fesse on a red ground. Right: a silver patriarchal cross rising from a green triple-mount

and crown. Raised silver embroidery.
Lining of red silk.   R. B.

b) Herald's staff
Vienna (?), 17th century
Blued iron, parcel-gilt, velvet; 89 cms
long (Inv. No. XIV 62)

On the top of the staff is a golden
sphere surmounted by the Hungarian
patriarchal cross. Red velvet haft. R. B.

c) Herald's staff
Vienna, mid-18th century
Wood, painted and gilded; 98.5 cms
long (Inv. No. XIV 61)

The staff is surmounted by the patriarchal cross rising from a triple-mount
and crown.   R. B.

**64 a) TABARD FOR THE HERALD
OF THE KING OF BOHEMIA**
Vienna, 17th century
Velvet, gold, silver and silk embroid-
ery, glass; 95.5 cms long, 114 cms wide
(Inv. No. XIV 63)

Front and back: crowned, rampant, silver lion, double-tailed on red. Armed
in gold. Appliqué work, partially embroidered. Eyes of glass. Red silk lining.   R. B.

b) Herald's Staff
Vienna, mid-18th century
Wood, gilded, silvered; 100 cms long
(Inv. No. XIV 64)

At the top: golden spheres with
crowned, rampant silver lion, originally double-tailed; one half broken off.
                               R. B.

**65 a) TABARD FOR THE HERALD
OF EMPEROR FRANZ
STEPHAN I OF LORRAINE**
Vienna, 2nd quarter of the 18th cen-
tury
Velvet, silk, gold and silver lamé; 94
cms long, 159 cms wide (Inv. No. XIV
73)

Front and back: two eagles bearing the
Cross of Lorraine on chains round
their necks flank the crowned shield,
which is surrounded by the neckchain
of the Order of the Golden Fleece and
the ribbon with the Star of the Tuscan
Order of St. Stephen. Arms divided
horizontally: above divided again into
three: Hungary, Naples, Jerusalem and
Aragon; below divided again into three:
Anjou, Guelders, Jülich and Bar.
Charged with a divided inescutcheon:
left, Lorraine; right Tuscany. The
tabard is strewn with the cross potent
of Jerusalem. Appliqué work, clumsily
transferred to a new backing at an unknown date.   R. B.

b) Herald's staff

Vienna, 18th century
Wood, painted and gilded; 105.5 cms
long (Inv. No. XIV 74)

This turned white staff ends in a gold-
en sphere with a crown, above which is
the Florentine lily with a banderole inscribed FLORENTIA, referring to the
Grand Duchy of Tuscany, which Franz
Stephan of Lorraine, under pressure
from France, had to exchange for his
native country on the occasion of his
marriage to Maria Theresia.   R. B.

66 EMPEROR FRANZ I OF
AUSTRIA (1768—1835)
IN THE AUSTRIAN IMPERIAL
VESTMENTS

Friedrich von Amerling (Vienna
1803—1887 Vienna), 1832
Canvas; 263 x 180 cms; signed *Fr.
Amerling, 1832;* Court Exchequer,
from Schloß Laxenburg (Inv. No. GG
8618)

Emperor Franz I is here depicted in
the Austrian Imperial vestments, the
mantle of which was made in 1830,
after a design by Philip von Stubenrauch, for the coronation of Ferdinand
I as the younger King of Hungary.

Beneath the mantle, Franz I wears a
white tunic, white hose and silk shoes,
although it is doubtful whether these
garments ever actually existed in the
form depicted here. In addition, he
wears the neckchains of the four Orders of the House of Austria, and the
crown of Rudolf II, and holds the
sceptre made for Emperor Matthias.
The matching orb is seen at the left-
hand edge of the picture. Franz I never
actually used the official insignia of
the Empire of Austria, and always
availed himself of a substitute Imperial
crown.

Friedrich Amerling was commissioned
to paint this portrait early in 1832,
breaking off his studies in Rome to do
so. A small oil sketch left by the artist,
showing the Emperor in a standing
pose, was formerly in private possession in Vienna.   K. S.

Ref.: Probszt 1927, p. 31, no. 248; Fillitz 1956,
p. 140.

67 THE MANTLE OF THE
AUSTRIAN EMPEROR

Vienna, 1830
Design: Philipp von Stubenrauch
(Vienna 1784—1848 Vienna), Director
of Costumes at the Court Theatre; execution: Johann Fritz, Master Gold
Embroiderer.
Red and white velvet, guimped embroidery in gold, paillettes, ermine,
white silk; 276 cms long (Inv. No. XIV
117)

This mantle with train, made of red
velvet, is pranked with a gold-embroidered scatter pattern formed of double
eagles with the *Bindenschild* surmounted by the Imperial crown. The
robe is edged with a yellowed band of
white velvet, on which the Imperial
crown and sprays of oak leaves are embroidered alternately. Parallel to the
edge is a wide border of oak and laurel
leaves embroidered in gold. The robe is
fastened by means of twisted gold
cords held by flat clasps, the cords ending in heavy gold tassels. The original
ermine cape and the strip of ermine
following the inside edge of the robe
had to be removed in 1874 owing to

This sword was transferred to the Treasury from the Court Chamber of Hunting and Saddlery in 1870, because the Treasurer of the time, Quirin von Leitner, believed it to be the sword which had belonged to the insignia of the Emperors Rudolf II and Matthias. However, the original must have disappeared, since its description in the inventory of the estate of Emperor Matthias from 1619 does not tally with the sword that has survived. Through Leitner's error the present sword became the State Sword of Austria, although it was only incorporated into the Imperial Arms in 1915/16. Upon entering the Treasury in 1870 it underwent restoration by the Viennese firm of Ratzersdorfer.   R. B.

moth damage. In 1954 a new ermine cape was donated by Mrs. Helene von Martinitz.   R. B.

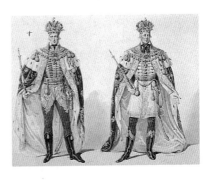

68 THE SWORD
Southern German, beginning of the 17th century
Steel inlaid with gold, gold, enamel, rubies, pearls; scabbard: mauve velvet, steel inlaid with gold, enamel, rubies; 115.3 cms long, with scabbard 123 cms (Inv. No. XI a 4)

69 DESIGNS FOR THE VEST-
MENTS OF THE EMPEROR
OF AUSTRIA
Philipp von Stubenrauch (Vienna 1784—1848 Vienna)

a) First design
Watercolour on card, signed: *Stubenrauch inv.;* 32.1 x 22.7 cms (Inv. No. XVI B 40)

The scatter pattern on the mantle consists of a crowned letter F. There is a broad border of foliate ornamentation around the edges, with crowned eagles' heads below the ermine cape.

b) Second design
Watercolour on card, signed: *Stubenrauch 1830;* 25.3 x 32 cms (Inv. No. XVI B 41)

This design shows two variants. The left-hand sketch with a cross against it shows the design that the Emperor gave his approval to and which was then made, with a few alterations in the ornamentation.

c) Third design

Watercolour on card, signed: *Entwurf v. Ph. v. Stubenrauch 1831* (Designed by Philipp von Stubenrauch, 1831) 33 x 24.6 cms (Inv. No. XVI B 42)

This sketch reveals that Stubenrauch was still working on designs for an undergarment for the Imperial mantle. However, it does not seem to have been made.   R. B.

70 a) TABARD FOR THE HERALD OF THE AUSTRIAN EMPIRE

Vienna, 1830
Gold lamé, velvet, silk, gold braiding, silk embroidery, paillettes, foils; 105 cms high, 104 cms wide (Inv. No. XIV 55)

Front and back: the double-headed eagle is represented in raised appliqué work, wearing the two crowns of Hungary and Bohemia, above which is the Imperial mitre crown. In one set of claws the eagle holds the sword and sceptre, in the other the orb. On the eagle's breast is the escutcheon of the House of Habsburg-Austria-Lorraine, hung with the neckchains of the Orders of the Empire: the Order of the Golden Fleece, the Military Order of Maria Theresia, the Hungarian Order of St. Stephen, the Austrian Order of Leopold and the Austrian Order of the Iron Crown. The whole is set with the escutcheons of the Austrian crown lands: Old and New Hungary, Bohemia, Galicia, Illyria, Austria below the Enns, Transylvania, Salzburg, Moravia-Silesia, Styria, Carynthia, Carniola and Tyrol. In the arms of Tyrol the embroiderer has made a mistake in the choice of colours, taking black and gold instead of red and silver. The herald's tabard was probably made by Johann Fritz in 1830, on the occasion of the coronation of Ferdinand I as the younger King of Hungary. Black silk lining.

b) Staff for the Herald of the Empire of Austria

Vienna 1830
Gilded wood, coloured; 101 cms long (Inv. No. XIV 57)

This turned staff ends in a golden sphere, above which rises the double-headed eagle with the Imperial Crown. In its claws the eagle holds the sceptre and the sword.   R. B.

THE AUSTRIAN HOUSE ORDERS

Secular orders had existed alongside the ecclesiastical orders ever since the late Middle Ages. One of the oldest secular orders in Europe is the *Order of the Golden Fleece,* founded by Duke Philip the Good of Burgundy in 1430, which passed to the Habsburgs together with the Burgundian inheritance (see p. 202). The knights of the Order, who had to fulfil certain conditions of birth (descent from the higher nobility, Catholic faith), lived according to statutes, to which they swore an oath, and pledged obedience to the sovereign. All their activities were supposed to be dictated by religious aims and chivalrous ideals. This was different to the orders of merit, the first of which were founded in the eighteenth century, which rewarded services performed for the state in military or civil matters. Austria's first order of merit, the *Military Order of Maria Theresia,* was founded by Maria Theresia in 1757 and was restricted to officers. On the occasion of her son Joseph's coronation as Holy Roman Emperor, Maria Theresia founded the *Hungarian Order of St. Stephen* in 1764 as an honour for exceptional services of a non-military nature. In 1808, Emperor Franz I founded the *Austrian Order of Leopold,* in memory of his father, Emperor Leopold II, although it had originally been planned to call it the Order of Rudolf, and after 1806 the Order of Franz. On 1. 1. 1816, after the province of Lombardy and Venetia had fallen to Austria, the Order of the Iron Crown, which had been founded by Napoleon in 1805, was reestablished by Emperor Franz I as the *Austrian Order of the Iron Crown.* In 1849 Emperor Franz Joseph created the Order named after him, although this, in contrast to all those already mentioned, no longer provided vestments for its members. The last time that vestments were used in the monarchy was in 1844, at the *Promotion* (ceremony of investiture upon acceptance into the Order) of the Golden Fleece. There were three classes of order which were awarded (although the Order of Franz Joseph later came to have four and finally even five classes): the Grand Cross, the Commander's Cross and the Knight's or Minor Cross. In the Order of the Iron Crown, members were designated Knights of the 1st, 2nd or 3rd Class.

There were also orders for ladies: in 1668, Empress Eleonore, the widow of Emperor Ferdinand, founded the *Order of the Star Cross* for Catholic women of the high nobility (see also Ecclesiastical Treasury, Cat. No. 135); in 1898, a few days after the death of his wife, Emperor Franz Joseph founded the *Order of Elisabeth* in honour of St. Elisabeth of Thuringia, as an order of merit awarded to women of all classes and any religion.   R. B.

Ref.: Auer 1949, pp. 151—152; Auer 1951, pp. 3—23; Měřička 1974, p. 108 ff., 137 ff.; Catalogue, Uniform und Mode 1983, p. 28 ff., p. 101 ff., p. 263 ff.

71 CEREMONIAL ROBES OF A KNIGHT OF THE HUNGARIAN ORDER OF ST. STEPHEN

(for the Bearer of the Grand Cross)
Vienna, c. 1764
(Monturdepot Inv. No. StO-218)

The robes consist of three pieces:

a) Mantle with cape
Green velvet, edged with imitation ermine, a border of gold-embroidered oak leaves. On the cape an imitation of the Grand Cross in gold and silver embroidery (crachard). Red silk lining.

b) Undergarment (Scapular)
The undergarment — in the form of an apron, consisting only of a length of red velvet fastened at the back with tapes — is entirely covered with golden oak leaves in guimped embroidery and set with paillettes.

c) Calpac (Hungarian busby)
Red velvet with gold embroidery and
imitation ermine. Osprey feathers. The
ceremonial robes of the Hungarian
Order of St. Stephen were used for the
last time in 1812.   R. B.

72 NECKCHAIN OF THE HUNGARIAN ORDER OF ST. STEPHEN

Vienna, 1836
Joseph Schmidt's Witwe, manufac-
turers of gold and fancy articles for the
Imperial-Royal Court
Gold, partially enamelled; 116 cms
long (Inv. No. XIa 55)

This neckchain is composed of three
repeatedly juxtaposed elements: the
Hungarian Crown of St. Stephen, the
letters SS (= Sanctus Stephanus) and
the monogramme MT (= Maria Theresia). The badge of the Order, a green
enamelled Greek patté cross, is suspended from the middle of the neckchain. At the front, on a red ground in
the small circular central part, is the
Hungarian patriarchal cross with the
initials M T, enclosed by the motto of
the order: PUBLICUM MERIT-
ORUM PRAEMIUM (Decoration for
Public Service). On the reverse is
S(ANC)TO ST(EPHANO) R(EG)I AP
(OSTOLICO) (Dedicated to St.
Stephen, the Apostolic King).
This neckchain, together with the
neckchain of the Orders of the Golden
Fleece, of Leopold, and of the Iron
Crown, was worn by the sovereign
(Emperor) as the Grand Master of the
Order.   R. B.

73 ROBES OF A KNIGHT OF THE AUSTRIAN ORDER OF LEOPOLD

(for the Bearer of the Grand Cross)
Vienna, 1808
Design: Joseph Fischer, engraver and
decorator to the Imperial Court
(1769—1822) (Monturdepot Inv. No.
III-LO/102)

The set of robes consists of:

a) Mantle with train and separate cape
The mantle, of yellowed silk rep (gros
de Tours), is edged with imitation ermine. Parallel to the edge is a motif executed in guimped embroidery in gold,
together with metal foils: a loosely undulating line of sprays of oakleaves and
the Imperial Austrian Crown (Rudolfine crown). On the cape of imitation
ermine is the embroidered Grand Cross
of the order (crachard); Below this is a
Grand Cross of the Military Order of
Maria Theresia. Gold cord with two
tassels. Lining of white silk.
b) Gown, with net lace ruff.
c) Knee breeches
d) Sword-belt with baldric
e) Baretta with gold cords and white
ostrich feathers
All these pieces are of red velvet. The
gown and breeches are embroidered
with oakleaf motifs in gold.
f) Sash of white silk with gold fringes.
g) Sword
Bronze-gilt, steel; 100 cms long. The
scabbard is of wood covered with red
velvet. On both sides of the flat pommel the letters F.I.A. (Franciscus Imperator Austriae).
The red silk stockings, red velvet shoes
and white leather gloves that originally
belonged to the set have not been pre-

served. The robes of the Order of Leopold were worn for the last time at the titular feast in 1824.   R. B.

74 NECKCHAIN OF THE AUSTRIAN ORDER OF LEOPOLD

Vienna, 1836
Joseph Schmidt's Witwe, manufacturers of gold and fancy articles for the Imperial-Royal Court
Gold, partially enamelled; 106 cms long (Inv. No. XIa 55)

This neckchain consists of two repeatedly juxtaposed elements: the intertwined letters F and L (Franciscus and Leopoldus) surmounted by the Austrian Imperial Crown and oak wreaths. The badge of the Order is hung from the middle: a red enamelled Greek patté cross with white edges. At the front, on a red ground in the small circular central part are the entwined letters FIA (Franciscus Imperator Austriae). Around it is the motto of the Order: INTEGRITATI ET MERITO (For Probity and Service). On the reverse, the motto: OPES REGUM CORDA SUBDITORUM (The wealth [power] of rulers is the hearts of their subjects).   R. B.

75 ROBES OF A KNIGHT OF THE AUSTRIAN ORDER OF THE IRON CROWN

(for a Knight of the First Class)
Vienna, 1815/16
Design: Philipp von Stubenrauch (Vienna 1784—1848 Vienna), Director of Costumes at the Imperial Court Theatre (Monturdepot Inv. No. EK III-3)

The robes consist of:

a) Mantle with train and cape
Mauve velvet with rich guimped embroidery in silver along the edges and on the cape, displaying the Crown of Theodolinda (cf. Cat No. 79) with sprays of palm fronds and laurel leaves inserted through the crown, together with wreaths of oak leaves, each encircling a letter. These letters together make up the device of the order AVITA

ET AUCTA (Inherited and increased). On the breast is an embroidered star (crachard) of the 1st class. Silver tassels. White silk lining.

b) Undercoat
Orange velvet with silver embroidery. A double, pleated ruff is wrapped around the neck.

c) Baretta
Mauve velvet, silver embroidery, silver cords, white ostrich feathers.

d) Belt and baldric
Mauve and dark blue velvet, silver embroidery, silver buckle.

e) Sword
Silver, steel; scabbard of wood covered with dark blue velvet; 101 cms long. On the front of the quillons, the letters F.P. (Franciscus Primus), on the back the date 1815.

f) Hose
The cream-coloured silk weave was specially designed for the robes.

g) Shoes
Yellowed velvet, rosettes of blue atlas with silver fringing. Fine leather lining.

h) Gloves
Fine napa; on the gauntlets laurel leaves in painted silver embroidery.

Ceremonial robes were only worn once, in this case on the occasion of the ceremony of investiture on 14. 10. 1838 in Venice, held after the coronation in Milan of Emperor Ferdinand I as King of Lombardy and Venetia (see below).
                                    R. B.

76 NECKCHAIN OF THE AUSTRIAN ORDER OF THE IRON CROWN

Vienna, 1836
Joseph Schmidt's Witwe, manufacturers of gold and fancy articles for the Imperial-Royal Court
Gold, partially enamelled; 96 cms long
(Inv. No. XIa 55)

This neckchain consists of three elements repeatedly juxtaposed: the intertwined letters F and P (Franciscus Primus), the crown of Theodolinda and oval wreaths of oak leaves. Hanging from the middle is the badge of the Order: above the crown of Theodolinda rises the double-headed eagle, charged with a blue shield. On the front: F (Franciscus), on the back: 1815. The double-headed eagle is surmounted by the Austrian Imperial Crown.   R. B.

THE KINGDOM OF LOMBARDY AND VENETIA

In the wake of the reorganisation of Europe that took place at the Congress of Vienna, the Italian provinces which had fallen to Austria were in 1815 combined into the Kingdom of Lombardy and Venetia. When Emperor Ferdinand I decided to have himself crowned King of Lombardy and Venetia in Milan on 6. 9. 1838, the question arose as to the choice of appropriate insignia and coronation vestments. Only the crown already existed: the venerable Iron Crown of Lombardy (today in the Cathedral Treasury of Monza). The rest of the insignia and vestments had to be newly commissioned. The painter Peter Fendi designed the sceptre, orb, sword and a support which made it possible to wear the undersized crown. These were all manufactured by Mayerhofer and Klinkosch, a silverware factory licensed by the Imperial-Royal Court, and by the court jewellers Pioté and Köchert in Vienna. The vestments were designed by Philipp von Stubenrauch and executed by Johann Fritz. After the coronation in Milan Cathedral, the coronation insignia and vestments were divided up between the two parts of the kingdom for safekeeping: the sceptre and orb were placed in the Cathedral Treasury of Venice, and the Iron Crown, sword and vestments were taken to Monza. This was meant to express the unity of Lombardy and Venetia. When the Austrians withdrew from Italy in 1859, the vestments and insignia were brought to Vienna and in 1861 placed in the Treasury. In 1866, the crown was also transferred from Italy. The sceptre, the orb and the support for the crown were broken up and sold in 1871/72. The only objects which have survived are those listed below.   R. B.

Ref.: Fillitz 1956, p. 143 ff.; M. v. Bárány-Oberschall, Die Eiserne Krone der Lombardei, Vienna/Munich 1966; Ch. Thomas, Ornat und Insignien zur lombardo-venezianischen Krönung 1838, Entwurf und Ausführung, in: Mitteilungen des österreichischen Staatsarchivs, vol. 32, 1979, pp. 165—197.

77 THE CORONATION VEST-
MENTS OF THE KINGDOM OF
LOMBARDY AND VENETIA

Vienna, 1838
Design: Philipp von Stubenrauch,
Director of Costumes at the Imperial
Court Theatre; execution: Johann
Fritz, Master Gold Embroiderer

a) Mantle

Blue and orange velvet, guimped embroidery in gold, ermine, coloured
foils, white silk; 269 cms long (Inv No.
XIV 118)

Design based on the mantle of the Austrian Emperor made in 1830 (Cat. No.
67). The faded orange velvet edging of
the mantle is accompanied by a line of
contiguous oval medallions in which
the Iron Crown is displayed. Parallel to
this runs a broad ornamental border
composed of sprays of palm fronds,
oak leaves and sprays of laurel. The
rest of the mantle is strewn with a motif
composed of a palm frond intertwined
with a spray of laurel.

b) Undercoat

White moiré, gold and silver embroidery, lace edging; 103.5 cms long (Inv.
No. XIV 119)

Knee-length, buttoned through flared
coat, the foliate pattern from the mantle repeated on both sides of the button
row and on the lower hem. Opens at
the back for the anointing of the king.

c) Baldric

Blue velvet, gold embroidery, silver-
gilt; 101 cms long (Inv. No. XIV 120)

The belt is embroidered with oak leaves
and sprays of laurel and has two loops
on the left from which the coronation
sword was suspended.

d) Sword of Investiture

Vienna, 1837/38
Design: Peter Fendi (Vienna 1796—
1842 Vienna); execution: Mayerhofer &
Klinkosch (hallmark); blade: Anton
Schleifer, civic cutler
Silver-gilt, steel, etched and inlaid with
gold, scabbard: blue velvet, silver gilt;
94.3 cms long, with scabbard, 97.4 cms
(Inv. No. XIV 120)

On the blade are the Imperial arms and
the following inscription: RECTA ·

TVERI (Observe justice). On the other
side, beside the arms of Lombardy and
Venetia: FERDINANDVS · AVS-
TRIAE · IMPERATOR · FRAN-
CISCI · IMP(ERATORIS) · LOMB
(ARDIAE) · VENET(IAE) · PRIMI ·
REGIS · FILIUS · INSIGNI ·
CORONAE · MEDIOL(ANAE) ·
MDCCCXXXVIII · SVM(P)TAE ·
PRIMVS (Ferdinand I, Emperor of
Austria, son of Emperor Franz, the
first King of Lombardy and Venetia,
first worn with the Milanese Crown in
1838).   R. B.

78 EMPEROR FERDINAND I OF
AUSTRIA IN THE CORONA-
TION VESTMENTS OF LOM-
BARDY AND VENETIA

Vienna, c. 1838
Watercolour, signed A. Weißenböck;
60 x 49 cms (Inv. No. XVI B 43)

The king is here depicted in full coronation regalia. This watercolour is our
only source of information regarding
the way in which the Iron Crown was
actually adapted. It shows a circlet set
with precious stones and fleurs-de-lys,
with a lining of blue velvet. Upon this
sits the Iron Crown itself, mounted with
gemstones and enamel. Four elongated
leaves rise from the rim of the crown

arms are surmounted not by the Iron Crown but by the Crown of Theodolinda (also in the Cathedral Treasury at Monza). Under the tabard a long, black velvet robe was worn; this item was listed in the Treasury inventory of 1842—1871, p. 415, but has since disappeared.

b) Herald's staff

Vienna, 1838
Academy sculptor Joseph Wandrak
Wood, gilded, silvered, lustred and painted, velvet; 95.2 cms long (Inv. No. XIV 66)

On the upper end of the staff are the arms of Lombardy and Venetia, surmounted by the crown of Theodolinda.

R. B.

and converge like an arch in the centre, which is surmounted by a cross. The form of the orb and the sceptre has obviously been influenced by the insignia made for the Rudolfine Crown (Cat. No. 57, 58). Neck-cloth, gloves, stockings and shoes have since been lost. R. B.

79 a) TABARD FOR THE HERALD OF THE KINGDOM OF LOMBARDY AND VENETIA

Vienna, 1838
Design: Philipp von Stubenrauch, execution: Johann Fritz
Blue velvet, silver lamé, gold braid and fringing, raised gold, silver and silk embroidery, coloured foils; 96.5 cms long, width at shoulders: 110 cms (Inv. No. XIV 65)

On both sides of the tabard the arms of the kingdom, divided vertically: right, Milan; left, Venice. Interestingly, the

80 STAFF OF THE HEREDITARY GRAND COMPTROLLER IN THE KINGDOM OF LOMBARDY AND VENETIA

Vienna, 1838
146 cms long (Inv. No. XIV 47)

Cane, varnished black; gilded silver mounts with the arms of Lombardy and Venetia and the monogramme of Ferdinand I beneath the crown of Theodolinda and the date 1838. R. B.

OBJECTS COMMEMORATING EMPEROR NAPOLEON, EMPRESS MARIE LOUISE AND THE DUKE OF REICHSTADT

Napoleon's marriage to Josephine Beauharnais having proved childless, the new French Empire proclaimed by him in 1804 lacked an heir to guarantee its dynastic continuity. For this reason Napoleon had his marriage annulled, in order to create the necessary legitimacy for his family, and attempted to forge a dynastic link with one of the old-established ruling houses of Europe. The preferred objects of his desire were a Russian Grand Duchess or an Austrian Archduchess. When Russia indicated her refusal to cooperate, it was left to Emperor Franz I of Austria to make the political sacrifice for peace and marry his eldest daughter Marie Louise (1791—1847) to Napoleon. The wedding ceremony took place with a great display of pomp on 2. 4. 1810 in a hall of the Louvre, which had been specially adapted for the occasion. When Marie Louise finally bore the desired heir to the throne on 20. 3. 1811, it seemed as if Napoleon had achieved the goal of his desires and the continuation of the French Empire and the Bonaparte dynasty had been secured. Immediately after his birth, the young prince, who was given the names Napoleon Franz Karl, received the title of King of Rome from his father, here in conscious imitation of the traditions of the Holy Roman Empire. However, shortly afterwards, on 11. 4. 1814, following the decisive defeat at Leipzig, Napoleon was forced to abdicate. Marie Louise returned with her son to her father in Vienna. As Napoleon went into his first exile on Elba, she was compensated with the Duchy of Parma by the Congress of Vienna. Thus the King of Rome became the Prince of Parma. However, the succession of the Prince in Parma failed due to the resistance of King Louis XVIII of France, who represented the rights of the Bourbons in Parma, whereupon his grandfather invested him with the title of Duke of Reichstadt. On 5. 5. 1821, Napoleon died in exile on St. Helena. The Duke of Reichstadt died of a lung disease on 22. 7. 1832 in Schönbrunn Palace in Vienna. Marie Louise reigned prudently in Parma and died there on 17. 12. 1847.   M. L.-J.

81 NAPOLEON I BONAPARTE (1769—1821) AS KING OF ITALY

Studio of Andrea Appiani (Bosisio 1754—1817 Milan)
Canvas; 99.5 x 75 cms (Inv. No. GG 2346)

Napoleon is portrayed in the ceremonial robes and with the insignia which he commissioned for his coronation in Milan as King of Italy on 26. 5. 1805. They were kept in the Treasury in Vienna until Italy demanded their return in 1920. The robes consist of a tabard of green velvet with gold embroidery and a green velvet mantle decorated with silver flowers with an embroidered white silk lining. Napoleon wears the

Grand Chain of the Legion of Honour, consisting of gold eagles and the five-pointed star of the order. No chain of this type is known today. Surviving examples follow another pattern, with eagles alternating with trophies. Orange with a green border, the Grand Riband of the Order of the Iron Cross, founded in 1805, hangs from the right shoulder to the left hip. Above it, on the left side of the breast is the Grand Star of the order, in the formation usual from 1807 onwards.

The painting is a studio replica of the official state portrait of Napoleon as King of Rome, of which numerous examples exist. Appiani, Napoleon's court painter in Italy, probably executed the painting in 1805, the year of the coronation. The Collection of Paintings possesses further, virtually identical versions, two of which are on display in the Portrait Gallery of Austrian History in Castle Ambras (Inv. No. 2347) and in the Museum of Military History (Inv. No. 2348) respectively.

K. S.

Ref.: Catalogue, Schatzkammer 1954, 5th ed. 1971, no. 114; Catalogue, Porträtgalerie 1976, 2nd ed. 1982, no. 165.

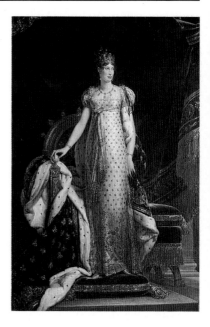

when Marie Louise was resident at Parma as the Duchess of Parma, Emperor Franz I asked his daughter for the painting as a gift. It was taken to Castle Laxenburg. A slightly altered copy made by Gérard's colleague, J. B. Guerin, remained in Paris (today in the Museum of Versailles).

K. S.

Ref.: Grimschitz 1926, pp. 87—89; Blauensteiner 1940, p. 127 f.

82 ARCHDUCHESS MARIE LOUISE AS EMPRESS OF THE FRENCH (1791—1847)

François-Pascal-Simon Gérard (Rome 1770—1837 Paris)
Canvas; 246 x 163.5 cms (Inv. No. GG 8682)

Napoleon married Archduchess Marie Louise, the eldest daughter of Franz I of Austria, by proxy in Vienna on 11. 3. 1810. This portrait, which was painted in 1812, shows Marie Louise in the Imperial vestments, a white dress embroidered with gold bees and a purple mantle lined with ermine and also embroidered with golden bees, which were the ancient symbol of the Frankish Kingdom.

After the fall of Napoleon in 1816,

83 EMPEROR NAPOLEON

Jean Baptiste Isabey (Nancy 1767—1855 Paris)
Paris, signed: *Isabey 1810*
Gouache on ivory; 24.8 x 16.5 cms; the frame brass-gilt; 31.9 x 24.2 cms (Inv. No. XIV 148)

The Emperor is shown full-length, standing in front of a throne of gilded bronze which has armrests in the form of winged lions and eagles flanking the back. Napoleon is portrayed in the garments he wore on the occasion of his marriage to Archduchess Marie Louise of Austria on 2. 4. 1810. Over a white silk tricot he wears a coat of cerise velvet, richly embroidered in gold, and over this a short cape of the same

material, lined with white satin. On his head he wears a black velvet baretta with white ostrich feathers inserted into a diamond agraffe. The bow of the white satin sash holds the sword, the hilt of which bears the *Regent,* the famous large diamond belonging to the French Crown Jewels. Over the salmon pink riband of the order lies the Chain of the Order of the Legion of Honour, embellished with brilliants, while the Grand Star of the Napoleonic Order of the Iron Crown is visible on the left side of the breast. To Napoleon's right, the Imperial Napoleonic Crown, a laurel wreath of gold, rests on a red velvet cushion. A heavy, blue velvet curtain with gold embroidery, fringing and tassels parts behind the throne to reveal a lofty gallery.

Companion piece to Cat. No. 84.

M. L.-J.

84 EMPRESS MARIE LOUISE
Jean Baptist Isabey (Nancy 1767—1855 Paris)
Paris, signed: *Isabey 1810*
Gouache on ivory; 24.8 x 16.5 cms; the frame brass-gilt; 31.9 x 24.2 cms (Inv. No. XIV 149)

The Empress is seen full-length, standing in front of a throne of gilded bronze, its back covered in blue velvet and decorated with golden bees and a laurel wreath surrounding an L (the monogramme of the Empress). Marie Louise stands with her left hand raised to her breast. She wears her long, narrow, low-necked wedding dress of white satin, richly embroidered with golden leafwork and bees. From her shoulders hangs a long, heavy, ermine-lined mantle of cherry-red velvet, the train of which has been thrown over the left arm of the throne. It too displays rich gold embroidery. Discernible are the Napoleonic bees, and stars and leafwork set with the N of Napoleon. This mantle had already been worn by Marie Louise's predecessor, Empress Josephine, at her coronation in 1804. The head and décolleté of the Empress are adorned with a diadem and a necklace of diamonds and rubies respectively. The two were Napoleon's costly wedding gift, which he presented to her in the box made by Biennais (Cat. No. 85). The necklace is furthermore hung with the miniature portrait of Napoleon by Isabey, set with twelve solitaires, which Marshal Berthier had presented to Archduchess Marie Louise on 8. 3. 1810 when he asked for her hand on Napoleon's behalf. A green-velvet curtain draping a pillar behind the Empress to the left reveals a glimpse of a colonnaded hall.

Isabey was the most popular miniaturist in the elegant world of Paris, and painted portraits for the high aristocracy of both the *ancien* and the *nouveau régimes*. A pronounced decorative talent enabled him furthermore to design the decorations for the coronation of Napoleon in 1804 as well as the wedding ceremony of Napoleon and Marie Louise on 2. 4. 1810 in the Salon Carré of the Louvre. Isabey was a favourite of Marie Louise and she took lessons in drawing and painting from him. She also sent him to Vienna to portray the numerous members of her family and remained loyal to him even after Napoleon's downfall. Called to Vienna by Talleyrand on the occasion of the Congress of Vienna, he portrayed the city's many contemporary notables and beauties. It was also at this time that the watercolour miniatures of the four-year-old Duke of Reichstadt were executed. Also preserved in the Treasury, it is no longer possible to display them in the permanent exhibition for conservation reasons. Isabey exhibited the two portraits of Napoleon and Marie Louise in the Salon in 1810, and an enthusiastic review of them was published: *". . . M. Isabey qui joint, avec un avantage qui est particulier, la grâce de la composition, le bon goût des accessoires, au charme du pinceau brillant et facile, a offert cette année les portraits de L. L. Majestés Impériales et Royales. Ces tableaux ont constamment attiré la foule au Salon, durant le peu de jours qu'ils ont été exposés."*
It seems that Marie Louise immediately sent the two portraits to Vienna. The green calico box lined with green velvet still survives today. How the two paint-

ings came into the possession of Archduke Rainer II, where they were still attested to in 1909, is unknown. After his death in 1913, they passed to Emperor Franz Joseph I. They were transferred to the Treasury in 1918.   M. L.-J.

Ref.: Basily-Callimaki 1909, pp. 116—119; Scott 1981, p. 2266.

85 THE JEWEL CASKET OF
**   EMPRESS MARIE LOUISE**
Martin Guilleaume Biennaise (Lacochère 1764—1843 Paris) and Augustin Dupré (Saint-Etienne 1748—1833 Armentières)
Paris, 1810
Silver gilt, green velvet and white silk lining. Signed on the lock: *Biennais Orf.(èv)re de S(a) M(ajesté) L'Empereur et Roi;* on the four reliefs of the 'Aldobrandini Wedding': *Dupré;* 28.8 cms high, 54.7 cms wide, 34.7 cms deep (Inv. No. XIV 153)

The casket is covered in green velvet, today somewhat faded, which provides an effective foil for the ornamental, partly ajouré silver-gilt appliqués. The decorative motives refer to Emperor Napoleon I and his second wife, Marie Louise of Austria. In the middle of all four sides are the grand sovereign arms of Napoleon; the one on the front covers the lock and can be raised. On the end of the ornamental bands is a crowned N in a roundel. In the frieze on the edge of the lid the Napoleonic eagle surrounded by a laurel wreath occurs four times, as does a bas-relief with the 'Aldobrandini Wedding', executed by the medailleur Augustin Dupré (after a fragment of a Roman fresco in the Vatican Collections that was highly regarded at the time). The large surfaces of the casket are strewn with bees, Napoleon's personal emblem, which he had adopted instead of the Bourbon fleur-de-lys. Finally, in the centre of the lid, surrounded by a laurel wreath, is the crowned monogramme of Marie Louise, formed from the intertwined letters M and L. The casket rests on four lion's paws. A pair of snakes, held in the jaws of two dog heads, form the handles on both of the shorter sides.

The combination of monogrammes, emblems and imperial arms with the symbols of strength and faithfulness, together with the 'Aldobrandini Wedding', would confirm the tradition (for which there is otherwise no definitive proof) according to which the casket contained the jewels that Napoleon gave to Marie Louise on the occasion of their marriage on 2. 4. 1810.

Martin Guilleaume Biennais, the Imperial Court goldsmith, was first and foremost an entrepreneur. He employed over 600 skilled workers and mostly relied on the designs of others (such as the architects Charles Percier and Pierre-Francois-Léonard Fontaine), which indicates that the design of the casket can probably be attributed to one of them. As with the tripod (Cat. No. 87), the casket was part of the estate from Castle Hernstein belonging to Archduke Leopold, and was bequeathed to Emperor Franz Joseph I in 1915 by his younger brother and heir, Archduke Rainer II. Theophil Hansen, the architect of Castle Hernstein (built between 1856 and 1880) designed the stand for the casket, basing his design on the tripod by the Manfredini brothers.   M. L.-J.

Ref.: Weixlgärtner 1916, p. 353; Fillitz 1971, p. 41—42, no. 121; Scott 1981, 2268; Fillitz 1986, p. 205, no. 48.

86 THE CRADLE OF THE KING OF ROME

Pierre-Paul Prud'hon (1758—1823), Henri-Victor Roguier (1758—after 1830), Jean-Baptiste-Claude Odiot (1763—1850) and Pierre-Philippe Thomire (1751—1843)
Paris, 1811
Silver-gilt, gold, mother-of-pearl, copper plates covered with velvet, silk and tulle with gold and silver embroidery; signed on the two of the feet: *Odiot et Thomire* and *Thomire et Odiot;* 216 cms high (Inv. No. XIV 28)

The cradle was the gift of the city of Paris to Empress Marie Louise on the occasion of the birth of her son Napoleon-Franz on 20. 3. 1811. This is commemorated by the inscription on the inside of the heavenly globe: OFFERT PAR LA VILLE DE PARIS L'AN 1811. It had been commissioned by the prefect of the *Departement Seine,* Count Frochot, when it became known that the Empress was expecting. The design was the work of the painter Pierre-Paul Prud'hon, who was paid 6,000 francs for it. The sculptor Henri-Victor Roguier made the models for casting, for which he received 4,487 francs. The work was actually executed by the goldsmith Jean-Baptiste-Claude Odiot and the bronze-caster and engraver Pierre-Philippe Thomire. They were paid 152,289 francs and 49 centimes, although this figure also included the high cost of materials (for instance, more than 280 kgs of silver alone were used).

The cradle was presented to Napoleon on 5. 3. 1811, only two weeks before the accouchement of the Empress. At his birth, the heir to the throne received the title of King of Rome. This was an act of state policy, which on the one hand ensured the continuity of the young Bonaparte dynasty and, on the other, was intended to announce its claim to world sovereignty. This had to be taken into account in the design and execution of the cradle. For this reason it is not an example of a cradle in the customary sense, but rather a bed in the shape of a throne, a piece of furniture for representative or ceremonial purposes. It originally stood on a ped-

estal beneath a baldaquin in the Tui-
leries. For everyday needs, Thomire
had delivered a simpler version made
of veined root wood with bronze-gilt
fittings. This is today in the Louvre in
Paris. The cradle's hood, which is in
the form of a half-cupola, and curtain
do actually recall a throne with a baldachin. According to Prud'hon's
elucidation, the wealth of details in the
iconographic design refer on the one
hand, to the event of the birth of the
prince and heir to the throne, on the
other to his illustrious father, Napoleon I, and the Empire founded by
him. Thus the cradle rests, as it were,
on the foundation of good government
of the state, which seems to be symbolised by the cornucopiae and the two
genii of Strength and Justice, which
will grow and mature with the prince.
Surrounded by floral motifs, the prince
is to lie in the midst of a colony of bees,
symbol of the industry and fertility of
his subjects. Napoleon had adopted
the bees as his personal emblem in
place of the fleurs-de-lys of the Bourbons. In doing so, he was following the
precedent of the 300 cicadas found as
burial offerings in the tomb of Chil-
derich I, the King of the Merovingians,
which had been discovered near Tournai in 1653. They had been sent by Emperor Leopold I to Paris as a gift to
King Louis XIV of France. Most of the
original 300 were stolen from the Cabinet des Medailles of the Bibliothèque
Nationale in 1831; only two examples
survive today.

Surrounded by branches of palm,
laurel and olive, the symbols of victory
and renown, the N of the father's
name, which at the same time was also
that of the prince, shines from the
centre of a sun-gloriole. That this fame
shall be everlasting is expressed by the
Goddess of Fame or Victory hovering
above a heavenly globe. (The model for
this was possibly the so-called Victoria
of Fossombrone, a Roman bronze
which is today to be found at Kassel
but which Napoleon had carried off to
Paris.) With both hands she holds a
laurel wreath above the child. It is the
crown of the Roman Caesars, of which
Napoleon had also made use at his
coronation as Emperor of the French
on 2. 12. 1804. Above it sparkles another diadem of stars. This represents
the firmament, and its largest, leading
and central star bears an N, standing
for Napoleon, who seems to have been
elevated to the realm of the immortals.
It is up at this star that the little eagle
at the foot of the cradle is gazing.
Aiglon was also the name given to the
little prince, and it thus seems as if he
is impatiently trying to fly up to the
father's star. The fact that the little
prince was already numbered among
the heavenly ones can be seen from the
two reliefs on the sides of the throne-
bed. Gliding down from the heavens,
Mercury places the boy on the lap of
the nymph *Seine,* distinguished by the
arms of the city of *Paris* and the ship of
Isis, as a gift of the gods. On the other
relief the new star of the King of Rome
rises above the city of *Rome,* symbolised by the she-wolf with Romulus and
Remus, and is hailed by the old river-
god *Tiber.*

The personal-dynastic sphere of the
iconography is finally elevated by the
Grand Imperial State Arms at the head
of the throne-bed, endowing the design
with general political significance.

The exceptionally fine execution is in
keeping with the status of this piece of
ceremonial furniture. The colours of
the costly materials used are brilliantly
matched, especially important being
the red velvet (restored after the original pattern in 1971) which forms the
coloured ground for the silver gilt and
mother-of-pearl decoration. Of the old
tulle cover only fragments have survived. Parts of an old tulle (?) curtain,
also embroidered with bees, is in private ownership in Belgium. However,
the cradle originally had two curtains:
one made of green taffeta, the other
also green, but made of 'levantine', a
veil-like material similar to tulle. The
present-day curtain does not correspond to the original, especially as
regards its colour. The scales which the
genius of Justice once held in its hands
have been lost.

After Napoleon's downfall in 1814,
Empress Marie Louise brought the
cradle with her to Vienna, where it

was deposited in the Treasury in 1832, presumably immediately after the death of the Duke of Reichstadt, the former King of Rome. It is first mentioned there in 1836.   M. L.-J.

Ref.: Weixlgärtner 1916, p. 353—371; Niclausse 1947, pp. 99—101; Fillitz 1971, p. 41, no. 119; Lullies 1974, pp. 319—326; Axel-Nilsson 1974—1976 (1977), p. 5 ff.; Baulez 1977, p. 194; Hernmarck 1978, p. 209; Catalogue, Napoleon 1969, pp. 186—188, nos. 509—511 and 515; Cohen 1986, p. 662 (illus. 4 shows the Vienna cradle and not the version in the Louvre); Fillitz 1986, p. 205, no. 47.

87 TRIPOD WITH BASIN

Luigi Manfredini (Bologna 1771—1840 Milan) and Francesco Manfredini (dates unknown)
Milan, 1811
Bronze-gilt, silver-gilt, lapis lazuli; signed on the underside of the bowl: *INVENTATO ED ESEGUITO DAI FRA(TEL)LI MANFREDINI NELLA R(EGI)A MANIF(ATTU)RA DELLA FONTANA NELL' ANNO 1811;* Height of tripod 81.5 cms; diameter of basin 37 cms (Inv. No. XIV 152)

The design of this tripod is based on an ancient bronze tripod from Pompeii, today in the Museo Nazionale in Naples. In formal terms it corresponds to the ancient model up to the lip of the basin. However, the combination of gilded bronze with the rich blue of the lapis lazuli, together with the silver-gilt bowl of the basin with its delicate, meticulously crafted ornamentation, is the work of the Manfredini brothers. The centre of the bowl is decorated with a medallion representing Neptune and Amphitrite on a shell drawn by two hippocampi. The sides of the bowl are decorated with a frieze formed of tendrilling motifs, with reclining nereids alternating with six oval medallions portraying various river gods. Decorating the edge of the bowl is another frieze, formed of tendrils held aloft by putti, which alternates with nine round medallions representing (clockwise) the gods Jupiter, Diana, Mercury, Ceres, Vesta, Apollo, Minerva, Juno, and Mars. The programmatic iconography of the piece suggests that it was used as a hand-basin and not as a baptismal font, as it has occasionally been described.

There is a tradition (for which there is no reliable evidence) that the tripod was a gift of the City of Milan to Napoleon I and his wife Empress Marie Louise on the birth of the heir to the throne on 20. 3. 1811.

The tripod in the Viennese Treasury is from the estate of Archduke Leopold (one of Archduke Rainer's sons, who was Governor of Lombardy from 1818), and stood in his castle at Hernstein in Lower Austria, which was rebuilt by Theophil Hansen. The Archduke's younger brother and heir, Archduke Rainer II, eventually bequeathed it to Emperor Franz Joseph I in 1915. We know that Eugène Beauharnais, Napoleon's stepson, and until 1813 Viceroy of Italy, whose residence was in Milan, also gave his father-in-law, King Max Josef I of Bavaria, a tripod of this type. It later came back to the estate of Beauharnais' descendants, the Dukes of Leuchtenberg, and can probably be identified as the one that is today in Castle Pawlowsk near Leningrad. A further signed example — but dated 1813 — from a private English collection, is today in the Victoria and Albert Museum in London. The brothers Luigi and Francesco Manfredini originally came from Bologna. Luigi, artistically the more important of the two, was in charge of the royal bronze foundry in Milan, established in 1807. A famous medallist, he was professor at the Milanese Academy. The artistic decoration of the bowl is thus probably his work.   M. L.-J.

Ref.: Weixlgärtner 1916, pp. 253—256; Fillitz 1971, p. 41, no. 120; Gonzales-Palacios 1970, p. 53; Ottomeyer and Pröschel 1986, I, p. 402. no. 5.19.1.

PIECES COMMEMORATING EMPEROR MAXIMILIAN OF MEXICO

Archduke Ferdinand Maximilian (1832—1867) was Emperor Franz Joseph's immediate younger brother. Responsible for reorganising the Austrian Navy, whose commander-in-chief he was, he was also Governor-General of Lombardy and Venetia from 1857 to 1859. On 10. 7. 1863, he was chosen as Emperor of Mexico, on the instigation of Emperor Napoleon III of France. He was, however, unable to prevail against the Republican forces, led by Benito Juáréz, and was taken prisoner. Condemned to death by court martial, he was shot on 19. 6. 1867. His body was brought back to Europe by Admiral Tegetthof on the frigate *Novara*. In 1857, Maximilian had married Princess Marie Charlotte of Belgium, a woman who took an active interest in politics. She died in 1927, after sixty years of mental illness.

A part of the following pieces and other commemorative pieces came into the possession of the Treasury in 1868 after Maximilian's death. Some went to Castle Miramar and were not transferred to the Treasury until 1925.   M. L.-J.

Ref.: Detailed biography in the catalogue to the exhibition Maximilian von Mexiko, 1974.

88 SCEPTRE
Mexican, 1863
Gold; 58.5 cms long (Inv. No. XIV 170)

Each of the three parts of the sceptre's shaft is made of gold of a different colour. On the lower and upper parts are branches of oak and laurel leaves; in between are two appliqués of the Mexican eagle with the serpent; the central section is smooth. At the top is an eight-arched crown. Inside the sceptre, which can be unscrewed at the bottom, is a document concerning the election of Archduke Ferdinand Maximilian of Austria as Emperor of Mexico by the Mexican Assembly of Notables on 10. 7. 1863. This document, together with its sceptre-shaped container, was presented to the Archduke in Miramar Palace on 2. 10. 1863 by a Mexican delegation led by Don Gutierrez.   M. L.-J.

89 SCEPTRE

Mexican, 1863
Silver, gold, emeralds and rubies (?);
40.5 cms long (Inv. No. XIV 171)

The smooth shaft is decorated with
ajouré floral motifs in the centre of
which is the Mexican eagle with the
snake of discord in its beak. At the upper end is a six-arched crown; at the
lower end the inscription: *Pachuca
1863 J. A.* In the hollow centre of the
shaft is a loyal address from the Mexican mining district of Pachuca, dated
8. 12. 1863.   M. L.-J.

90 SCEPTRE

Mexican, M. Rivera, 1863/64
Gold, parcel-gilt, diamonds, emeralds,
rubies; 43 cms long (Inv. No. XIV 169)

On the central boss is the dedicatory
inscription: LA H.VE/RACRUZ/A.S.
M/I.MAXI/MILIAN/O 1.°. In green
enamel lettering on a banderole on the
handle is the motto: EQUIDAD EN
LA JUSTICIA (equality before the
law). Gift of the city of Vera Cruz to
Emperor Maximilian.   M. L.-J.

91 THE CANE OF EMPEROR MAXIMILIAN OF MEXICO

Mexican, between 1864 and 1867
Tortoiseshell, gold, diamonds, emer-
alds, rubies and pearls; 94 cms long
(Inv. No. XIV IIe)

On the gold pommel of the cane is the
Emperor's monogramme MIM below
the Imperial Mexican crown.   M. L.-J.

92 NECKCHAIN OF THE ORDER OF OUR LADY OF GUADELOUPE

Vienna (?), c. 1864/65
Silver-gilt, partially enamelled (Inv.
No. XIV IIb)

The order was founded by Emperor
Augustin de Iturbide, and its statutes
were modified by Emperor Maximilian.

The neckchain consists of 30 links, alternately taking the form of the Mexican eagle and the wreathed monogramme AI (Augustin de Iturbide).
The jewel, a patté cross enamelled in
red, white and green with concave
sides, little spheres at the tips and an
aureole between the arms, lies on a
wreath of laurel and palm branches. In
the middle of the front is a medallion
with the representation of the Madonna of Guadaloupe, surrounded by
the inscription: RELIGION IN-
DEPENCIA UNION (religion, independence, unity). On the back, on a
white ground, is the inscription: AL
PATRIOTISMO HEROICO (for
heroic patriotism). The Mexican eagle
forms the connecting link to the neckchain. Presumably manufactured in
Vienna by the firm of C. F. Rothe, the
suppliers of the Chancellery of the
Mexican Orders.   M. L.-J.

Ref.: Měřička 1966, p. 99.

93 NECKCHAIN OF THE MEXICAN ORDER OF THE EAGLE

Vienna, 1865
Silver-gilt, partially enamelled (Inv.
No. XIV IIa)

Emperor Maximilian founded the
Mexican Order of the Eagle on 1. 1.
1865 as the highest order of merit of his
empire. The neckchain consists of a
double chain, with the fifteen intersti-
tial links formed by the Emperor's
monogramme (MIM) below the imperial crown, together with fifteen
Mexican eagles. The pendant is likewise formed by the Mexican eagle, here
with sceptre and sword. It rests on the
nopal cactus, the emblem of Mexico,

and is biting the green snake of discord to death. It is linked to the neckchain by the imperial crown of Mexico. The neck-chain was made by the Viennese firm C. F. Rothe, the official suppliers to the Chancellery of the Mexican Orders. The firm still possesses the original dies.   M. L.-J.

Ref.: Měřička 1966, p. 100; Catalogue, Maximilian von Mexiko 1974, nos. 188—190.

IMPLEMENTS AND GOWNS FOR HOLY BAPTISM

At the Imperial court, the dispensing of the sacrament of holy baptism was not merely a familial celebration, attended by the arrival of relations with their retainers; it was also an act of state, marking the entry of the newborn infant into public life. Weeks before the birth of a child of archducal rank, the Imperial Treasurer enquired of the Grand Chamberlain whether he might have the baptismal implements delivered to the chamber of Her Majesty or of the Archduchess. Shortly beforehand, a safe delivery was prayed for in the churches of the city. If all went well, general rejoicing broke out all over the city: the streets were illuminated, candles were placed in windows and to the sound of trumpets, money and wine were distributed among the population. The child was generally baptised a few hours after birth, or at the very latest, on the following day. The ceremony was performed — with a very few exceptions — not in the chapel of the Hofburg, but in a room specially prepared for the occasion, at the residence where the birth had taken place — the Hofburg, Schönbrunn or Laxenburg. The persons invited were disposed according to strict protocol in the christening room, where the golden christening set had been prepared. Those persons who entered with the Emperor grouped themselves round him. The infant, clothed in the hooded gown from the set of christening robes donated by Maria Theresia, was carried by its nurse or by the Grand Comptroller on the cushion belonging to the set. Two chamberlains held the corners of the smaller coverlet that covered the child. The larger coverlet was spread out over a small table beside the altar. On this table, the nurse took off the heavy, pearl-embroidered gown and clothed the child in the lighter cambric gown. (Cat. No. 97). After the baptism by water, to which were added a few drops of water from the River Jordan, kept by the court priest, the nurse put the child into the pearl gown once more. If the child was a crown prince, and thus to be made a Knight of the Order of the Golden Fleece, a neckchain of the order and a sword for the knighting ceremony were laid ready on a special stand. This ceremony was performed immediately after the baptism and all the Knights of the Order were required to kiss the baby's swaddling bands in place of the fraternal embrace. The Emperor performed three cuts of the sword over the child, while offering a short prayer.   R. B.

Ref.: Thomas 1963, pp. 388—397; A. Stöckelle, Taufzeremoniell und politische Patenschaften am Kaiserhof, in: MIÖG, 90, 1982, pp. 271—337.

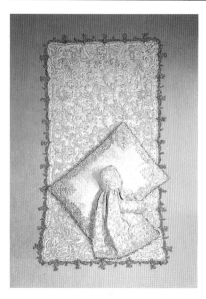

The borders embroidered to match the rest of the set.

On 16. 1. 1757, three christening sets (one blue and two white) were removed from the Ecclesiastical Treasury at the instigation of Maria Theresia and their pearl trimmings used for a *"larger and more richly"* furnished christening set. On 22. 6 of the same year it was placed *"in a brand new chest of red saffian leather mounted with silver"* in the Ecclesiastical Treasury, where it was kept until 1780. As from 1785 it appears in the inventory of the Secular Treasury.

R. B.

94 CHRISTENING SET DONATED BY EMPRESS MARIA THERESIA

Vienna, 1757
Silver lamé, patterned, richly embroidered with gold and pearls, passementerie trimmings.

a) Large coverlet
158 x 129 cms (Inv. No. XIV 8)

Embroidered in pearls on the short sides: *M.T. — 1757.* Embroidery: meandering patterns formed of two rows of pearls intertwined with sprays of flowers and leaves.

b) Small coverlet
171.5 x 92 cms (Inv. No. XIV 9)

Embroidery as on the large coverlet.

c) Christening gown with hood
64.5 cms long (Inv. No. XIV 12)

Fully embroidered with the same motifs as the coverlets.

d) Pillow
71 x 51 cms (Inv. No. XIV 13)

The patterned silver lamé is most evident on the pillow; intersecting meandering patterns in flushing silver tinsel (largely missing) form rhomboid areas, each containing a spray of blossoms.

95 BAPTISMAL COVERLET

Vienna, 1762
Silver moiré patterned with floral and foliate motifs in atlas, hand-made gold lace; 178 x 116 cms (Inv. No. XIV 10)

This coverlet was entrusted to the safekeeping of the Treasury on 16. 4. 1762 on the orders of Maria Theresia, after the *Hervorgang* (issuing forth, i.e. churching) of Archduchess Isabella of Parma, the first wife of the later Emperor Joseph II. This was the mother's first appearance in public after the birth, when she and the child were blessed in church. Isabella's *Hervor-*

95, 98

gang was held on 20. 3. 1762, after the birth of Maria Theresia's first grand-daughter, who was named after her. This coverlet, probably specially made for the occasion, was used *"because the others were too heavy"*.   R. B.

97

96 THE CHRISTENING SET DONATED BY MARIA LUDOVICA

Vienna, 1790
Unpatterned silver lamé, gold embroidery, gold bobbin lace.

a) Large coverlet
169 x 146 cms (Inv. No. A 171)

Embroidered on the short sides with silver paillettes: *ML — 1790*. Embroidery: borders of three loosely intertwined meandering patterns. In the central area, parallel meandering tendrils of delicate blossoms; in between intersecting zigzag lines.

b) Small coverlet (not exhibited)
171 x 99 cms (Inv. No. A 172)

Embroidered like the large coverlet.

c) Christening gown with hood
65.5 cms long (Inv. No. A 173)

Embroidered on the borders and seams.

d) Pillow
67 x 53 cms (Inv. No. A 174)

The embroidery along the borders matches that of the rest of the set.
Maria Ludovica, wife of Emperor Leopold II, donated this christening set, based on the one donated by Maria Theresa, on the occasion of the birth of her first grandchild Archduchess Ludovica on 17. 2. 1790. That this set could not eclipse the earlier one in importance is shown by the fact that in all the succeeding christening ceremonies it is always the set from 1757 which is mentioned and never the later one, which was, incidentally, entered in the inventory of the Ecclesiastical Treasury.   R. B.

97 CHRISTENING GOWN
Vienna, end of the 18th century
Cambric, gold embroidery, bobbin lace; 65 cms long (Inv. No. XIV 11)

The embroidery is arranged in parallel vertical bands with a scattered pattern of tiny leaves in between. The gown,

96

which belongs to the set ordered by Maria Theresia, is described in later inventories as *"a small gown with hood"*.

R. B.

98 SMALL CHRISTENING GOWN FOR (EMPEROR) FRANZ JOSEPH AND HIS BROTHERS AND SISTERS

Vienna, 1830

Satin, net lace with bobbined appliqués; 72 cms long (Inv. No. A 208)

Long, pink silk gown, fastened with ribbons at the back. The silk covered by net lace with richly-worked borders of flower bouquets and scattered patterns. Pink satin bow, faded. The gown has a small matching tulle hood with silk ribbons. This set was used for the baptism of the later Emperors Franz Joseph, (1830) and Maximilian of Mexico (1832), as well as that of the Archduke Karl Ludwig (1833), the Archduchess Maria Anna (1835) and the Archduke Ludwig Viktor (1842).

R. B.

99 CANDLE

Vienna, 1868

Wax, painted with oils; 73 cms long (Inv. No. D 109)

Painted with festoons of flowers, this candle was used at the christening of Archduchess Maria Valerie (born 22. 4. 1868), the youngest daughter of Emperor Franz Joseph and his wife, Elisabeth.

R. B.

100 CANDLE

Vienna, 1883

Moulded wax, gilded, velvet, gilded silver foil; 96 cms long (Inv. No. D 75)

In an oval medallion on the front is the inscription: *Archduchess Elisabeth, born 2. 9. 1883.* On the back: *Baptised: 5. Sept: a. 1883.*

Archduchess Elisabeth was the daughter of Crown Prince Rudolf and his wife, Stephanie of Belgium.

R. B.

101 BAPTISMAL EWER AND BASIN

Spanish master, 1571

Gold, partially enamelled; dated 1571 on handle; ewer 34.5 cms high, basin 61.5 cms diameter (Inv. No. XIV 5, 6)

This set, for which about 10.5 kgs of gold were used, was, together with 10,000 gulden, the wedding present of the Carinthian estates to Archduke Karl of Inner Austria and Maria of Bavaria. It was formally presented in Graz on 11. 9. 1571 by the Provincial Governor, Georg Khevenhüller, the wedding having taken place on 26. 8. in Vienna. The two costly pieces must have been the property of Maria, since they appear not in the inventory of Karl's estate of 1590, but in an early will of Maria's, dating from 1591, in which she bequeaths them to her son, Ferdinand (afterwards Emperor Ferdinand II). Since Maria lived until 1608, they presumably remained in her possession until then. Ferdinand must have subsequently taken the set with him to Vienna. Descriptions of the Treasury from the second half of the 17th century already refer to them as being used for the christening of the Archdukes.

Both ewer and basin are richly chased and ornamented with champlevé enamelling and present the art historian with considerable problems as to their localisation, thus necessitating thorough examination.

The slender *ewer* with its long neck and high handle has an almost ovoid body, the ornamentation of which is divided into four zones, each with either three or six subdivisions respectively. The foot, however, starts off with five divisions. The broad, slightly convex surface of the outer zone is decorated with five mascarons, alternating with bunches of fruit. Above a small, vertical moulding are five concave double tongues separated by mannerist strapwork. The bottom of the ewer is decorated with six convex double tongues with strapwork between them. There follows a zone of densely-embossed scrollwork or strapwork ornamentation, flanking three medallions deco-

rated with grotesques in colourful champlevé enamel. (Characteristic of the grotesques, an ornamental device composed of plants, animals and abstract elements, is their vertical orientation, i.e. they cannot be inverted — unlike the mauresques, which are vertically and horizontally symmetrical [cf. basin]). The main zone of the ewer also bears three applied roundels, two of which have grotesque ornamentation, while the third, set in front, bears the arms of Carinthia in enamel. The areas in between are occupied by a circular niche displaying a chased female mask at the centre flanked by bunches of fruit. These ornaments are repeated, in similar form but without the masks, on the outer border of the basin. Two pearl chaplets mark the upper and lower limits of this zone. On the shoulder, corresponding vertically to the lower zone and to the female masks, are two further applied enamel roundels, which also repeat the motif of the medallions below; the base of the handle, which terminates in a female head, takes the place of the third. The scroll and strapwork in between the medallions is here

arranged on three axes. The slender neck, bisected in the middle by a chaplet, again takes up the concave double tongue motif from the stem. The long, curved lip, edged with strings of gold pearls, is engraved with grotesques on the upper side and on the under side with bird motifs and strapwork. The pierced strapwork and numerous volutes on the handle enclose a helmeted warrior figure holding a disc. At his feet lies a tiny plaque with the date 1571.

The large *basin* matches the ewer in its formal conception. On the broad border, enclosed on the outside by a wreath of leaves with a chaplet and on the inside by a denticular profiled ring, lie six oval medallions with brightly coloured mauresques and six blue-enamelled satyr masks with black horns and golden hair. The embossed fields in between, repeated twelve times, match those on the main zone of the ewer. The sides of the basin are formed by smooth, concave tongues with a web in pointillé technique between imbricated bands. In the centre, two convex rings rise from the bottom of the basin, joining it to the foot of the ewer. The outer ring bears six small winged enamelled putti heads, corresponding radially to the medallions on the border; the inner ring again has six medallions, which correspond in turn to the satyr masks. This radial correspondence is continued in the ewer. In the centre, hidden by the foot of the ewer, the arms of Carinthia are repeated in enamelwork, with the same dimensions as those on the ewer.

The set is not marked, and its provenance can thus only be deduced by stylistic comparison. Although it has until recently been described as Southern German or Italian work, it does not really belong to either of these artistic traditions. A third possibility, suggested by Hayward, is that it is the work of a Spanish master, a hypothesis which is supported by the greatest number of arguments, despite the fact that we have only fragmentary knowledge of Spanish goldsmiths' work of the 16th century. Typically Spanish features are the combination of applied enamelled medallions with embossing, and the slender form of the ewer. Further features from the Spanish tradition include the concave and convex double tongues, the double convex rings of the bottom of the basin and individual details of the mannerist scrollwork and strapwork. The form of the handle, too, the way it swings out over the straight, vertical attachment and the figure enclosed in the ornamentation — which was perhaps influenced by ornamental engravings from Antwerp, for example those by Cornelius Bos, — is also to be found in the Spanish tradition. Finally, the relatively rough surface of the basin, particularly on the underside, corresponds to the working methods of Spanish goldsmiths. None of these arguments alone would suffice to attribute this piece to a Spanish artist, yet as a body of evidence, they carry considerable weight.

It is known that several Spanish artists were active at the court of Maximilian II in Vienna, among them goldsmiths. Furthermore, contact between Austria and Spain was particularly intensive at

this time. The Archdukes Rudolf and Ernst spent a large part of their youth at the Spanish court. On 1. 8. 1570, their sister, Archduchess Anna, left Vienna to marry King Philip II of Spain, and travelled via the Netherlands to Spain, arriving on 4. 10. Among her retainers was Moritz Christoph Khevenhüller and the Spanish goldsmith Juan Mazuelo, who had previously been active in Vienna. Later the same month, Georg Khevenhüller arrived in Munich as a member of the embassy sent to petition Duke Albrecht V for the hand of Maria for Archduke Karl. Couriers were constantly travelling between Vienna and Madrid and between the Khevenhüllers. The question thus remains open of whether the Spanish artist who made the set belonged to the court circle at Vienna or Madrid.   R. D.

Ref.: J. Hayward, Virtuoso Goldsmiths and the Triumph of Mannerism 1540—1620, London, 1976, p. 392 f., nos. 564—567.

102 SMALL BAPTISMAL EWER
Imperial Court workshop (Jan Vermeyen, † 1606 Prague)
Prague, beginning of the 17th century
Gold, partially enamelled, rubies; 15.5 cms high (Inv. No. XIV 7)

This small ewer is a masterpiece of goldsmiths' art. It has an extremely elegant profile, and its decoration resembles that of the setting of a precious stone. The smooth ovoid body is entirely decorated with colourfully enamelled cast-gold ornamentation, giving the impression of a double-layer. It rests in an openwork basket of eight red tongues framed in white, and colourful spikes of leaves, whose centres are occupied alternately by a ruby or a bunch of fruit. This is balanced by the narrow decoration on the shoulder, which is set with rubies. On the body are small, ornate cherubs' heads with colourful wings and large rubies. Each of them is connected to the next by garlands in which hang bunches of fruit. The little heads and the gem settings bear delicate sprays of

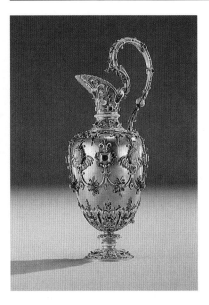

flowers. On the base, the neck and the sweeping, protruding lip, the gold is slightly roughened, singularly delicate enamelled tendrils set with rubies rising in relief from the surface. The elegantly raised handle, whose edges are bordered by white bands, and which is also decorated with rubies, ornate blossoms and leaves, bears the Habsburg arms (vertically divided shield with the arms of Austria and Burgundy) near the top. Every detail is a feast for the eyes.

The arms do not display an emblem of sovereignty, from which one may surmise that the small ewer was made for an Archduke. The little cherubs' heads indicate that it was used for ecclesiastical purposes, and thus that this costly piece was intended as a baptismal ewer from the first, an assumption also supported by its small dimensions. The standard of the work which has gone into the little ewer links it to the finest works of art produced at the court of Rudolf II. However, the latter was unmarried, and Matthias did not marry until 1611, and then remained childless. The piece appears neither in the inventory of Rudolf's *Kunstkammer*, nor in that of Matthias' estate. The only other possible recipient is Archduke Ferdinand (later Emperor Ferdinand II),

who married Maria Anna of Bavaria in 1600, and had seven children by her. The first three came into the world in 1601, 1603 and 1605 respectively, i.e. at a time when Ferdinand was not yet in possession of the large golden set. Bearing this in mind, we may conclude that the small ewer was made as a baptismal ewer between 1601 and 1605 in Prague. In this case it can only have been made by Jan Vermeyen, the master of the Rudolfine crown (Cat. No. 56), whose style it in fact most closely resembles.   R. D.

Ref.: Weixlgärtner 1928, p. 290, note 49; Distelberger 1985, p. 281.

103 CABINET HOLDING THE KEYS TO THE COFFINS OF THE HABSBURGS

Alexander Albert, Court cabinetmaker
Vienna, 1895
Walnut and other woods; 243 cms high, 149 cms broad, 64 cms deep (Inv. No. XVI A 24)

Whenever a member of the Imperial family was buried, their coffin was reopened on its arrival in the crypt of the Church of the Capuchins, at which point the Grand Chamberlain asked the Guardian of the Capuchin Monastery whether he recognized the deceased. After the affirmative answer, the two separate locks of the coffin were closed. One key was entrusted to the Guardian, the other placed in the Treasury. Apart from the keys to the coffins that lie in the crypt of the Church of the Capuchins, the Treasury also possesses the keys to the coffins of those Habsburgs buried in Seckau, Bozen, Gmünd, Gran, Linz and Mantua. In 1870/71, during the renovation of the crypt in Neuberg, new metal coffins were made for the Habsburgs buried there and the keys to these also placed in the Treasury. Thus the line of Habsburgs whose coffin keys are preserved here goes back to Duke Otto the Merry († 1339). However, the keys are all of a later date, the oldest belonging to the 17th century. In all, the keys to 139 coffins are preserved in this cab-

inet, the central section being reserved for the keys of Emperors and their next-of-kin, while the two side sections contain the keys to the coffins of all the other archdukes.

The Crucifix in the Cabinet with the Coffin Keys

Gabriel Grupello? (Geraardsbergen 1644—1730 Ehrenstein/Kerkrade)
Düsseldorf, c. 1695
Ivory; cross 56 cms high, 17.6 cms wide; corpus 26,7 cms high (Inv. No. XIV 33)

Four nails pin the figure of Christ to the cross, the legs placed side by side and the arms raised almost vertically. The elongated contours of the body are scarcely interrupted by the loincloth draped around the hips. This type of corpus with the arms outstretched in a V had become widely known and imitated through the works of Peter Paul Rubens. It had an added advantage in that the figure could be carved from a single piece of ivory. The cross is stylistically related to a cross in the Couven Museum in Aix-la-Chapelle, ascribed to Gabriel Grupello (cf. Cat. No. 178 from the Eccesiastical Treasury). The surface is characterised by the softness of the modelling, which imbues both body and hair with a fascinating, almost painterly quality. The cross was donated privately to the Treasury in 1821.   S. K.

Ref.: U Kultermann, Gabriel Grupello, Berlin 1968, p. 247, no. 27 (crucifix in the Couven Museum).

JEWELLERY AND COMMEMORATIVE PIECES

104 EMERALD UNGUENTARIUM
Dionysio Miseroni († 1661 Prague)
Prague, 1641
2,680 carat emerald, enamelled gold;
10.9 cms high, 8.5 cms long, 7.2 cms
wide (Inv. No. Pl 2048)

This vessel is an absolutely unique
piece of inestimable value. The dark-
green emerald is of outstanding quality
— it is one of the largest in the world
— and comes from the mine at Muzo
in Columbia, where the extraction of
emeralds first began in 1558. The uncut
stone is already recorded in the inventory of the estate of Emperor Matthias,

dating from 1619, as *"a large piece of
emerald, uncut, as it occurs in nature,
about the size of a big fist"*.

It was Emperor Ferdinand III who had
it turned into its present form, promising the stone-carver Dionysio Miseroni
some land or a small estate upon com-
pletion of the work. In the event, the
master received the handsome sum of
12,000 gulden, guaranteed and paid in
installments, for this difficult task,
which took him some one-and-a-half
to two years.

In order to avoid too great a loss of
material, the cutting work followed the

form of the natural stone, which has resulted in the vessel's irregular shape. Despite this, a great number of carats were lost in engraving it with the four leaves that hang from the shoulder — a lobate and a pinnate leaf, alternately — and the acanthus leaf on the base. Between the leaves, curving grooves follow the stone's natural 'terrain'. The two small emerald feet have been inserted into the base with gold mounts. Since the vessel's rim remained uneven, the goldsmith provided it with a green enamelled gold border, upon which lies the heavy, rose-cut lid, attached to the mounting by a small, serpentine eyelet. The lid alone, with its convex underside reaching into the vessel's mouth, is 3.6 cms high and has a diameter of 4.9 cms. The whole of its underside is mounted in gold, engraved with flowers and covered by green translucent enamel. The lid and the feet have been worked from the material excavated from the vessel. When carving the side of the inner cavity the loss of material amounted to circa 2.5 mms, i.e. 5 mms of the diameter. Taking into account this considerable loss during cutting, the decision to carve a vessel from the stone has to be described as highly questionable and its modest decoration as genuinely expensive. Dionysio Miseroni presented the finished work to the Emperor together with several fragments of the gem, for which jewellers were supposed to have offered him 2,500 gulden in gold or gems.

The famous emerald vessel became a *mirabilium* (wonder) of the first rank in the Imperial Treasury. In 1645, when Ferdinand III, at the end of the Thirty Years War, wanted to raise money with the emerald in Genoa, the jewellers refused to value it because they did not trade in such large pieces. The chancery clerk of the legation for Saxony-Weimar, Müller, who visited the Treasury in 1660, noted in his travel journal that *"the Muscovites offered to give several chests of pearls"* for the vessel. A description of the Vienna Treasury dating from 1677 records that the Grand Duke of Florence wanted to offer three tons of gold for it. However, these are obviously stories that 17th century visitors to the Treasury were told in order to illustrate the uniqueness of the piece, and perhaps also to draw a comparison with the unique position of the Emperor.   R. D.

Ref.: R. Distelberger, Dionysio und Ferdinand Eusebio Miseroni, in: Jahrbuch 1979, p. 126 ff.

105 THE CROWN OF STEFAN BOCSKAY

Turkish, c. 1605
Gold, rubies, spinels, emeralds, turquoises, pearls, silk; 23.2 cms high, 18.8—22 cms diameter (Inv. No. XIV 25)

This crown is associated solely with a short historical episode. Counter-refomatory policies caused the Lutheran mining towns of Upper Hungary and the Saxon community of Transylvania to turn away from Emperor Rudolf II. The Calvinist aristocrat Stefan Bocskay (1557—1606) placed himself at the head of the dissatisfied factions and in February 1605 was elected Prince of Transylvania. He had styled himself as such since 1604 and had even had the title recognised by Sultan Ahmed I (1603—1617). Following his military successes, even in the western regions of Hungary, against the Imperial army led by General Basta, he was elected Prince of Hungary by the rebellious Hungarian nobles on 20. 4. 1605. Bocskay now turned to the Sultan to have himself recognised as king. The Sublime Porte, at war with the Emperor, seized the opportunity to exercise supreme sovereignty and simultaneously to commit the Prince to Turkish interests. Sultan Ahmed recognised Bocskay and his heirs as Kings of Hungary with full authority, and had him ceremonially crowned by the Grand Vizier Lala Mehmed Pasha on 11. 11. 1605 on the Field of Rákos outside Pest with this crown. Out of consideration towards the Emperor, Bocskay somewhat hypocritically de-

clared that he regarded the crown as a gift of the Turks rather than as a sign of sovereignty. On 23. 6. 1606, the Peace of Vienna was signed, guaranteeing religious freedom. In November of the same year, a peace was signed with the Turks in Zsitva Torok. Bocskay died on 29. 12. in Kaschau and his successor, Bálint Drugeth Hommonay († 1609) assumed the crown. In 1608, Emperor Matthias was crowned King of Hungary and in November 1609, the Representative Assembly of the Hungarian Estates voted to surrender the Bocskay crown to Matthias. It was taken from the heirs of Hommonay, who had died in the meantime, and the Palatine Georg Thurzo brought it to Vienna on 4. 10. 1610.

The crown comprises two main parts: the broad circlet with a wreath of fleurs-de-lys, and the closed, spherical helmet rising from it. The two parts are joined together with gold wire. The entire surface of the thick sheet gold is chased. Between the gemstone settings there are deep cut lanceolate leaves with smooth, blackened webs. The jewels consist of extremely irregular gemstones of varying size and quality, some of which have evidently been used before in other pieces. The majority are cabochon; some are facetted.

The base of the circlet is formed by a wreath of leaves, with a string of pearls lying close in front of it and crowned by pierced pearls. The circlet itself is decorated with three rows of gems, each with an alternating pattern of red and green stones, with larger stones in the middle row. In the wreath of fleurs-de-lys, eight larger leaves alternate with eight smaller ones. The sickle-shaped perforations between the lilies are backed with small pieces of faded rose-coloured and light green silk. In the large fleurs-de-lys, an emerald lies at the top of the central leaf with two turquoises in the leaves on either side; the small lilies each contain a ruby. On the vertical axis, all the stones of the circlet are offset in successive rows, thus resulting in diagonal rows as well. The tips of these lilies are crowned with irregularly polished and pierced pink stones in settings forming a small coronet of leaves, five of which are now missing. The frontal lily bears a Greek cross with a ruby at its centre and a pearl at its tips and in its angles. This frontal lily is not distinguished by any difference of form but by the presence of a fine triangular emerald. The fact that the cross is worked in the same technique as the other parts would seem to refute the opinion, held until recently, that this was a later addition made for Bocskay.

The helmet, its lower edge marked by a blackened band with a motif of intertwining leaves, is divided radially into eight segments by rows of pearls which start above the tips of the larger lilies. Within each of the eight segments lie three vertical rows of stones, the two outer ones again consisting of alternating rubies and emeralds. The second stone of the middle row is considerably larger than the others. The tapering towards the point of the helmet leaves only the middle row of stones, consisting of a ruby between two turquoises. The stones are also arranged in horizontal correspondence to one another, with the turquoises — as in the lilies of the circlet — forming a row of their own, no other stones occurring in these rows. The arrangement of the stones probably possesses symbolic significance. The motif on the base of the crown is repeated at the point of the helmet in a wreath of leaves forming a miniature coronet with eight pierced pearls. A high, facetted emerald decorates the point, encircled by a further row of eight, smaller pearls. The smooth, sheet gold of the inside of the crown is unlined.

The shape of the crown recalls the metal helmets of Orthodox bishops, which in turn are descended from the Byzantine *kamelaukion* (the closed Imperial Byzantine crown). Crowns were not worn in the Ottoman Empire and thus there were no Turkish models available. It is thus not improbable that the Grand Vizier had the cross put on the crown; he must have known that Bocskay, who had until then been loyal to the Emperor, had turned away from Rudolf II for religious reasons. The goldsmith work is Ottoman.   R. D.

Ref.: K. Nehring, Die Bocskai-Krone als Objekt des patrimoine intellectuel, in: Südostforschungen, XLIII, 1984, pp. 123—133.

106 CASE FOR THE CROWN OF STEFAN BOCSKAY

Turkish, around 1605; the fabric Persian, c. 1600

Wood, silk, silver-gilt; 26.8 cms high, 28 cms diameter (Inv. No. XIV 184)

This decagonal domed case is made of wood and covered with fabric. The clasp at the front and the hinges at the back are silver-gilt. The fabric of the cover is costly Persian silk and is decorated with a figural scene surrounded by flowers. Half sitting, half reclining, a lady is reading a book. Beside her kneels a servant with a wide, sweeping turban, offering her a bowl with his right hand and holding a bottle in his left. Between the two figures lies a bowl containing fruit. In the lady's open book can be read the signature of the artist, *Mu'min,* in Arabic script. On the inside of the case, the fabric retains all the freshness of its original colours, and is typical of the refined taste of the court of Shah 'Abbās the Great (1587—1628) at Isfahan. Technically, it can be described as a double-woven lampas of coloured silk. Glued to the floor of the case is an Italian fabric from the early 17th century. Its ground is warp satin in red silk; the pattern, which takes the form of pinnate leaves and blossoms, is yellow silk woven in twill and interwoven with silver.   R. D.

Ref.: D. Duda, Islamische Kunst und der Westen: am Beispiel Wien (14.-18. Jh.), in: Europa und die Kunst des Islam. 15. bis 18. Jh. XXV Internationaler Kongress für Kunstgeschichte. CIHA. Vienna 4.—10. 9. 1983, vol. 5, Salzburg 1985, p. 50. C. Bier, Woven from the Soul, Spun from the Heart, Washington 1987, p. 246.

107 TWO BOUQUETS OF FLOWERS

Florence (or Vienna), late 17th century, partial readaptation of older parts
Gold, partially enamelled, silver-gilt, diamonds, emeralds, rubies, blue sapphires, jacinths and hessonite; both 25.2 cms high (Inv. No. Pl. 1080, 1081)

The flower bouquets stand, attached by only one stem, like tiny trees, in silver-gilt vases with siren handles. The fronts of the vases are decorated with silver foliate ornamentation, set with emeralds and small, facetted diamonds. The flowers are backed by a structure of fairly coarsely-worked, enamelled leaves. Closer inspection of the various parts reveals a considerable difference in terms of style, quality and technique. The only pieces deriving from the late 17th century, the date of the small vases and the 'skeleton' of the bouquets, are the two simple flowers composed of white and green leaves surrounding a central stone, which flank the large emerald rosette.
These are hung with old, pierced sapphires and rose-coloured spinels respectively. All the other flowers have enamel of considerably better quality and an older type of setting. When they were set into the bouquets, the translucent enamel on their backs was damaged in many places and in some cases has been renewed. These flowers were obviously taken from older pieces of jewellery and deserve closer attention.
In the centre of the base of each bouquet are small jewels — probably from the 16th century — with the stones arranged in the form of a cross. They are flanked by beautiful aquilegias enamelled in blue and set with sapphires, with pendant sapphire drops. The bouquets are also crowned by aquilegias. The centre of each bouquet is formed by two large rosettes, the lower composed of emeralds and the upper of rubies. These four costly pieces have been worked using different techniques. Possibly the most beautiful of the four is the large emerald rosette on denticulated leaves tipped with red. Belonging to it are the two stelliform flowers flanking the ruby rosette. These correspond formally to the emerald jewels in the second bouquet. Next follows a row of three large yellow labiate flowers resembling lady's slippers. These are set with jacinths and hessonites (a type of garnet), which were at that time indistinguishable. All of these jewels date from the first quarter to the middle of the 17th century. The rosettes had probably been used as jewellery sewn onto ceremonial robes; the aquilegias and lady's slippers on the other hand were perhaps used to decorate elaborately-coiffed hair. They are merely individual examples of a formerly plentiful trove of jewellery. As can be seen from portraits of the 17th century, ceremonial clothing was decorated with dozens of rosettes of this type.
These jewels were made into the two bouquets because they had fallen out of fashion as dress ornamentation.

Thus it was that these two cabinet pieces, made for the Kunstkammer, and later the Treasury, have ensured the survival of jewels that no longer exist anywhere else, since jewellery was invariably reset.   R. D.

108 DIAMOND SABRE

Turkish, 2nd half of the 17th century
Set with diamonds, Vienna, c. 1712
Damascened steel (with meteoric iron?), gold, silver, parcel-gilt, diamonds, one zircon, wood, leather; 91.5 cms long, scabbard 82.5 cms long (Inv. No. XIa 50).

On the blade are Arabic inscriptions damascened in gold; in the medallion beneath the tang: *"In the name of God the All Merciful"* and along the back: *"Help from God and approaching victory and glad tidings for the faithful".* The hilt and cross-guard of this sabre, as well as the top-locket, mid-locket and chape of the scabbard, were originally only covered with silver gilt, and chased with floral decoration. The flower sprays on the hilt are of higher quality than those on the other parts, even though they all date from the same time. Treasury descriptions from the second half of the 17th century mention several costly Turkish scimitars with diamonds. It is, however, clear that the precious stones were only added at a later date, since hardly any attention has been paid to the Turkish style of decoration and all the cuts and mounts are European. This may have been done for the coronation of Karl IV as King of Hungary in 1712, at which the sabre was supposed to have been worn. On the inner side, where the gilded silver plates are only sparingly decorated, the ajouré silver tendrils have been set with diamonds. Many of the larger stones have been reused. While the diamond roses have been cut in a variety of ways, the seven large table cuts and two pointed diamonds are particularly striking on account of their very old mounts, which

presumably date from the late Middle Ages. They are attached with wire. Only the large table stone on the middle of the cross-guard is a zirkon, and at that time it had still not been conclusively identified as such. The table stones on the mid-lockets, as well as the three stones of the chape at the tip of the scabbard, have gold mounts. The inventory of 1871 not only notes that the sabre was *"procured by Emperor Karl VI for the Hungarian coronation"* (22. 5. 1712), but also that it was *"worn by Maria Theresia for her coronation at Pressburg"* (25. 6. 1741).

R. D.

109 REMAINS OF A SUBSTITUTE IMPERIAL CROWN OF EMPEROR FERDINAND III

a) Four plaques representing the Evangelists Matthew, Mark, Luke and John
German (?), probably 1653
Silver-gilt (no hallmarks); 8.1 cms, 8.3 cms, 8.2 cms and 8.1 cms high (Inv. Nos. Pl. 1006, 1008, 1007, 1009)

The plaques are embossed from thin sheets of silver. Whether the representations of the four Evangelists were based on graphic models is not known.

The four relief plaques were assigned to the Imperial-Royal Collection of Castle Ambras by the Treasury in 1872; they came to the Kunsthistorische Museum, together with the rest of the collection, in 1891.

b) Two Neckchains of the Order of the Golden Fleece.
Vienna, 1873
Court jeweller A. E. Köchert, incorporating older parts
Gold, partially enamelled, diamonds, rubies (one missing); no hallmarks or maker's marks; c. 120 and 102 cms long respectively (Inv. No. XIa 58)

The longer of the two neckchains consists of 21 spark-emitting flints and 42 fire steels, the shorter of 18 spark-emitting flints and 36 fire steels. These elements are linked together by chains. According to an entry in the inventory of 1874, both neckchains were fashioned by the court jeweller out of parts of the *"substitute Crown of the Roman-German Empire",* which had been broken up in 1872. The longer neckchain was apparently made for Emperor Franz Joseph and the shorter for Crown Prince Rudolf. The Golden Fleece pendant is missing in both cases.
The fact that the extremely high price

of 2,228 gulden was paid for the work indicates that the pieces were in fact virtually new, and merely included the existing gemstones, partially in their old bezel settings. The element of the spark-emitting flints, at least, must have been new, since this emblem of the Golden Fleece would have been inappropriate for a copy of the Imperial Crown. The rubies, together with their old bezel settings, are newly-set. The fire steels, however, would seem to be adaptations of older decorative elements.

The Treasury used to possess a crown, a detailed description of which appears for the first time in the inventory of 1750, which would seem to have been a fairly free reproduction of the Crown of the Holy Roman Empire. It was later called the *"substitute Imperial Crown".* Instead of the four enamelled plaques of the original, it had these four silver plaques with reliefs representing the four Evangelists, together with 1,251 diamonds, 53 table-cut rubies and white enamel foliate work, none of which corresponds to the original crown either. The crown was deposited in the Treasury by Emperor Ferdinand III in 1654. At the coronation of Joseph II as Roman King in Frankfurt in 1764, it is documented that the crown was carried at the head of the procession as it left

the cathedral. The enamel work was badly damaged on this occasion. In 1872 it was finally broken up: the only pieces now remaining are the four reliefs of the Evangelists and the gemstones in the two neckchains.

It is probable that the crown was made in 1653 for the coronation of Ferdinand IV as Roman King, as the insigne of the Imperial Treasurer, whose priviledge it was to carry it at the head of the coronation procession. This office had been bestowed on Karl Ludwig of the Palatinate in 1650 as the Imperial office of the eighth Electorate, which he had received as compensation for the Electorate that had been taken from his dynasty and given to Bavaria after the Peace of Westphalia in 1623. A portrait of Karl Ludwig of the Palatinate by J. B. Ruel in Heidelberg shows the Elector with a copy of the Imperial Crown in his hands. This crown also seems to have the reliefs of the Evangelists in place of the enamelled plaques. However, the disposition of the coloured gemstones corresponds almost exactly with that of the original Imperial Crown, which prompts the question of whether the House of the Palatine Elector might also have possessed a copy of the crown.   M. L.-J.

Ref.: Weixlgärtner 1928, pp. 304—308; Kugler 1986, pp. 117—123.

110 HYACINTH "LA BELLA"

Mounting: Vienna (?), c. 1687
Garnet (almandine), gold, silver-gilt, enamel; weight of the gem: 416 carats; dimensions: 6.8 cms high, 3.9 cms wide; the mounting 19.9 cms high, 15.8 cms wide (Inv. No. XIa 51).

This gemstone has a double setting. The inner setting, composed of white enamel branches, would appear to date from the 15th century. The outer setting takes the form of an Imperial double-headed eagle, which holds in its right talons a sword and the arms of Hungary, in its left a sceptre and the arms of Bohemia, while its two heads bear the Imperial crown. Curling around the necks is a white enamel banderole with the inscription *Hiacent / La Bella.*

Despite the date of the older setting, the stone first receives mention in 1619 (in the inventory of the estate of Emperor Matthias), as *"Ain schön jochzinck La bella"* (A beautiful hyacinth La bella). At some point in time, today unknown, it was removed from the Treasury and had to be repurchased from a Hungarian private collection by Emperor Leopold I in 1687. The following inscription on the back of the stone's covering plate refers to that event: *"ANNO 1687 Hat / Leopoldus der Er/ste Romischer Kayser / dieses VNschatzbare / Kleynodt so HIACENT / LABELLA genannt vnd / 416 CARAT wiegt von / der HVMANAYIschen / FAMILIA aus Hungarn / erkaufft vnd in Dero / Kayserliche Schatz/Camer gelegt"* (= ANNO 1687 Leopoldus the First, Holy Roman Emperor, bought this invaluable jewel, known as HIACENT LABELLA and 416 carats in weight, from the Hommonay family of Hungary, and placed it in his Imperial Treasury).   M. L.-J.

111 MILK OPAL

Setting: Southern German or Prague, c. 1600
Milk-white opal, gold; 4.2 cms high (Inv. No. Pl. 1825)

This three-sided stone has shallow facets; on each side lie vertical facets, each divided into triangular sections, resulting in a zigzag pattern. The point is flattened and also cut into triangular facets. The culet is divided into four bands and has similar facetting to the sides.

The brackets of the gold setting are formed of finely-chased foliate scrollwork, out of which winged sirens grow, their pointed helmets following the edges of the stone. In the centre at the bottom is a pin with a thread, which probably indicates that the setting originally stood on a support. The opal is listed in the inventory of Emperor Rudolf II's Kunstkammer of 1607/1611. This extraordinarily beautiful jewel has no function as such, for example as the decoration of a particular item, being an aesthetic object in its own right.

The scholarly personal physician of Emperor Rudolf II, Anselmus Boetius de Boot, wrote in his 'Gemmarum et Lapidum Historia' of 1609 that the opal was the most beautiful precious stone, to be preferred above all others, echoing the reverence accorded to the opal in the Middle Ages: at that time the *'Waise'* in the frontal plate of the Imperial Crown, probably a Hungarian opal, was deemed to be the 'stone of stones'.   R. D.

Ref.: Weixlgärtner 1928, p. 287; Bauer/Haupt 1976, no. 2440.

112 HUNGARIAN OPAL

Setting: Southern German, c. 1600
Opal, enamelled gold; 7.2 cms high (Inv. No. XIa 52)

This drop-shaped, polished stone sits in an enamelled gold setting with three clasps which separate below and enclose a red enamelled leaf-rosette. The joint in the curve of the clasps covers a small rosette, which is also red. Above, the setting continues beyond the stone, providing room on all three sides for a further three red rosettes in front of the green tendrils which constitute the stone's mount.

The places where the so-called Hungarian opal is found lie in the Libánka and Simonka mountains (present-day Czechoslovakia). Hungarian opals are still the most highly valued of all opals. Pieces of this size and quality were extremely rare.   R. D.

Ref.: M. Bauer, Edelsteinkunde, revised by K. Schloßmacher, 3rd ed. Leipzig 1932.

113 HAIR AMETHYST

Setting: Spanish, last third of the 17th century
Amethyst (= quartz), gold, emeralds; 11.8 cms high (Inv. No. XIa 53)

In 17th century Spain, where amethysts were found in Catalonia, they were valued almost as highly as diamonds. It was not until the 19th century and the import of gemstones from South America that the prices of all gem-

stones fell dramatically. The original value of the stone explains the heavy, costly setting of gold in the form of a crown, which is closely set with emeralds of the highest quality. Inside the crown is an openwork, rosette-shaped helmet.

This pear-shaped stone of remarkable size contains inclusions of goethite and veinings of iron oxide, which have given it the name of hair amethyst. It was said to have been a gift to Emperor Leopold I from King Charles II of Spain (1665—1700).

A jewel of this size was of course not intended to be worn, but displayed as a cabinet-piece in the Treasury.   R. D.

114, 115, 116 a, b

114 GRAND CROSS OF THE MILITARY ORDER OF MARIA THERESIA

J. A. Schöll (Frankfurt goldsmith working in Vienna)
Vienna, 1765
Silver, gold, diamonds, emeralds, rubies; signed beneath the central disc: *1765* and: *J. A. Schöll de Franckfurth fait à Vienne le 20. Dec 1765;* 10.6 cms high and wide (Inv. No. XIa 16)

The Military Order was founded by the Empress Maria Theresia in 1757, to commemorate the victory of the Austrian troops over the army of Friedrich II of Prussia at Kolin. The emblem of the Order consists of a white enamel cross with incurving sides and undée ends. It displays a round shield bearing the colours of Austria and surrounded by the inscription FORTITUDINI ('for the brave'). On the back, in place of the Austrian colours, is the monogramme of Maria Theresia.

This particular Grand Cross is set with diamonds and rubies instead of enamel, and is also underlaid with a laurel wreath, the leaves of which are made of emerald mounted in gold.

The cross derives from the estate of Emperor Joseph II, who wore it as the Grand Master of the Order and in 1789, after the capture of Belgrade, presented it as a gift to Field Marshal Gideon Loudon. Repurchased from his widow in 1790, Emperor Franz II awarded it to Prince Philipp Josias von Coburg in 1794. Repurchased anew from the latter's heirs, the cross was finally placed in the Treasury.   M. L.-J.

115 STAR OF THE MILITARY ORDER OF MARIA THERESIA

Court jeweller Johann Michael Grosser
Vienna, 1757
Gold, silver, diamonds, rubies, emeralds; signed on a scrap of paper inside the capsule: *Jo: Mich. grosser. hoff. Jubilir fecit 1757;* including suspension ring 6 cms high (Inv. No. XIa 17)

This cross, which was made in the year of the Order's foundation, is probably that worn by the Emperor himself from the time of Franz I onwards. Franz II placed it in the safe-keeping of the Treasury in 1792.   M. L.-J.

116 STAR AND CROSS OF THE HUNGARIAN ORDER OF ST. STEPHEN

J. and A. Biedermann, court jewellers
Vienna, 1st half of 19th century

The 'Royal Hungarian High Order of Saint Stephan, the Apostolic King', founded by Maria Theresia in 1764 to commemorate the election of her son Joseph II as Holy Roman Emperor, was the monarchy's highest civil order of merit.

a) Star

Gold, silver, diamonds, emeralds, enamel; on the reverse, signed: *Jos: & Ant: / Biedermann / k.k. Hofjuveliere / in Wien;* diameter 10.4 cms (Inv. No. XIa 20)

Upon the mounted diamonds of the star lies a wreath of oak leaves made of emeralds in gold settings. This surrounds a diamond-rimmed medallion displaying the arms of New Hungary and the initials M.T. (Maria Theresia) composed of diamonds and emeralds on a red enamelled ground.

b) Cross

Gold, silver, diamonds, enamel; with the crown 8.3 cms high (Inv. No. XIa 20)

The green enamelled cross is surrounded by diamonds and displays a medallion, at the centre of which are the arms of New Hungary and the initials M. T., composed of diamonds and red and green enamel. It is surrounded by a white hoop with the inscription PRAEMIUM PURE IGIM MERITOR (usually: PUBLICUM MERITORIUM PRAEMIUM = Award for Distinguished Public Service). On the reverse, on a white ground surrounded by a laurel wreath, is the inscription: S(ANC)TO ST(EPHANO) R(EG)I AP(OSTOLICO) (For St. Stephen, the Apostolic King). Above the cross is a stylised Hungarian crown set with diamonds.

In 1854, this particular Star and Cross of the Order was awarded to Field Marshal Count Josef Wenzel Radetzky. In 1858 it was repurchased from his estate, and placed in the Treasury.   M. L.-J.

117 CROSS OF THE HUNGARIAN ORDER OF ST. STEPHEN

Vienna (?), 2nd half of the 18th century

Gold, silver, diamonds, emeralds, rubies, enamel; without the ring for the ribbon of the Order 6 cms high (Inv. No. XIa 22)

This cross, from the estate of Emperor Franz I, was deposited in the Treasury on 22. 1. 1766 on the orders of Empress Maria Theresia after his death. It is remarkable for the fine quality of its stones.   M. L.-J.

118 CROSS OF THE HUNGARIAN ORDER OF ST. STEPHEN

Vienna (?), 1746/1765

Gold, silver, diamonds, emeralds, rubies, enamel; without the ring for the ribbon of the Order 5.7 cms high (Inv. No. XIa 21)

From the estate of Archduke Ferdinand, Duke of Modena, who died on 24. 12. 1806, this cross was repurchased for the Treasury by Emperor Franz II in 1807.   M. L.-J.

119 GOLDEN CROSS OF CIVILIAN MERIT

Vienna, 1814

Gold, black and yellow rep ribbon; diameter 3 cms (Inv. No. XIV 16)

Plain patté cross. On the front the inscription: GRATI / PRINCEPS ET PATRIA / FRANC(ISCUS) / IMP (ERATOR) AUG(USTUS) (in gratitude — Sovereign and Fatherland — Emperor Franz). On the obverse: EUROPAE / LIBERTATE ASSERTA / MDCCCXIII / MDCCCXIV (For those who ensured Europe's freedom 1813/1814).

Emperor Franz I of Austria established this decoration on 13. 5. 1814 after Paris had been taken by the armies of the Alliance, for people who had rendered great service in the efforts to bring about Napoleon's downfall, without having taken part in military actions. The Civilian Cross of Merit was awarded in silver or gold. This cross is the decoration worn by the Emperor himself.

Parallel to this, the Emperor also established a Military Cross, which was made from the metal of the captured canons and was thus called the *Kanonenkreuz* ('cannon' cross).

M. L.-J.

120 MILITARY CROSS WITH DIAMONDS

Vienna (?), 2nd half of the 19th century
Gold, silver, diamonds, rubies, enamel; with the ring for the ribbon of the Order 7.3 cms high (Inv. No. XIa 24)

This Order was founded by Emperor Franz Joseph on 22. 10. 1849, after the victories of Custozza and Novara, and at the suggestion of Field Marshal Radetzky. The bearer of this particular version, which is set with precious gems, remains unknown.   M. L.-J.

121 COMMEMORATIVE TOKEN OF ALLEGIANCE

Rudolf Marschall (1874—1967)
Vienna, 1908
Platinum, diamonds, rubies, enamel; 7.5 cms high, 6.3 cms wide (Inv. No. XIb 64)

This token was presented to Emperor Franz Joseph by the Austro-Hungarian Army in 1908, in celebration of the 60th year of his reign. In the centre is the date 1908 on a red-enamelled ground and a cross set with diamonds, surrounded by a laurel wreath. Over this rests the Austrian Imperial Crown backed by two crossed swords. On the front the inscription: EXERCITUS / UNIVERSUS (the entire army) in raised lettering over red enamel. On the obverse, engraved and enamelled, the inscription: FRANCISCO/JOSEPHO /I./IMPERATORI/REGI/DOMINO / NOSTRO / HOC / FIDEI / PERPETUAE / SIGNUM. (To Franz Joseph I, Emperor and King, our Lord, this sign of eternal loyalty.)
Transferred to the Treasury in 1981.

M. L.-J.

122 PRUSSIAN MARSHAL'S STAFF

Court goldsmith Sy & Wagner
Berlin, 1895

Gold, silver, enamel, brilliants, rubies, velvet; 49 cms long (Inv. No. XIb 65)

The shaft of this staff is covered with blue velvet, and decorated with the Prussian eagle and the Prussian Royal Crown alternately appliquéd five times in four rows. The pommels at both ends of the staff can be unscrewed (on the inside of each is the name of the firm SY & WAGNER / BERLIN). On white enamelled banderoles surrounded by mounted brilliants or rubies, is the inscription: WILHELM II KÖNIG VON PREUSSEN SEINEM HOCHVEREHRTEN / BUNDESGENOSSEN FRANZ JOSEPH KAISER VON ÖSTERREICH KÖNIG VON UNGARN 27. FEBR. 1895 (Wilhelm II King of Prussia to his highly esteemed confederate Franz Joseph Emperor of Austria, King of Hungary). On the ends of both pommels is a large brilliant and the interentwined monogramme WR (Wilhelmus Rex), also of brilliants, above golden yellow translucent enamel and surrounded at the top by bands of brilliants and rubies respectively. On the upper pommel is the royal crown, surrounded by the motto SUUM CUIQUE (Each to his own); on the lower pommel, the Prussian eagle.
The marshal's staff was a gift of Emperor Wilhelm II of Germany to Em-

peror Franz Joseph, from whom he had taken his leave on 27. 2. 1895, after having been present at the funeral in Vienna of Archduke Albrecht, who was also an honorary Prussian Field Marshal. It was probably on this occasion that Emperor Franz Joseph was himself made Royal Prussian Field Marshal.

Transferred to the Treasury in 1918.

M. L.-J.

123 CITRINE
Setting: Nothern Italian or Southern German, last 3rd of the 16th century
Citrine (quartz), enamelled gold; 9.3 cms high, 5.9 cms wide (Inv. No. Pl. 1600)

This oval, honey-coloured stone was formerly held to be a topaz. It is uncut, but polished, whereby there are some smoothed hollows on the flatter side, probably undertaken to remove inclusions in the stone. The other side is cut as a regular cabochon.

The setting consists of a continuous band of white enamel with small cartouches, alternating in blue and red with red or green centres, between which are rosettes, flanked by club-shaped, black enamelled ornaments. The localisation of the goldwork is problematic: the individual motifs resemble Milanese work; the execution, however, suggests it was made by a Southern German master. The pendant pearl is missing.

R. D.

124 CITRINE
Setting: Vienna(?), mid-17th century
Citrine (quartz), gold, partially enamelled, 2 pearls, 1 diamond; 8.9 cms high (with pearl), 4.5 cms wide (Inv. No. Pl. 1897)

This oblong, octagonal stone was originally held to be a topaz. The deep pavilion exhibits a step cut, the crown a phantasy cut: the extremely flat facets divide the surface lengthways and crossways through the centre, as well as from corner to corner, giving rise to right-angled sections. These, in turn, are facetted in the form of a table

stone. The cutting reminds one of those later works with complicated facetting which Ottavio Miseroni made from 'Bohemian topaz' (quartz) around 1620. Certain inaccuracies in the cutting also resemble his work, which he was at the time delivering unmounted to Vienna from Prague.

The cartouche of the suspension ring bears a pearl in a black enamelled gold rosette. The pendant pearl sits in a black enamelled calix of leaves.

R. D.

125 CITRINE
Setting: Vienna (?), 17th century
Citrine (quartz), gold; 3.9 cms high (with hanging rings 4.8 cms), 2.8 cms wide (Inv. No. Pl. 1904)

This oblong, octagonal stone, formerly held to be a topaz, is step cut on the pavilion and phantasy cut on the crown: the facets divide the surface horizontally and vertically, intersecting in the middle, and from each corner, thus creating rectangular sections. These are divided by diagonals, also running from corner to corner. Both in design and technique, the cut resembles that of the larger, facetted citrine (Cat. No. 124).

R. D.

126 EMERALD CAMEO WITH BUST OF EMPEROR LEOPOLD I
Daniel Vogt († 1674 Breslau)
Vienna, c. 1669/70
Emerald, enamelled gold, diamonds;

on the shoulder the signature: *D. VOGT FECIT;* the cameo 3.3 x 2.9 cms, with mounting 5.6 x 4.6 cms (Inv. No. Pl. XII 69)

The cameo, carved from Columbian emerald, depicts the young Emperor Leopold I (born 1640) in right profile, wearing a laurel wreath to indicate his emperorship, and with long tumbling locks. A cloak is draped over his shoulder and breast. The figure overlaps the bevelled edge. The artist differentiates the surface by alternating matt areas with shining, polished ones. At the end of the sixties Vogt was working in Vienna, during which period he must have carved this exceptional gem.

The setting, also dating from that time, with its delicate, enamelled, ajouré tendrils, is only in keeping with the high value of the piece in its eight large diamonds, seven of them rose cuts and one (that beneath the suspension ring) a naville cut.   R. D.

Ref.: Eichler/Kris 1927, No. 497.

127 FAMILY TREE WITH THE KINGS AND EMPERORS OF THE HOUSE OF HABSBURG

Tree: Vienna, c. 1725/1730
Intaglios: Christoph Dorsch (Nuremberg 1676—1732 Nuremberg), Nuremberg, c. 1725/1730
Gold, chalcedony; signed: *DORSCH;* 29.2 cms high, 17.4 cms wide, base 12.8 cms diameter (Inv. No. Pl. XII 783)

The crown of this sturdy gold tree, with its fanciful branchings from which 16 portrait medallions of chalcedony are suspended, is conceived on the outlines of a rhombus. The distribution of the medallions, which have been wrought onto the branches, displays perfect correspondence, both vertically and horizontally, although there is slight three-dimensional divergence. The intaglios of chalcedony are inscribed and arranged from bottom to top and left to right in the chronological sequence of the kings and emperors portrayed: Rudolf I, Albrecht I, Albrecht II, Friedrich III (the Handsome, anti-king to Ludwig IV of Bavaria), Friedrich IV (today counted as Friedrich III), Maxi-

milian I, Karl V, Ferdinand I, Maximilian II, Rudolf II, Matthias, Ferdinand II, Ferdinand III, Leopold I, Joseph I and Karl VI. The last medallion bears Dorsch's signature on the lower edge. The circular base is shaped in the form of a hillock in the centre of which the tree is rooted. The goldsmith's work is not marked. The fact that Christoph Dorsch died in 1732 and that the last of the emperors, Karl VI (b. 1685), is portrayed in old age, indicates a date of around 1725/1730.

The sequence of emperors was of course interrupted by rulers from other dynasties. They are linked here with the motif of the family tree, which is at the same time a memorial to the House of Habsburg.   R. D.

128 EGG-CUP FROM THE ESTATE OF KING LOUIS XVI OF FRANCE (1754—1793)

Silver-gilt (Paris Poincon de décharge from the period 1774—1780, with the monkey's head for 958/1000 silver); 10.1 cms high (Inv. No. XIV 145)

tions. The crown is brilliant cut and its facets are multiplied by the fact that the table is not flat but slightly convex. The delicate gold setting holds the stone in an à jour gallery with an alternating pattern of one or three teeth, which is swivel-mounted on two hinges. Four snakes with delicate scales and acanthus leaves on their heads bear the jewel, and a fifth, smaller than the rest, knots them together in the centre under the stone. The piece bears no mark, but the cut, together with the goldwork, probably date it to around 1800.   R. D.

Underneath a tree, a stag starts back in fright from a barking dog and in doing so lets himself be captured by an armour-clad hunter. In the open crown of the tree there would have been a matching piece made of glass or porcelain. According to entries made in the inventory of the estate of King Louis XVI of France, it was bought from the Paris Mint in 1794. From the fragments of a piece of paper inside the casket, all that can now be distinguished is: *"Coquetier du Roi Louis XVI. acheté a la Monnaie Nationale le 4 . . . . / pa . . . ."*
Deposited in the Treasury in 1916.
                                              M. L.-J.

130 SET OF JEWELS FROM THE ESTATE OF ARCHDUCHESS SOPHIE (1805—1872)
Paris (?), between 1809 and 1819
Gold, silver, diamonds, emeralds and rose-coloured topazes; hallmark: left profile of a cock's head with an open beak; length of the chain 41 cms, length of the earrings 4.3 cms (Inv. No. XVII 31)

This set consists of a necklace and ear-pendants; the latter are adapted to the

129 AQUAMARINE
Setting: Vienna (?), c. 1800
Aquamarine, gold; 5.8 cms high, 7.4 cms long, 4.55 cms wide (Inv. No. Pl. 1911)

This oval, 492 carat aquamarine is possibly of Russian provenance, to judge by the optical refraction. The so-called 'mixed' cut has been executed with extraordinary precision. The pavilion, with 24 vertical facets, has nine grada-

form of the pendants on the double gold chain. Especially delightful are the alternating hues of the gold and the colourful silver-mounted stones. Pasted to the underside of the case, which is made of red and green saffian leather, is a piece of paper with the words: *"No. 63, Dieser Schmuck stammt aus dem Nachlasse weiland Ihrer kaiserl. Hoheit der dl. Frau Erzherzhogin Sophie. † 28. Mai 1872."* (No 63, These jewels come from the erstwhile estate of Her imper. Highness and Serene Ladyship, the Archduchess Sophie. † 28. May 1872).

As is suggested by the older hallmark, the jewels were probably not made upon commission for the Archduchess but either bequeathed or presented to her by a party today no longer known. Procured in 1884 from the court jeweller Köchert in Vienna for 1,200 gulden and placed in the Treasury.

M. L.-J.

131 CAMEO WITH THE PORTRAIT OF EMPEROR FRANZ I

Giovanni Beltrami (Cremona 1777—1854 Cremona), before 1840
Onyx; 5.9 cms high, 4.4 cms wide; setting: gold, enamelled; 10.5 cms high, 7 cms wide (Inv. No. Pl. XII 54)

The cameo shows a bust of the Emperor in old age, portrayed in left profile and wearing a laurel wreath.

Signed on the lower edge of the bust: BELTRAMI. On the obverse the inscription: F.I. / GEB. XII. FEBR. MDCCLXVIII / † / II. MAERZ. MDCCCXXXV.

On the front of the setting, on a ground of black enamel, the Emperor's device in raised lettering: IVSTITIA · REGNORVM · FVNDAMENTVM (Justice is the fundament of empires). On the obverse on the inside of the setting: MEINE LIEBE VERMACHE ICH MEINEN UNTERTHANEN: ICH HOFFE DASS ICH FÜR SIE BEY GOTT WERDE BETEN KÖNNEN. TEST. 14. §. 1. MÄRZ 1835 (I bequeath my love to my subjects. I hope I may pray for them before God). On the outside of the setting: *Ihre Majestät die Kaiserin Carolina Augusta ließ dieses Bildniß ihres unsterblichen Gemahls für das k. k. Münz- und Antikenkabinet arbeiten und übergab es den 14. Apr. 1840* (Her Majesty the Empress Carolina Augusta had this portrait of her immortal spouse made for the Imperial-Royal Cabinet of Coins and Antiquities and presented it on 14th April, 1840).

M. L.-J.

132 ONYX CAMEO: THE VIRGIN MARY AND CHILD

Rome (?), 2nd quarter of 19th century

Onyx, gold; with setting: 7.1 cms high, 6 cms wide (Inv. No. XIV 23)

The motif of this cameo is a variation of two laterally inverted pictures of the Madonna by Raphael: the Madonna della Sedia in Florence and the Madonna della Tenda in the Munich Pinakothek. It deviates from its models most of all in the gesture and attitude of the child. The gold setting is neo-baroque. The cameo derives from the estate of Archduchess Sophie, the mother of Emperor Franz Joseph. According to the inventory, it was she who wrote the following lines about it: *"Dieser geschnittene Stein, welcher vom heiligen Vater dem Grafen Radetzky, Feldmar-*

133

schall meines Sohnes Kaiser Franz Joseph, geschenkt worden war, wurde mir durch den Feldmarschall selbst übergeben zu Schönbrunn am 5. Juni 1851." (This carved stone, presented by the Holy Father to Count Radetzky, Field Marshal of my son Emperor Franz Joseph, was given to me by the Field Marshal himself at Schönbrunn on 5th June 1851.)   R. D.

133 BRACELET FROM THE ESTATE OF EMPRESS CHARLOTTE OF MEXICO (1840—1927)

French (?), 3rd quarter of the 19th century
Gold, partially enamelled, diamonds, glass; no hallmarks; greatest width of bracelet: 7.1 cms (Inv. No. XIV 252)

The à jour work of the bracelet is par-

tially covered in blue, red and green translucent enamel. The armband bears a medallion with a miniature of Queen Louise of Belgium (1812—1850), surrounded by ten large diamonds. She was a daughter of King Louis-Philippe of France, wife of King Leopold I of Belgium and mother of Empress Charlotte of Mexico. On the back plate of the medallion is the engraved inscription: *Souvenir / de famille / Offert à notre bien / aimée Charlotte / par ses oncles / et ses tantes.* (Family memento, presented to our dearly-beloved Charlotte by her uncles and aunts). It was perhaps a wedding present from Queen Louise's brothers and sisters to their niece in 1857.
Donated to the Treasury in 1962.
                                    M. L.-J.

134 FOUR PIECES OF JEWELLERY FROM THE ESTATE OF THE EMPRESS ELISABETH OF AUSTRIA (1837—1898)

1. Brooch
2nd half of the 19th century
Chiselled gold, silver, diamonds, pearls; no hallmarks or maker's marks; 12.2 cms long (Inv. No. XIV 193)

In the middle and at the ends of the gold pin are three jewelled pieces in the form of three-leafed clovers, each set with numerous small diamonds and three club-shaped pearls.

2. Brooch
2nd half of the 19th century
Gold, silver, diamonds and pearls; on the clasp is the Viennese hallmark for foreign goldware, in use between 1872 and 1902; on the pin is an indistinct

135

maker's (?) mark F.H. (?); 3.55 cms high; 3.9 cms wide (without pin) (Inv. No. XIV 194)

The brooch takes the form of a three-leafed clover. Set into each of the diamonded leaves is, respectively, a white, rose-coloured or dark-grey pearl.

3. Brooch

Alexander Emanuel Köchert (1825—1879)
Vienna, between 1872 and 1879
Gold, silver diamonds and pearls; on the clasp the Viennese hallmark A and the Viennese assay mark with the fox-head for 580/1000 gold, in use after 1872; on the pin, too, the Viennese hallmark and an indistinct maker's mark, presumably Æ K (Alexander Emanuel Köchert); diameter 2.9 cms (Inv. No. XIV 195)

This brooch takes the form of a buckle, although it can also be interpreted as an uncial E (Elisabeth).

4. Brooch

2nd half of the 19th century
Gold, silver, diamonds, pearls; no hallmarks; 5.6 cms long (Inv. No. XIV 196)

At each end of the clasp-shaped, dia-

monded brooch is a club-shaped pearl. These four pieces of jewellery were donated to the Treasury in 1956. M. L.-J.

135 HUNGARIAN OPAL JEWELLERY

Egger Bros.
Budapest, 1881
Gold, enamelled, Hungarian opals, diamonds, rubies; the buckle of the girdle bears an indistinct mark and the signature: *KÉSZITETTEK EGGER TESTVÉREK / BUDAPESTEN 1881* (Inv. No. XIb 41)

This extremely decorative parure consists of a girdle, collier, pendant earrings, ten bodice clasps, two armlets and five hairpins. It was modelled both on jewellery of the Renaissance and on so-called Hungarian 'magnate' (=aristocrat) jewellery. The latter, together with the rich use of Hungarian opals, the arms of Budapest on the central medallions of the girdle and those of Belgium on the pendant of the collier indicate the occasion for which the parure was made. It was a gift of the City of Budapest to Princess Stéphanie of Belgium on the occasion of her marriage to Crown Prince Archduke Rudolf on 10. 5. 1881. As the bodice clasps indicate, it was intended to be worn with the Hungarian national costume. After the Crown Princess' remarriage in 1900, to Count Elemér Lonyay, ownership of the jewellery reverted to Emperor Franz Joseph, who had it placed in the Treasury.

M. L.-J.

136 THE GOLDEN ROSE

Giuseppe Spagna (Rome 1765—1839 Rome) and Pietro Paolo Spagna (Rome 1793—1861 Rome)
Rome, 1818/19
Gold; stand made of verde antico. On the vase's cover-plate the signature *GIUS. / SPAGNA / ROMA*. On the neck and the smooth band around the body of the vase, respectively: the maker's mark of Giuseppe Spagna G$_I$S (Bulgari No. 983) and the Roman hallmark for at least 18-carat gold. At the foot is the maker's mark of Pier Paolo Spagna  (Bulgari No. 985), the Roman hallmark for gold of at least 18 carats and a further unidentified mark resembling a horse's head on a lozenge-shaped ground. Without stand c. 60 cms high (Inv. No. XIV 19)

The stem of the Golden Rose is inserted into a two-handled, bellied vase. At the bulge of the vessel alternate emblems taken from the arms of Pope Pius VII Chiaramonti: the patriarchal cross growing from a triple-mount, with its stem transfixing the A of the word PAX, is the heraldic device of the reformed Benedictine Order, to which the Pope himself belonged, while the star and the head of a Moor with a headband are elements from the arms of Count Chiaramonti. Other sections of the vessel display an alternation of lobate acanthus, fluting, rows of fleurs-de-lys, laurel wreaths and Ionian kyme. From the inner ends of the handles, which are shaped like volutes, hang two delicate garlands of flowers. The 'Rose' itself consists of a stem, from which grow twelve branches with leaves and, at the end of each, a blossom. The thirteenth rose crowns the top of the stem.

The vessel is made of embossed and engraved gold, and decorated with matt and hand-polished elements set apart from one another. The handles, the stem and the branches are hollow. The thorns on the stem have been made by prising up chips of the metal, while the blooms are made of chased gold foil, as are the leaves; the latter are matt except for the nervures, which were hand-polished. The rose-blooms, their petals arranged in seven layers, have also been brushed, so that they, too, gleam. In the centre of the upper rose, instead of the inner petals, there is a hollow space closed with a sieve-like lid.

This particular golden rose is distinguished by the special balance of its form, the delicacy of its ornamental details and the exceptional subtlety of its technical execution. In all probability it goes back to Giuseppe Spagna in its most basic elements, although it was completed by his son Paolo. The presence of the maker's marks of both the father and the son is explained by the fact that, in 1817, Giuseppe Spagna renounced his master's authorisation, possibly in favour of his son, and that the piece was officially presented by the latter. At any event, this Golden Rose could hardly have been made before 1818/1819, since it was consecrated by Pope Pius VII in 1819 and then sent by him as a present to Empress Carolina Augusta, the fourth wife of Emperor Franz I of Austria.

On Laetare, the fourth Sunday in Lent, the Pope consecrated a Golden Rose, which he then presented to a high-ranking personage or an ecclesiastical institution. This ceremony probably goes back to the old festival of the Wednesday before Mid-Lent, when the rose served as a reminder of the joys of the coming Easter celebrations. Ceremonies involving the consecration of a rose are recorded as far back as the middle of the 11th century. They originally took place in the Basilica of Santa Croce in Gerusalemme in Rome, when the Rose was carried by the Pope as he rode on horseback from the nearby Lateran palace to the Basilica. After the consecration he would fill the Rose with musk and balsam, thurify it with frankincense and sprinkle it with holy water. In addition to this, the Pope gave a sermon in which he elucidated the meaning of the ceremony. The texts of the sermons by Innocence III and Honorius III have come down to us from the 13th century. They start out from the idea of the beauty, redness and scent of the rose *("de flore et rubore rosae et odore")*, which, in its turn, is based on the verse *"Ego sum flos campi"* ("I am the flower of the field") from the Song of Solomon. The form of the rose, which is narrow below and wide open at the top, is allegorically related to Christ's earthly poverty which nevertheless fulfils the whole world. In the same way, the golden material of the rose symbolises Christ the King, and the red colour of the gold the suffering of Christ, while the scent of the rose prefigures his resurrection — although it is also a reference to the women who hurried to the tomb of Christ to embalm his body. Similarly, the gold of the rose stands for the divinity of Christ, the musk for his human body and the balsam for his spirit. The golden rose also becomes a symbol of the Holy Trinity if one equates the gold with God the Father, the musk with Christ and the balsam with the Holy Spirit. In the case of the golden rose in the possession of the Treasury, musk and balsam were poured into the hollow of the topmost rose. The fragrance came out through the sieve opening. Even today a slight perfume provides a reminder one of its one-time contents. The topmost rose symbolises Christ, while the twelve other branches were, in this particular rosebush, probably intended to represent the Twelve Apostles. The golden rose also expresses the joys of the Church militant and triumphant, with the intention of suggesting to the recipient his or her successorship to Christ. According to all appearances it was originally the privilege of the prefects of Rome to receive the Golden Rose as a gift from the hand of the Pope. In later times the recipients were in general high-ranking persons or ecclesiastical institutions. In 1368, Johanna of Naples-Sicily became the first woman to receive the Golden Rose, although since the 17th century it has been almost exclusively women who have been distinguished with the award.

Empress Carolina Augusta, who received this particular Golden Rose in 1819, died in 1873. The rose was first recorded as being in the Treasury in 1874.   M. L.-J.

Ref.: Bulgari II 1958/59, p. 426 and 428; Cornides 1967.

THE TWO INALIENABLE HEIRLOOMS OF THE HOUSE OF AUSTRIA

Emperor Ferdinand I died on 25. 7. 1564. Soon afterwards, on 11. 8. 1564, his successor Emperor Maximilian II came to an agreement with his brothers Archduke Ferdinand II and Archduke Karl about the chattels left to them by their father, and in particular about the agate bowl and the *'Ainkhürn'* (unicorn). For these two pieces seemed to the brothers to be too precious to be inherited by any one of them alone. It was therefore determined that *"these two sightly and exquisite treasures should from now on and for all time eternal remain with our laudable House of Austria, nor should either of them ever be alienated or altered by sale, gift, pawn or other like means, by whatever name it be called, but rather for all time remain in the keeping of the eldest Prince of Austria."* Maximilian subsequently confirmed receipt of the treasures. On the one hand, this agreement pronounced the inalienability of the two pieces; on the other, it established the right of inheritance by seniority instead of primogeniture. Thus, after the death of Maximilian II, the heirlooms did not pass to his eldest son Rudolf II, but to Maximilian's brother Ferdinand II (of Tyrol), as a result of which they were then transferred to Innsbruck. In fact, they did not find their way into Rudolf II's *Kunstkammer* in Prague until 1596. Brought back to Vienna by Emperor Matthias, they thereafter constituted the *pièces de resistance* of the Treasury's collection.
                                                                                          R. D.

137 THE AGATE BOWL

Constantinople (?), 4th century
Agate; diameter 58 to 58.5 cms, span including handles 76 cms (Inv. No. XIV 1)

An aura of the mysterious and extraordinary surrounds this bowl. Cut from a single, massive block of agate, it is the largest gemmoglyptic bowl in the world, and although more than one thousand six hundred years old, it is completely undamaged. Its history has long been shrouded in obscurity. Since its first documented reference as an inalienable heirloom of the House of Austria in 1564, it has been revered as a unique object of inestimable value, being designated the *"best and most important piece"* in the whole Treasury in the 17th century. In formal terms the bowl is a masterpiece of the lapidary's art. The taut, sweeping curves of the bowl's sides rise over a shallow, concave foot, measuring a third of the bowl's diameter and demarcated by a groove. The bifurcated openwork handles unfold in tendrils along the lip and cleave in long, lanceolate leaves to the underside of the bowl, as if moulded from pliable wax, not carved from precious stone harder than steel.
The form of the bowl alone has an almost magical fascination: broad, self-contained and chthonic, it simultaneously opens up, as if with arms spread wide, into the immensity of space. As if the unique grandeur of the stone and its masterful shaping were not enough, sources attest to a miracle of nature, to the existence of a mysterious inscription: the inventory of the estate of Emperor Matthias made in 1619 records that *"the word KRISTO is to be seen in quite large letters in the nature of the stone."*
A number of other readings of the inscription have come down to us from the 17th century — e.g. JEHOVAH, CHRISTOS (in Greek characters) among others — giving the impression that none of these authors had ever seen the inscription themselves. All of them, however, agree on the nature of the miracle, namely that the name of Christ is not engraved or painted on the bowl, but appears in the substance or natural veining of the stone itself. They invoke the authority of the Gospel of St. Luke, 19,40, where Jesus says on entering Jerusalem: *"If these should hold their peace, the stones would immediately cry out."* The Jesuit scholar Petrus Lambecius (Lambeck) published the inscription in 1665, together

with an engraving of the bowl in full size, since anybody who had not seen it would find its dimensions incredible. *"By means of this inscription, which should not merely be marvelled at but rather worshipped, that is formed in the natural veining,"* he writes, *"Nature herself has dedicated this inestimably precious stone of astounding size to Christ, her God and Creator, with the following words: B. XRISTO R. S. XXX."* According to the engraving, the large but faint letters lie on the side of the bowl where the banding begins near the lip. If a line were to be drawn across the bowl between the centres of the last leaf-scroll on each handle, it would run straight through the inscription, which begins approximately above the light agate cloud on the left and ends just before the small, angular white patch on the right. Thus its exact position was established. The Treasury inventory of 1750, with a reading of B. XRISTO RI XXPP, is almost identical to Lambeck's. In the 19th century it was corrected to XRISTO F XXI.

There would be little point in dealing with this inscription in such detail were it not for the fact that there have been witnesses for it in this century, as well as others who claim it has never existed. In 1934, one source claimed to have seen the initial letters XRI clearly in the structure of the stone when a particular amount of light struck the bowl. In 1951, while the bowl was being cleaned, the inscription appeared again, and in 1953, the epigraphist Rudolf Egger saw it and published a description *(It was a day with wonderful light and the inscription was easily legible.)* He transcribed it as FL B ARISTO TRFXXP and deciphered it as the artist's signature: FL(a)b(ius) Aristo Tr(eviris) f(ecit) XX P(ondo) (Made by Flabius Aristo of Trier, XX pounds). Unfortunately, Egger gave no description of the physical character of the inscription. This reading is in any case incorrect. Firstly, lapidaries signed their work using their own technique, i.e. engraving, and there are no traces of this here. Secondly, as Rudolf Noll has pointed out, XXP cannot be interpreted as the weight of the bowl: 20 Roman pounds are equivalent to 6,549 grammes and the bowl weighs 10,635 grammes. The inscription exists in its own, miraculous way. It eludes the grasp of scientific verification and the mystery remains unsolved. The miracle of nature is transformed into the charisma of vision. It is axiomatic that the power of perception must always operate on the level of the object to be perceived: miracles can only be seen by an eye capable of perceiving them. The letters lie beneath the surface and appear only when the right amount of light strikes the bowl.

The name of Christ in the bowl may have led to its being venerated as the Holy Grail, into which the blood of Christ flowed at the Crucifixion. In the 18th century, reports were still current of the bowl having been plundered from Constantinople in 1204, and of its having come into the possession of the Dukes of Burgundy, from whence it passed to the Habsburgs through the marriage of Maximilian I to Mary of Burgundy. This tradition has not yet been proved or disproved.

To understand the myth of this miraculous masterpiece, one must consider the ancient view of Man's interaction with Nature, to which we now give the arid name of technology. Before Man merely exploited Nature, he saw himself as a part of it, as the self-revelation and reflection of the Creator. The work of an artist was the imbuing of lifeless matter with *the powers of the soul.* The miraculous nature of the bowl lay in the perfect conjunction of this unique gift of Nature, this precious stone of rare size, and the consummate skill of the artist. Nature's creations were greater than those of Man, yet it is precisely in the realm of Nature that he has always wanted to test the limits of his possibilities.

The making of the bowl was a monumental undertaking for the gem-cutter of late antiquity, and a task that must have taken years to complete. The first step was to square off the rough block with hammer and chisel, like a sculptor. A hammer with a serrated peen was used to give the stone its

rough outline, small strokes being used to trace out the shape of the bowl. After this stage, a rotating instrument with a steel bit was used, the bit being either a ball, a disk, a cylinder or a hollow tube. The artist had to construct this tool according to the specific requirements of the task he needed it for. It was mounted on a horizontal spindle, driven by a belt or rope-drive via a flywheel with the aid of a treadle (like a spinning-wheel or an old-fashioned sewing-machine), could achieve fast speeds of rotation. The especial difficulty here was that the 'lathe' was mounted with the spindle itself and thus the stone had to be held or pressed as required against the bit. Since the stone was harder than the metal of the bit, the latter was charged with oil and diamond or corundum powder. During abrading, the powder had to be renewed frequently and the bit cooled with water. In unending effort, the desired shape gradually emerged. The polishing was done with increasingly softer bits and grinding agents. First the inside of the bowl was hollowed out and only then was the outside shaped. The small irregularites — slight corrugations in the bottom, discrepancies in the profile of the sides and the lip — give an idea of the difficulties involved

in achieving an evenness of form. Seen in strict profile, the lip of the bowl diverges slightly from the horizontal. On the deepest point of the lip, discernible vestiges of what was perhaps a porous impurity are present. Traces of the gemcutting process are to be seen all over the openwork handles. The convex handles were hollowed out by a repeated process of horizontal drilling. Holes were drilled vertically close to each other to achieve the bifurcation and perforation for the foliate decoration. Here, in the inside of the curves, one can still make out the exact diameter of the bit used. At one point on the right handle, one can see where a borehole was not completed, perhaps intentionally. For these boreholes, a drill with a flywheel on the spindle was used, which gave it more weight. The process of polishing was extremely difficult, especially in the case of the handles, and it is evident that the artist has here had to dispense with the highest polish. The innumerable small irregularities give the bowl life and at the same time attest to the artist's involvement and struggle with the material, right up to the limits of his capabilities. Both the exceptional stone and the skill and painstaking effort expended in its shaping make it obvious why the bowl was from the very beginning an Imperial possession without compare.   R. D.

Ref.: Petri Lambecii Hamburgensis Commentatorium de augustissima bibliotheca caesarea Vindobonensis, Vienna 1665, p. 26 f.; R. Egger, Kostbares Zaubergerät, in: Festschrift für Alphons A. Barb, Wissenschaftliche Arbeiten aus dem Burgenland, Heft 35, 1966, p. 66 ff.; W. Oberleitner, Nochmals zur "Inschrift" der großen Achatschale in der Wiener Schatzkammer, in: Jahreshefte des Österreichischen Archäologischen Instituts, vol. 60, 1990, Hauptblatt, pp. 121—128. Contains references to further literature.

138 THE 'AINKHÜRN' (UNICORN)

1st half of the 16th century
Narwhal tusk; 243 cms long (Inv. No. XIV 2)

The name used for this narwhal tusk derives from the fabulous unicorn. Although the mythical creature was supposed to have been small, it was credited with great powers. It could not be caught by hunters, yet it laid its head in the lap of a virgin and allowed itself to be captured by her. This myth, which originated with Physiologus around the year 200 A.D., was widespread in the Middle Ages, and interpreted using Christian allegorisation in numerous paintings. Even Physiologus saw it as a symbol for the incarnation of Christ and the Virgin Birth. Yet, as the conqueror of evil and herald of salvation, Christ was also the *unicornis spirtualis* (spiritual unicorn), which also expresses his oneness with the Father. The unicorn's horn became a symbol of his divine power and of his message of salvation for all humanity. The equation of the narwhal's tusk with the unicorn first occurred around 1200. Great powers of healing were attributed to this rare natural specimen and unicorn horns were bought for enormous sums even by popes. There are numerous records of the purchase of unicorn horns in the 16th century, when they sometimes fetched as much as 30,000 ducats, and in the first half of the 17th century certain examples were valued at more than twice that amount.

Physiologus also writes that the unicorn once detoxified a spring by making the sign of the cross in the water with its horn. For this reason the 'horn' was credited not only with exceptional medicinal healing powers but also with great efficacy as an antidote to poisons. Powdered 'rare unicorn horn' was one of the most essential and expensive medicines in a 17th century apothecary.

With its references to the power and dominion of Christ, the unicorn symbolism predestined the costly material for use in both secular and ecclesiastical insignia. Examples of both kinds are to be found in the Treasury: in the Secular Treasury as the sceptre belonging with the Rudolphine Crown (Cat. No. 58), and as the Burgundian Ainkhürn Sword (Cat. No. 204); and in the Ecclesiastical Treasury as the bishop's crozier (Cat. No. 3). The throne of the Danish kings in Rosenburg Castle in Copenhagen (from the period 1662—1665) was almost wholly made of narwhal tusks. The unicorn's horn in the Vienna Treasury is an especially large specimen and was presented as a gift to King Ferdinand I by King Sigismund II of Poland in 1540. Ferdinand then had it sent to the sculptor Silvester Lechner in Innsbruck, where it was provided with a pedestal, to which was attached a slip of paper with a rhyme on it. Although the pedestal itself has been lost, the poem has nevertheless survived and describes not only the unicorn as a creature but also the history of the piece itself. It is here given in standardised German orthography:

"Durch Gottes Schickung und Gewalt / bin ich schwach von Art und Gestalt, / mein Größ ein Reh nicht viel übertrifft / die vorderen Füß sein höher als die hintern geschifft; / ein langer Hals, ein Kopf subtil und klein / darauf steht mir dieser und etlichen nur ein Khürn allein, / das hält an den hohen Buckeln, und hintern Füß sein schart (geteilt, paarhufig), / von Adler Augen hab' ich ein Art, / mein Woll vergleicht einem Schäflein schier, / an Wildbret übertreff' ich all ander Tier. / Mit meinem Lauf tu ich überschreiten / Pferd, Wind, Luchs, Panthertier zu allen Zei-

*ten. / Mein Wohnung hab ich bei
zweien Wassern breit / so Asiam und
Europam von einander scheidt. / In
das Königreich Polen ich mich verging
/ darin mich Bernhard Prettwitz fing;
nahm mir das Khürn zu derselben
Stund, / schenkt es dem edlen König
Sigismund. / In Europa ward mein
nicht viel gefunden / drum schickt
mich der König von Stunden / weiter
hin ins deutsche Land / dem groß-
mächtigen König Ferdinand."*

(By the design and power of the Lord /
I am fashioned meek of kind and form,
/ In stature not greatly exceeding a deer
/ With forelegs higher than those at the
rear; / A neck which is long, and a
head small and fine / Which bears this
singular horn of mine / On shoulders
strong; hind-feet even-toed, / And eyes
quite like the eagle's own, / Pure as a
little lamb's is my wool, / As animal
game I excel one and all. / My legs can
at any time carry me further / Than the
horse, the wind, the lynx or the pan-
ther. / My home is beside two waters
wide / Where Asia and Europe in two
divide. / In the Kingdom of Poland I
once roamed free / Where Bernhard
Prettwitz captured me; / At that time
this horn of mine did he take / And a
gift to the high King Sigismund make;
/ In Europe there were not many of my
kind / And thus the King sent me, at
that very time, / Further abroad to this
Germanic land / To the great and
powerful King Ferdinand.)

The Bernhard Prettwitz mentioned in
the poem came from Silesia and at the
time of Sigismund I and II was in Polish service as the Starost of Bar and
Trembowla (Podolia). He made a great
contribution to the defence of Poland
against the Tartars, Turks and
Walachians, which in Poland earned
him the honorific title of *Murus Podo-
liae et Terror Tatarorum* (Wall of
Poland and Terror of the Tartars). He
died in 1561 (according to Ulrich von
Prittwitz, of Regensburg).   R. D.

Ref.: Schönberger 1935/36, p. 196 ff.; R.R. Beer,
Einhorn, Fabelwelt und Wirklichkeit, Munich
1972; J. W. Einhorn, Spiritualis Unicornis. Das
Einhorn als Bedeutungsträger in Literatur und
Kunst des Mittelalters, Münsterische Mittelalter-
Schriften, vol. 13, Munich 1976.

139 EMPRESS MARIA THERESIA (1717—1780) AND EMPEROR FRANZ I, STEPHAN OF LORRAINE (1708—1765)

Matthäus Donner (Esslingen 1704—
1756 Vienna), 1750
Bronze, surface chased and cold-ham-
mered after casting, brown patina,
marble; both signed on the left-hand
side of the base: *M. Donner, Fecit.
1750;* 68 and 69 cms high (Inv. NO:
Pl. 6142 and 6143)

These busts were made for two wall
niches in the Cabinet of Coins and
Medals in the Imperial Treasury, which
had been refurbished in 1750. They are
already listed in the Treasury inventory
of the same year. The site for which
they were originally intended accounts
for both the antique style of dress of
both rulers and, in particular, the in-
scriptions on the fronts of the bases:
MAR(IA) · THERESIA · AVSTR
(IACA) · REG(INA) · AVG(VSTA) ·
ANTIQVIT(ATIS) · HONORE ·
REST(ITVTO) · IVNO · MON(ETA).
(Maria Theresia of Austria, Queen and
Empress; she restored the ancient
world to its place of honour: Juno
Moneta) and
FRANCISCVS · LOTHARING(VS) ·
IMP(ERATOR) · P(IVS) · F(ELIX) ·
AVG(VSTVS) · AMPLIATO · NVM

(ORVM) · THESAVRO · APOLLO · MON(ETARIVS). (Franz of Lorraine, gracious, blessed Emperor, for increasing the Coin Treasury: Apollo Monetarius). The casting models used to make the busts are to be found in the Collections of the National Mint in Vienna.

M. L.-J.

Ref.: Kábdebo 1880, p. 76.

THE HABSBURGS AS KINGS OF BOHEMIA, ELECTORS OF THE HOLY ROMAN EMPIRE

In 1077, the Imperial Princes gathered at Forchheim to depose Emperor Heinrich IV, who had been excommunicated by Pope Gregory VII. Flouting ancient blood-right, they elected Rudolf of Swabia king, thus setting the course for an institutionalisation of the royal election, the Reich becoming an electoral kingdom. However, the right of election became increasingly restricted, eventually becoming the priviledge of a very few spiritual and temporal Princes of the Empire, whose number had been essentially laid down by the beginning of the 13th century. The *Sachsenspiegel* (a compendium of medieval law) compiled before 1235, names six Princes of the Empire as having the right to vote at the royal election: three spiritual — the Archbishops of Mainz, Trier and Cologne, — and three temporal — the Count Palatine of the Rhine, the Duke of Saxony and the Margrave of Brandenburg. From 1257, the King of Bohemia was included in the Electoral College as its seventh Elector.

In the 'Golden Bull' (so called after the golden seal on the capsule), proclaimed in 1356 by Emperor Karl IV, the election of the king, together with the highest offices of the Empire, was finally conferred on the seven Electors, thus giving them a share in Imperial power.

In order of rank they were: 1. The Archbishop of Mainz as Archchancellor of Germany; 2. The Archbishop of Trier as Archchancellor of Burgundy; 3. The Archbishop of Cologne as Archchancellor of Italy, 4. The King of Bohemia as Archcupbearer; 5. The Count Palatine of the Rhine as Archdapifer; 6. The Duke of Sachsen-Wittenberg as Archmarshal and 7. The Margrave of Brandenburg as Archchamberlain. The summoning of an electoral meeting was the official responsibility of the Archbishop of Mainz in his capacity as Archchancellor of Germany. It was he who counted the votes at the election, which was now decided by majority, not unanimous vote. The casting of the first vote belonged to Trier, followed by Cologne, then followed Bohemia with the first temporal vote. The important and often decisive final vote was reserved for Mainz. The election was held in the Church of St. Bartholomew (today the Cathedral) in Frankfurt, the coronation by the Archbishop of Mainz took place in Aix-la-Chapelle (from 1562 in Frankfurt) and the first assembly of the German Diet was held in Nuremberg. The Golden Bull also determined the protocol of rank of the Electors, whereby the King of Bohemia was assigned foremost rank among the temporal Princes as a crowned and anointed king. The position of the Electors was further consolidated by the Golden Bull in that their office was made hereditary and that the Electoral Principalities became indivisible and could only be inherited by the first-born son in the male line. The Electors were granted the regalia and the right of supreme judicial authority over their subjects. From that time on in the Empire, in contrast to the other monarchies of Europe, it was not the passive, but the active right to election that was hereditary.

The provisions of the Golden Bull excluded the Habsburgs and the Wittelsbachs, — at this time, besides the Luxemburgs, not only the most important dynasties in the Holy Roman Empire, but also its most powerful rivals — from any share in Imperial power. Duke Rudolf IV of Austria attempted to compensate for this limitation of his power with the famous forgery of the *Privilegium majus.* Subsequently, Habsburg efforts concentrated on the acquisition of neighbouring Bohemia. They achieved their object, albeit only for a brief period after the extinction of the Luxemburgs in 1437, finally succeeding, however, in 1526, after the death of the Jagellon king, Ladislaus of Hungary and Bohemia. As Kings of Bohemia, the Habsburgs were from then on represented in the College of Electors. Eventually the Bavarian Wittelsbachs also attained this elevation in rank during the Thirty Years' War, when the Palatine Electorate was transferred to them in 1623. The Palatine Wittelsbachs were compensated in the Peace of Westphalia with a new electorate, together with the newly-created office of Imperial Treasurer. In 1692, Braunschweig-Lüneburg was granted the ninth electorate, but the number of Electors was reduced again to eight in 1777, when, after the Bavarian Wittelsbachs had died out, the old Palatine electorate reverted to the Palatine branch of the dynasty and the office of Imperial Treasurer was transferred to Braunschweig-Lüneburg. When in 1803 with the *Reichsdeputationshauptschluss* the spiritual electorates were dissolved, four new temporal electorates were created: Hessen-Kassel, Baden, Württemberg and Salzburg, recently secularised. The Salzburg electorate, which the Tuscan line of the Habsburgs had received in compensation for the loss of Tuscany, was dissolved only two years later in 1805 at the Peace of Pressburg; all the other electorates ceased to exist in 1806, with the establishment of the Confederation of the Rhine, as did the Holy Roman Empire itself, whose formal end was marked by the abdication of Franz II as Holy Roman Emperor. Hessen-Kassel alone continued to bear the title of an Electorate.

                                                                                    M. L.-J.

140 THE ROYAL BOHEMIAN ELECTORAL ROBES

Vienna or Prague, before the mid-17th century
Fabric: Italian, 2nd quarter of the 17th century; silk, gold; 131 cms long, diameter 270 cms (Inv. No. XIV 122)

The mantle is made of gold lamé with a red silk chain, patterned in gold (pattern repeat: H 5.5 cms, W 8.5 cms) and cut in the form of a semi-circle. Belonging with it are an elector's coronet with ermine trimming (renewed 1986) (Inv. No. XIV 121) and a pair of gloves with gold lace trimmings (Inv. No. XIV 123). Since the Bohemian coronation vestments in Prague, consisting of a mantle trimmed with ermine, a stole and a belt, were made from the same gold-patterned red silk, decorated with meandering pod-shaped and foliate motifs, it follows that the three Viennese pieces originally formed part of the Bohemian electoral robes. At one time, they also included an *"undergarment of red silk"* (Treasury inventory of 1773). These robes must have been made in connection with the Bohemian coronation vestments, probably for King Ferdinand IV (crowned King of Bohemia in 1646 and Roman-German King in 1653). The King of Bohemia

was at the same time Prince Elector of the Empire.   R. B.

Ref.: J. Petraschek-Heim, Ein Ornat der Wiener Schatzkammer, in: Waffen- und Kostümkunde 1976, pp. 1—21.

141 FULL-LENGTH PORTRAIT OF EMPEROR MATTHIAS (1557—1619) AS KING OF BOHEMIA

Hans von Aachen (Cologne 1552—1615) and studio, c. 1613/14
Canvas; 200.5 x 95.7 cms (Inv. No. GG 3254)

Emperor Matthias wears the Bohemian Coronation Vestments, consisting of a long, button-through undergarment of white silk lampas with a varicoloured pattern, and a green mantle with pearl embroidery. He wears the Crown of Wenceslas and holds the sceptre in his right hand and the imperial orb in his left. Matthias commissioned a new sceptre and orb for the Rudolfine crown; consequently the insignia formerly used with the Rudolfine crown were put with the Bohemian coronation insignia and the old Bohemian insignia from the 14th century, portrayed here, were put with the insignia of the Austrian Hereditary Homage (Cat. Nos. 1, 2). Through the door in the background on the right is a view of a battle field with the King on horseback.

Matthias confirmed Hans von Aachen's appointment as court painter after the death of Emperor Rudolf II and summoned him to Vienna. There von Aachen executed a series of portraits of the Emperor and of his wife, Anna. Eleven of these portraits are listed in a bill submitted to Emperor Matthias by the painter's widow after his death in 1615. Whereas the full-length portrait of the Emperor in slightly differing regalia in the Paintings Gallery in Prague Castle (Inv. No. 0 304, until 1894 in the Kunsthistorische Museum, former Inv. No. 2741) was largely painted by Aachen himself, in this portrait only the head seems to be by his hand and the rest the work of his studio. R. an der Heiden supposes that Jeremias Günther executed a large portion of it, a theory which has lately been challenged by Da Costa-Kaufmann.   K. S.

Ref.: an der Heiden 1970, pp. 176, 204, No. A 33; Da Costa Kaufmann 1985, p. 207, Cat. nos. 1—83.

THE HOLY ROMAN EMPIRE

HISTORICAL PREMISES FOR THE INTERPRETATION OF ITS INSIGNIA AND REGALIA

The medieval concept of the divine origin of imperial authority, and of the Emperor being chosen by God to directly execute divine will, is alien to us today. The Emperor ruled over an empire whose Latin title *Sacrum Imperium Romanum* (Holy Roman Empire) referred neither to the extent of its territory, nor to any common nationality or language of its inhabitants. It was called the Holy Roman Empire because it was considered to be the renewal of the *imperium Romanum* of the ancient world, the last of the four great empires of antiquity. This made it possible to reassert the old claim to universality in the exercise of imperial power, a claim which remained effective, albeit as an unfulfilled hope, until after the Middle Ages. From the very beginning of the new empire, the idea of political unity found support only among the Roman Catholic peoples of Christendom, and even this form of desired unification of the West was not fully achieved at any time in its history. Thus the development of the West proceeded solely from the western half of what had been the late Roman Empire, as the Greek-Orthodox East was ruled over by the Byzantine Emperors, who for reasons of historical continuity continued to bear the title of Roman Emperor.

The extension of the title to that of 'Holy Roman Empire' becomes customary from the 12th century onwards. It arose at a time when a renaissance of Roman law was occurring as a result of a more secular concept of empire in comparison with that of early medieval times. Thus the time-honoured standing of Roman law began to gain in importance at the very point in time when a vigorous papacy was challenging the ecclesiastical sacredness of the Holy Roman Empire. In accordance with the political order in the Carolingian and Ottonian eras, there existed a theocratic unity of the spiritual and temporal realms, i.e. one which was derived from the concept of divine power. The Emperor had until then ruled over the Empire and its Church as the executor of divine will. This theocratic concept of sovereignty is symbolically expressed in the most important insignia (emblems of sovereign power) of the Holy Roman Empire. It thus seems appropriate to trace the essential features of the historical development of the emperorship, which in the Middle Ages went hand in hand with the Germanic concept of kingship.

Mankind has always sought security in the past and endeavoured to endow the present with significance by drawing on the past. His picture of the past has frequently been coloured by his ideas of what would be desirable in the future. Given certain intellectual as well as political conditions, it could happen that in decisive historical situations great rulers chose to adopt foreign ideals as an act of self-determination, and in their new orientation came to regard themselves as being part of a tradition that was not that of the history of their own nation.

EMPEROR CONSTANTINE AS THE MODEL RULER OF THE EMPIRE IN THE MIDDLE AGES

One of the fundamental characteristics of medieval art had already been established in late antiquity and the early Christian era, with the development of equal status for court and ecclesiastical art during the age of Constantine. After the long and beneficent reign of Emperor Constantine (306—337), whose divine vocation and conversion later ecclesiastical historians never tired of propagating, the claim to sovereignty in the *imperium Romanum* is justified in Christian terms. Divine vocation had been the prerequisite for the election of every emperor in the Roman Empire from the age of Augustus onwards. Regardless of how the emperor had acquired his imperial power, he was considered as having been chosen and 'sanctified'. Elevated to the level of the divine, the Imperator and Augustus possessed a power that inspired trust and fear in equal measure. The common people saw in him their saviour and protector; from him they hoped for the continuation of the Empire and peace and prosperity. Moreover, political good fortune was regarded as a visible sign of the sovereign's status as one chosen from above. In this way, a course had already been mapped out in which the new conception of the Christian emperors could be proclaimed in cult and ceremonial. Emperor Constantine, who had been chosen by the grace of God, was granted the title of Vicar of Christ on earth by the bishops who had gathered at the Council of Chalcedon, because his word was also binding in religious matters. His Christian successors in the Empire were accorded equal rank with that of the Apostles. With reference to Constantine's own words, they regarded their power as a service willed by God: the Emperor's mission was to ensure the spread of the Christian faith. Christ, as the invincible victor over death, granted the Emperor victory both over his own enemies and over the adversaries of the unity and the idea of the Empire.

The wealth of imperial power and the confident anticipation of victory were expressed in the overwhelming importance attached to pomp, court ceremonial and sacred titles. Claims to universal sovereignty had already been made at the end of the 3rd century A. D. by the tetrarchy, with its two chief rulers *(Augusti)* and co-regents *(Caesares)*. Since Constantine's time, the emblems of imperial rank had been the diadem and purple robe, rather than the armour of the imperator. In the Eastern Roman Empire, the wearing of purple remained the priviledge of the Emperor and his immediate family. The colour combination of the blue, white and green of the jewels on their purple ceremonial vestments also remained an imperial priviledge, any infringement of which entailed severe punishment.

However, the forms of the insignia of Constantine's sovereignty and of the imperial ensign — the labarum — revealed his subordination to a vastly superior power: with the mutually corresponding symbols of the christogramme and the cross, the claim to power of the victory-bringing Christian God entered a new epoch. Constantine had put himself and his army under the protection of these victory-bringing symbols in 312, and in doing so had spontaneously effected their reintroduction as the future emblems of the Empire. The christogramme came to have more significance for the Eastern half of the Empire, which was divided up under Constantine's successors, than for the Western part, where the jewelled cross became a more potent symbol of the unity of the *imperium Romanum* and the hope of the *imperium Christianum*. Together with the eagle of ancient Rome, which was retained, the imperial insignia were now complete.

Unforeseen perspectives now opened up both to Christianity, which had been elevated to the status of a state religion, and to Christian art. Through the instrument of art, the protection and triumphal invincibility of the Cross of Christ, together with the celestial glory in which the faithful hoped to share eternally after the return of the Saviour on the Day of Judgement, were to be impressed as effectively upon the heathen as on the baptised believer. The Christians projected the image of the earthly emperor onto the image of Christ, with Christ Pantocrator (the Almighty), duly reflecting his divine radiance back onto the earthly emperor. As the Vicar of Christ on earth, the emperor was Christ's image, surrounded by the aura of a new sacrality. Reference was also made to the priest-kings of the Old Testament, the rank of apostle being supplemented by that of high priest: in encomia the emperors were extolled as the new David or Solomon.

The imperial insignia of the western *imperium Romanum* which date from the high Middle Ages display several layers of programmatic theological ideas and concepts of sovereignty. They are based on a fusion of concepts taken from the ancient Roman Empire and Christianity, and related ideas derived from the Old Testament. Some of the imperial insignia were adapted to contain relics, in which divine strength and grace were believed to reside, yet in terms of their form and programmatic content, which made frequent reference to the great models of the past, they were more an attestation of their bearer's divine mission of power than a statement of the actual political situation at the time they were made.

Under Emperor Constantine, Empire and Church became one. Spiritual and temporal history seemed bound up with one another, *Romanitas* had become united with *Christianitas. Roma aeterna* was regarded as the guarantrix of the eternal peace of the Roman Empire and the perpetuation of the ethos, civilisation and culture of ancient Rome.

When Emperor Constantine moved his seat of government and the fulcrum of imperial politics to the East, Byzantium, renamed Constantinople after its new founder, became Rome's rival and — as the ''New Rome'' — the imperial capital. The political catastrophe which occurred when the Western Empire collapsed under the incursive hordes of the barbarians, extended into the religious sphere as well. To those Christians oriented towards the ideology of the Roman Empire, and now plunged into doubt, even regarding their expectation of salvation, St. Augustine pointed out that ''Empires change, and even perish''. With his image of the ''glorious City of God'', St. Augustine demonstrates to all those who had too optimistically regarded the Roman state as the ultimate fulfilment of the imminent Second Coming, that while the Church on earth is indeed dependent on the secular authority of the state, her true goal lies elsewhere, albeit in the unforeseeable future. According to St. Augustine, the Christian is obliged to make his contribution to the political system of his community ''for the sake of conscience''.

The Roman hierarchy, inasmuch as its existence continued on Italian soil after the barbarian invasions and the founding of the Germanic kingdoms, no longer looked to the distant Byzantine emperor as its leader and protector. The continuity that did remain was transferred to the Church. It provided security as a spiritual and moral power, and ultimately it was the Church that proved to be the protector and preserver of art and culture. Jacob Burckhardt named the ancient world, Christendom and Germanic civilisation as *''the three great powers of the world'',* which led to the birth of the West as *''a new, living entity.''*

CONDITIONS FOR THE IMPERIAL REVIVAL IN THE FRANKISH KINGDOM

In the Middle Ages, the memory of Constantine was still powerful enough to influence the development of the ideal of an emperor's greatness and to predetermine his political policy-making. Within the spiritual continuity of the traditions of the Roman Empire, reference is always made to the binding example of Constantine. Important rulers were celebrated as the new Constantine in the same way as they were regarded as the reincarnation of certain biblical figures.

The establishment of the Frankish kingdom by King Clovis (482—511), who extended his kingly power over the Germanic tribes in imitation of the rigidly centralised administration of the Roman Empire before it had been overwhelmed by the turmoil of the Great Migration, gave Christendom the opportunity to develop an independent Frankish Church in Gaul and in the Rhine-Meuse area. Clovis' conversion to Christianity was motivated by his recognition of the superior, victory-bringing powers of the Christian God. Under his successors, the expansion of Frankish power went hand in hand with the spread of Christianity. Seemingly without a break, the pagan-Germanic concept of *'Geblütsheiligkeit'* — i.e. the sacred character and cultic duties of kingship that mediated between the gods and the tribe — led, in the Frankish and Germanic kingdoms, to the king's patronage over the Frankish Church.

In the Carolingian era, the relationship between state and church was redefined. Working closely with the Frankish rulers, St. Boniface, converter of the heathen and, as the Pope's mandatory, entrusted with the establishment of bishoprics, had, by the year 751, renewed the interrupted relations between the Frankish and the Roman churches by instigating a series of fundamental reforms. The alliance with the papacy consolidated the Franks' political position. When, in response to the Pope's urgent cry for help, King Pippin marched into Italy with his army to fight for St. Peter, a new era of Frankish politics began. The *defensio ecclesiae Romanae,* the defence of the Roman-Catholic Church, now became the main task, if not the actual raison d'etre, of the emergent western empire.

THE ORIGIN OF THE PAPAL STATES

Pippin's military campaign in support of the Pope, which was to be followed by the armed marches to Rome of later Roman Emperors, was linked to the question of the Papal States. The Papal States were a new creation. An attempt to provide them with some kind of historical justification had resulted in the production by the Curia of a document called the Donation of Constantine, the most notorious of all 'diplomatic' forgeries. According to this document, Constantine the Great had granted Pope Silvester equivalent rank to the Emperor and thus sovereignty over Rome and the Italian provinces. Since oral transmission of the truth counted for more than a written document in the Middle Ages, the Pope based his claim on transmitted reports, according to which the desired privilege had a legal foundation.

Nevertheless, the political sovereignty for Rome and the Papal States claimed by the Pope in the Donation of Constantine was not to be finally achieved until almost 500 years later, in the 12th century. Deliberately using the forgery as legitimation, and well aware that his rank was already equivalent and would soon be superior to that of the Emperor, the Pope began to pursue an independent political course. In order to emphasis the honorary imperial rights named in the forgery, the purple mantle became the supreme symbol of investiture for a newly-elected Pope. The first dualistic conflict between Emperor and Pope concerning supremacy in Italy occurred when the Hohenstaufen dynasty inherited the Norman kingdom of Sicily, which had been created by King Roger II. Emperor Friedrich II (crowned King of Sicily in 1198 and King of Rome in 1212, † 1250) strove to extend his power over the whole of Italy. Significantly, it was at precisely this juncture that the purple coronation mantle, together with the rest of the Sicilian-Norman regalia, was incorporated into the treasury of insignia and jewels belonging to the Holy Roman Empire.

CHARLEMAGNE AND THE CAROLINGIAN EMPIRE

Under Charlemagne (768—814), France expanded its power to an extent that was to remain unique in the history of the West. With the subjection and Christianisation of the Saxons and the securing of his eastern frontier, Charlemagne created the conditions for the emergence of the future German nation. Responding to a new call for help from the Pope, Charlemagne went to war against the Lombards, declaring himself their king in 774, after the capitulation of Pavia. Never again was the political unification of the West to seem so near to fulfillment as then. Even before Charlemagne's coronation as Emperor by Pope Leo III in Rome on Christmas day 800 A.D., the Frankish king's empire was being referred to as the *imperium Christianum,* his court palace at Aix-la-Chapelle as the "second Rome", and his sovereignty over Gaul, the Germanic lands and Italy was largely undisputed. Religious turmoil in the Eastern Church — caused by the iconoclast controversy (726—843), which revolved around the worship or abolition of religious icons — provided the Frankish king with an opportunity to challenge the ecumenical authority of the Byzantine Emperor. The name of the Greek *Basileus,* whom the Pope had until then addressed as his 'lord', disappeared from papal documents, and moreover as early as 796, Leo III had sent his protector Charlemagne the banner of the City of Rome. Thus both the Pope in the coronation ritual and the Romans in their acclamation of the emperor were merely giving formal recognition to what had long been an established state of affairs. In Charlemagne's full title as Emperor, the name *augustus* refers to his divine elevation to power, that of *imperator* to his role as supreme commander of the army, and the formulation *Romanum gubernans imperium* can be identified with the title of the Roman Emperor in post-Justinian documents (Here the official nature of sovereignty over the Roman Empire becomes evident). The position of the Franks as the ruling nation of the Empire remained untouched. Under the influence of feudal law, an estate gradually emerged consisting of participants in imperial power (the *'Reichsaristokratie'*), who had exclusive rights to all the important titles and offices of the Empire.

In the splendour of the Imperium, the Emperor represented the unity of the West and claimed the leadership of Christendom on its path to salvation. A contemporary encomium extols how God had raised Charlemagne to power for the protection and guidance of all Christians as Governor in God's stead. As the representative of Christ, even the bishops took second place beside him. Spiritual, political and secular interests were closely interwoven in the early mediaeval *ecclesia universalis (christianitas),* the Church Universal, the corresponding equivalent of Christendom. The emperorship was intended as the cohesive force behind the Christian unity of the Empire. It suited Charlemagne, the 'new David', to be placed in the line of succession of the Roman rulers who had been sovereigns before him in the *imperium Christianum.* In the motto on Charlemagne's bull, *renovatio Romani imperii,* his circle of advisers, the court prelates, were not merely referring back to late Roman tradition alone. With the concept of *renovatio,* taken from the Bible, they were invoking the renewal of the Empire from within, pinning their hopes on a new creation, while renewal as the restoration of the past remained the supreme goal in the realms of art and culture. The Church ensured not only religious but above all cultural unity. It is to the Church that the West owes its common (Latin) language of culture and education and a largely uniform world view. All centres of learning were dominated by religion and the Church. Nevertheless, although much ancient art did survive, only fragments of the broad cultural consciousness in which it had been embedded had been preserved. The isolated pockets of humanist learning remained confined to the court, moving between palaces, the higher echelons of the clergy and the imperial monasteries. Very few could understand Latin and read documents. Those who could were, almost without exception, members of the clergy, since few people outside their ranks had access to any education. Priests had to be able to read, write and speak Latin, since it was the language of the Church.

A Christian king's political power over the comprehensive, unified entity of the *ecclesia universalis,* which spanned both the secular and ecclesiastical spheres, could only be derived from God. The doctrine of political Augustinianism comprehended the *regnum* only in its religious function. In the unified concept of *rex et sacerdos,* the sacramental character of consecrated kingship is expressed as participation in the priesthood and kingship of Christ, and the ecclesiastical hierarchy's dependence upon the ruler is clearly and concisely defined. However, it also contained the seeds of future crises and emergent tendencies towards emancipation. Because the Augustinian concept of theocracy accorded no independence to a secular political will, it was in contradiction with the existing balance of power from the very outset, because it was directed solely towards a religious goal. Rulers' political power-struggles inevitably involved religious and ecclesiastical concerns. Charlemagne's emperorship saw no changes in the constitution. It was only with the conscious foundation of the Roman Empire on the *imperium Romanum* that the Frankish feudal lords' attention was first directed towards the entity of the *res publica,* the common weal, as a concept of suprapersonal greatness. The personal Germanic warrior-kingdom based on relations of mutual loyalty began to be penetrated by the emerging concept of the theocratic nature of imperial office.

The interplay between king and nobles occupies a large part of the mediaeval history of the Germanic-Roman peoples and was to prove decisive for further constitutional development. One of the unsolved problems under the Carolingians was the relationship between Frankish 'royal' law and 'tribal' rights. As a counterweight to the feudal system, the Frankish Church, which had been endowed with imperial estates, assumed responsibility for the king's obligation to conduct military campaigns. On the other hand, in the stem duchies it was the aristocracy which rallied strongest support against the centralising tendencies of the kingship.

Under Charlemagne's successors, the ideal of imperial power was demolished. Louis the Pious (814—840) made a vain attempt with his legislative reforms to promote the idea of imperial unity, to mould a single Christian people from the numerous different peoples within the Empire. He and his central instrument of administration, the *Hofkapelle,* increasingly regarded sovereignty as an office of the *ecclesia universalis.* However, the necessary will to realise this idea was lacking. In the division of the empire, which was negotiated at Verdun in 843, the empire of Lothar was limited to that part of the empire already granted to him, together with Aix-la-Chapelle and Rome; the Empire of the western Franks was granted to Charles the Bald, and the eastern Frankish part of the empire to Ludwig the German, as independent kingdoms. As the Carolingian Empire disintegrated, so too did the Imperium, which was eventually limited to Italy, and it gradually dwindled away until finally only the idea remained.

THE IMPERIAL KINGDOM OF OTTO THE GREAT AND THE REVIVAL OF THE IMPERIUM ROMANUM

The renewal of the *imperium* in the Carolingian empire would have remained little more than an unsuccessful experiment had not the memory of its successes been accompanied by the bold hope of reviving the myth of emperorship anew, and of reestablishing the continuity of the imperial tradition as a binding and universal concept of empire in the succession of Charlemagne. Despite the turmoil of the previous centuries, the magical and alluring power of imperial elevation remained undiminished. Imperial power was bound up with the myth of imperial Rome, and Aix and Rome were its magnetic poles. The aura surrounding Aix derived from the *Pfalzkapelle* (palace chapel), whose octagonal walls symbolised eternity, the eight-sided tomb promising resurrection and rebirth in the Celestial City of Jerusalem, the realm of perfection, for the mortal remains of the great Emperor. In the gallery, however, Charlemagne's marble throne seemed to be waiting for whoever God should deem as worthy of ruling over the earthly empire. Rome on the other hand was eternal, the quintessential city, of which Otto III was to say: *"We have proclaimed Rome the capital of the world."*

Like France and the *regnum Italiae,* the German Kingdom was a successor state of the Frankish kingdom. The *Königsheil* (the king's charismatic power) passed from the Franks to the Saxons. The ancient Saxon Dukes, later known as the Ottonians, began their rise to Imperial power with King Heinrich I. Carolingian traditions played the most important role in the politics of the Ottonian state and empire. In contrast to the old feudal stem duchies, the Saxon kings had succeeded in preserving a balance of power. They made it the central task of the empire to secure the Imperial frontiers against the Slavs and Hungarians, and it was Otto I's victory over the Hungarians at Lechfeld in 955 which gave German kingship the upper hand against feudal self-interests. Prior to this, Heinrich I had regained Lotharingia, ruled according to Carolingian administrative law, established a *Hofkapelle* (court chapel) with central powers of domain and revived the Frankish Church. With donations from Imperial estates to diocesan churches and imperial abbeys, the Ottonian kings developed the Church into the central institution of the Empire.

In the art of the Ottonian and early Salian Empires the tradition of Augustan patronage and an echo of the classical Roman concept of art lived on. The classical Roman ideal of the emperor as the fount of all knowledge and wisdom was revived. Otto III, *"the wonder of the world"* at the turn of the millenium, had received a priest's education and even presided over learned disputes. Knowledge of Latin, the language of the Church, gave a tiny circle of people access to the classical, humanistic heritage, the culture of the ancient world. The precious objects that had survived from late antiquity — among them numerous cameos and codices embellished with miniatures — ended up in the king's treasury or the treasuries of the Imperial Church. With its imitation of classical forms, court art derived its impulses from the formal concepts transmitted from classical antiquity, and the close relationship between artisans' workshops and the royal and ecclesiastical treasuries reinforced this continuity.

The Emperor was liberal in his distribution of costly materials and objects, as well as holy relics (which were deemed more precious), to all who enjoyed his special protection. When he appeared in the full splendour of his regalia as sovereign, everyone recognised him as the Vicar of Christ over whom God spread his abundant grace. The abundance of riches that a ruler had at his disposal to reward loyal followers fed the affection of his subjects. No ruler could exist without riches in his Treasury; his power diminished in proportion with his riches.

There was one emblem which stood out above all the other secular emblems of sovereignty in terms of its symbolic power, because it signified victory and legitimised the Emperor's sovereign power as that exercised in the name of Christ the Ruler of the Universe: the Cross as the *crux gemmata* (jewelled cross). Only the relics of the Passion — since Christ himself was present in them — were more potent in bringing victory than the jewelled cross, and these were thus accorded pride of place in the emperor's treasury. Magnificent ceremonial crosses, embellished with cameos and gemstones from the imperial treasury, were donated to the cathedrals and abbeys of the imperial Church by pious rulers as proof of their favour and as a symbol of their inviolable power.

Harmony in spiritual and temporal concerns remained the ultimate goal of the Ottonian Empire. The imperial duties performed by the church — whether in the secular administration or the religious services of liturgy and mission — were regarded as one and the same religious and ethical duty. This concept of imperial service explains the theocratic forms of investiture. Theocratic priest-kingship elevated the sovereign to the rank of *vicarius Christi*. His participation in the spiritual pastorate legitimised his distribution of secular possessions among the bishops; they also received their ecclesiastical office from his hand, with ring and staff. Thus the concept of investiture also included the act of installing bishops in episcopal office, and created among them a special relation of loyalty to the king. The bishops eventually became princes of the Empire, and their bishoprics imperial bishoprics. The armies of the imperial Church now fought the battles of the kings. However, despite the strong ties between the hierarchy of the imperial

Church and the sovereign, the state Church remained as always a member of the Church Universal.

The military dominance of the Saxon and early Salian kings developed from the Germanic warrior-kingdom. Their leadership within the German kingdom was based on this hegemony and the arrière-ban over the tribes. The centralistic power of the king found support among the ever-loyal higher clergy of the state Church against the territorial self-interests of the powerful Dukes, of whose loyalty he could never be sure.

Not only were the preconditions for national consciousness lacking entirely: the idea of the unity of the Frankish kingdom still lived on. Otto I (936—973) was not content with his inherited position as ruler of the German Kingdom. As Charlemagne's successor he had himself crowned and consecrated king in the minster at Aix-la-Chapelle, seated upon Charlemagne's throne, which was furnished with the holy relics belonging to the latter, among them presumably the Burse of St. Stephan. From his father, Otto had inherited the Holy Lance (Cat. No. 155), the victory-bringing relic and weapon held to be the legendary lance that had once belonged to Constantine. As an emblem of imperial sovereignty it signified his claim to Italy. Otto's preeminence among the western monarchs left one last honour to be attained. Following repeated calls for help from the Pope, the German king prepared to assume sovereignty over Italy before continuing on to Rome.

In 962, Otto I, together with his wife, was crowned and consecrated over the tomb of St. Peter, the Prince of the Apostles. In the ritual of the coronation, the Pope was merely bestowing his sacramental blessing on what had already been decided. As long as the Ottonian and early Salian theocracy lasted, the empire was free of papal influence. It was the Germans who emerged as the imperial people, and their kingdom which assumed imperial character.

Otto's election as emperor, formally acclaimed by the Romans, did not increase his power as ruler, which remained fundamentally that of a king. The revived Christian empire strove to be Roman, yet saw its mission as universal. The Emperor was responsible for the protection of the Church, the propagation of the faith, conversion of the heathen and the persecution of heretics. In these duties lay a cultural, missionary task which endowed imperial policy in the East with a higher purpose. The power of the Ottonian dynasty did not essentially extend beyond the Alps. No emperor was able to prevail in Rome for any length of time, not even Otto II, although during his reign the imperium that had been resurrected under the German kings did become more Roman than it had ever been under Charlemagne. To affirm the universal character of the Empire, Otto III transferred his seat of government to the Aventine.

However, the means to power required to create a universal Christian Roman Empire were lacking. What in fact constituted ''imperial Italy'' was northern Italy, which had been subjugated by Otto I. Yet when Heinrich II was crowned King of Lombardy, he granted Italy a greater degree of national independence again. With the territorial acquisition of Burgundy under Konrad II (1033), the kingdoms of Burgundy and Arelat (Provence) then became allied to the imperium and were to remain so for centuries. To all appearances, the empire and its politics had reached their zenith. However, the territory over which the emperors actually ruled was that of the Germans and Lorraine. The emperors had styled themselves *imperator Romanorum* ever since Otto II, despite the fact that imperial power over the Romans was never achieved for any significant length of time. Considering the contingencies of politics, it is easy to understand why the sources of the age frequently mention the *translatio imperii,* the translation of the empire, referring to the fact that it was now the Germans and not the Romans who constituted the imperial people. This change was expressed in the titles of the emperors from Heinrich III onwards, who bore the title *rex Romanorum* instead of rex Francorum. From Konrad III, the addition of *(et semper) augustus* established the claim of the German kings to the Roman emperorship. However, neither Otto I nor his successors demanded — or even expected — the subjection of the other Christian kings in the West on the strength of their imperial title. Surpassing all other monarchs in dignity and authority, the Emperor of the West seemed to occupy the Universal Throne, chosen by God to unite temporal history with the process of salvation.

Emperor Heinrich III, who in 1046 divested three anti-popes and installed three successive imperial bishops on St. Peter's throne, was the last of the Roman emperors to hold sway over the Church. Internal ecclesiastical reforms, together with a papacy which was becoming increasingly aware of its paramount spiritual power, led to a redefinition of the relations between *regnum* and *sacerdotium*. From this time on, ecclesiastical authority was to be responsible for both the spiritual and political aspirations of the Church.

ECCLESIASTICAL REFORM AND THE INVESTITURE CONTROVERSY
THE CHANGE FROM UNIVERSAL EMPERORSHIP TO PAPAL SUPREMACY

Owing to the supranational unity of the ecclesiastical hierarchy and the uniformity of Church law, the papacy enjoyed enough support to enable it to assume the leadership of western Christianity. The right of papal election had been transferred to the College of Cardinals as an electoral body in 1059. From this time on, whenever one of the spheres of power was obliged to pass judgement on the other, it was the judicial authority of the Pope as spiritual pontiff and his privilege of excommunication and divestment which prevailed. The Church now claimed all penal authority for itself, expressed in the symbol of the sword. This included not only the spiritual sword of anathema, but also the material sword of military command — whether exercised through the secular ruler or on the Pope's own authority, with the latter himself issuing the call to arms. The anathema hurled at Heinrich IV by Pope Gregory VII in 1076 had far-reaching consequences. The controversy concerning the investiture of bishops and abbots by their sovereign princes soon developed into a more fundamental conflict between spiritual and temporal power. During the course of the controversy, the relationship between Church and Empire was reversed. From then on, the Pope enjoyed precedence over the Emperor, who had to be consecrated and crowned by the Pope, and was committed as the secular arm of the Church to its protection and defence. From Rome's point of view, western unity was based on a common faith and membership of the same church. In stark contrast to the previous incorporation of kingship into the scheme of salvation, the Pope was now intent on devaluing the mystic, sacral significance of kingship, and diminishing the position of the anointed king by stripping him of his redemptive character. He secularised the kingship, limiting the sovereign's office to the temporal sphere alone.

In a countermove, the *regnum* transformed its power into a kingdom by divine right with its own, independent spheres of law and action. The demotion of the king to the level of a lay monarch led to the development of a concept of the divine right of kings that was not solely based on ecclesiastical principles. In part it drew on ancient sources: on the one hand the continuation of ancient Roman imperial law with its sacralisation of ruler, law and empire, and on the other hand derived from the Germanic concept of the *Königsheil* that adhered to the ruling dynasty.

The papal anathema was followed by a turning point in the constitutional history of the German kingdom. In 1076, the nobles won a decisive victory over the kingship and the concept of imperial unity when they elected an anti-king. This opposed the right of free election by the princes to the royal blood-right. For the first time there were two kings in Germany fighting for papal recognition, and as such they recognised the Pope's role as arbiter. It was the combination of blood-right and the right of election that was to determine the history of German kingship. The princes, as the Electors, would not tolerate royal authority established by virtue of dynastic descent alone.

Installation in ecclesiastical office by laics, including the king, had been declared uncanonical by the Pope, who had thereby destroyed the fundament of the imperial Church system, since both state and king lost the Church as their mainstay. At the Concordat of Worms in 1122 a compromise solution was arrived at: Heinrich V relinquished his right to investiture with ring and staff for ecclesiastical office and conceded free canonical election of the bishops to the Church. The Pope granted the Emperor the investiture of the high clergy as part of the rights and attributes of sovereignty under the temporal symbol of the sceptre. In political terms, this resulted in the promotion of bishops from imperial official to spiritual prince of the Empire.

The authority of the papacy as based on primacy, i.e. supreme ecclesiastical authority, was not confined to the spiritual and political leadership of western Christendom. The independent state politics pursued by the papacy have already been mentioned above in connection with the rise of the Papal States. The relationship of the Church Universal and the papacy on the one hand to the divided temporal rulership in Christendom on the other was determined over the centuries by a dualistic component, although the interplay of both elements was to influence the course of medieval history decisively. The papacy attained the height of its power under Innocence III (1198—1216), when the Curia achieved the leadership of the West and victory over Emperor Friedrich II († 1250). However, the increasing orientation of the papacy towards France and the flowering of scholasticism at the universities was accompanied by the disintegration of ecclesiastical unity and the emergence of a schism in Christendom.

In his reform of 1246, Emperor Friedrich II argued from basic principles, referring the Church and the Pope to their fundamental duties, to the original ecclesiastical apostolic ideal of subordination of the Church to divine authority. Subordination of the Roman Curia to temporal authority could no longer be seriously considered. Not until the Age of Enlightenment were effective attempts made to achieve a definitive separation of Church and State.

The figure of the Hohenstaufen *'Bamberger Reiter'* (Knight of Bamberg), the absolute ideal of western knighthood, is a perfect illustration of the binding example provided by Constantine and of sovereignty legitimised by divine election. As with the spiritual image of Constantine in previous epochs of the Middle Ages, the issues here are the position of the Christian ruler in relation to God and the conception of the virtues he was supposed to possess. The king, mounted in majestic pose on his horse, may be Emperor Constantine himself, or perhaps St. Stephen, the Hungarian king, related by marriage to the Ottonian dynasty since 995, who converted his country to Christianity. It is questionable whether the ideal of the High Gothic period coincides in this figure with the ideas of the ruling emperor, or whether Friedrich II as an individual actually had very different ideas. He had, after all, reconstructed his Sicilian-Norman kingdom as a rationally organised and centralistic bureaucracy. In any case, this monumental Gothic sculpture inside the cathedral at Bamberg — its style deriving from French cathedral sculpture and ancient equestrian statues of emperors — is an expression of the need to represent the High Gothic concept of sovereignty in an appropriate form, endowed with sacred significance and a sense of universal mission.

IMPERIAL PIETY AND THE WORSHIP OF RELICS IN THE LATE MIDDLE AGES
DREAMS OF THE SACRED CHARACTER OF THE EMPIRE SIGNIFY THE BEGINNING OF A FLIGHT FROM REALITY

With the erection of the fortified castle at Karlstein, Emperor Karl IV (1346—1378) undertook one last, yet artistically convincing attempt to give visible expression to the sacral character of the emperorship. He succeeded in this by creating a mystic sphere of piety in a small sacral chamber fitted out with precious relics, gemstones and paintings. As King of Bohemia, Karl IV was Elector of the Palatine, and later became Roman king, being crowned Emperor in Rome in 1355. He aspired as no other ruler before him in the Holy Roman Empire, to bind the emperorship to a fixed location, i.e. a capital. It was this intention that led to the founding of the Neustadt at Prague. Imperial donations made Prague the 'Golden City'. However, neither Prague nor the later capital and residence, the Baroque city of Vienna, ever managed to achieve the same standing as Rome, which served as their fundamental ideal. Even Emperor Friedrich I Barbarossa, during whose reign the first mention of *sacrum imperium* was made in 1157, was unable to solve the problem of the centre of power. Barbarossa regarded Frankfurt as the place of election, but Aix as the *sedes regni* (seat of government) of the German kingdom, since Aix was the place of the coronation of its kings. However, the case was in fact much more complex.

The images of the rulers on the front of all the lead and gold bulls reflect the German kings' conception both of themselves and their claim to be King of the Romans. Charlemagne's bull bore on its obverse an image of the Eternal City, *aurea Roma,* the golden city. This was intended both as a reference to the Roman origins of the Empire and as an expression of the belief that it would endure until the Day of Judgement. From the reign of Konrad II until the end of the Middle Ages, the obverse of all the bulls bore as their legend a verse composed in 1033: *Roma caput mundi regit orbis frena rotundi* (Rome, the head of the world, directs the reins of the earth). The legend encircles the image of the city, usually referred to as *aurea Roma* from the reign of Otto III onwards. In hallowed tradition, Rome is conceived of as the *urbs regia* (royal city) of the western emperorship, as the centre of the Church and, symbolically, as the City of God.

The same imperial and Roman device is repeated in the audience chamber at Karlstein, its other walls being decorated with frescoes displaying the genealogy of the Luxemburg dynasty. In the late Middle Ages, the sacred aura of the imperial ideal was to be given expression, in terms of mystical experience, in the Chapel of the Cross. Emperor Karl IV expanded the castle at Karlstein, which lay not far from Prague, into a sacral citadel, a treasure hoard of relics and precious jewels, a place of meditation and prayer. In the temporal sphere, the art of princes was the art of their castles, whose strength was proof of their owners' authority. In Karlstein, Karl IV was concerned to erect a splendid monument to imperial power. Its highest, crowning tower glorified his power; the chapel inside the tower shows the ruler to be a monarch possessing charismatic strength and miraculous power. The chapel functions as a reliquary with the treasury of holy relics that it contains increasing the power of imperial intercession. Courtly art was created as cult and liturgy. The most precious materials surround the relics and the devout Emperor in his majesty. This marriage of liturgy and the cult of the sovereign had been expressed 500 years earlier in the palace chapel of Emperor Charlemagne at Aix, and long before that in the Byzantine east.

In the spring of 1350, Karl IV had received from the sons of Ludwig of Bavaria, his adversary and predecessor on the imperial throne, the imperial insignia, *quem imperium dicuntur,* 'which is called the empire'; among them the Imperial crown, said to have been first worn by Charlemagne, the reviver of the empire, who had been canonised during the Hohenstaufen era. Around 1200, Charlemagne became the obligatory model for future rulers. For Karl IV, the crown of the

canonised Emperor acquired the character of a holy relic. The transformation of
the imperial insignia from emblems of rulership into holy relics emerges clearly
in a missive to the Pope requesting permission to exhibit the relics annually. In
August 1350, Karl IV had applied for papal sanction to display as holy relics all
the insignia and treasure known collectively as the *reliquiae imperiales*. In particular, the Holy Lance, which Karl IV misinterpreted as being the lance belonging to Longinus containing a nail from the True Cross, was greatly venerated by
the monarch. The Emperor proposed to the Pope the introduction of a holy day
(the second Friday after Easter) which was subsequently called the 'Day of the
Holy Relics', and dedicated to the veneration of the lance and nail.

For the greater honour of "the holy implements of the martyrdom of Our Lord",
the Chapel of the Holy Cross was consecrated in the highest, most imposing tower
of Karlstein. In the walls, which are encrusted with precious stones, and whose
panels are placed in such a way as to form crosses set with holy relics, in the
painted walls above these, where panel paintings depict the Crucifixion and the
company of saints, and in the gold-painted vaulting set with crystal at the very
top, is displayed the whole formal wealth of treasury art in the High Middle Ages.
The bejewelled facing of exterior surfaces, as in the Carolingian Burse of St.
Stephen and the Ottonian imperial insignia, here recurs as monumentalised en-
crustations on an inner surface, on the inside walls of the room. This is unique
to Karlstein. The chapel forms as it were a protective casing for the holy relics,
which are contained in a niche over the altar.

The use of gem-symbolism, the skilful mise-en-scène to induce intense sensual
perceptions and evoke mystical experience and the recreation of the ultimate
truths of faith, all accord with the aura of piety surrounding Karl IV. The simplicity of the holy relics themselves, which were of incalculable value for the devout,
their jewelled receptacles of gleaming gold and the insignia which had themselves
become holy relics, as well as every symbolic reference and even the pomp itself,
find their resonance and parallel in the precious appointment and the programmatic design of the room. Here, in acordance with the traditional equation of
sacral space and conceptions of the cosmos, a mystical image of the Celestial city
of Jerusalem arises in a spiritual vision.

From Charlemagne onwards, every sovereign who was crowned emperor in the
former Constantinian basilica of Old St. Peter's in Rome saw in front of him in
the mosaic of the apsis during the coronation rites the visionary representation
of the twin cities of Bethlehem and Jerusalem, their walls magnificently adorned
with gemstones, as an allegory of heaven. They flanked a representation of God
in Majesty containing at its centre the *crux gemmata* (jewelled cross) over the
Lamb of God: the symbol of lambs issuing from the celestial cities stood for the
Apostles, who gather round the symbol of Christ. These mosaics from the era of
Constantine are probably the earliest pictorial references to the apocalyptic vision
of the Celestial City of Jerusalem, the realm of perfection. In the language of Ottonian art, the octagon of the Imperial Crown (Cat. No. 153) also stands for the
jewel-encrusted Golden City. The people of the Middle Ages needed a symbol,
some kind of visible sign, in order to grasp abstract ideas or messages of salvation
which went beyond the perception of the senses. These symbols were used to illustrate a higher meaning. Interpretations of these, however, were never clear-cut and
cannot be explained by the language of the gemstones alone. Several meanings
can be contained in one symbol. The equation of the Imperial Crown as an allegorical concretisation of the Celestial City of Jerusalem, the Golden City, with its
gem-encrusted walls, is most probably only one of several possible interpretations. The magical fascination of the stones and their religious significance already underlay the form of the jewel-encrusted, victory-bringing crosses of the
Constantinian era, as is the case with the early Salian Imperial Cross (*crux gemmata* with a representation of the Lamb of God; Cat. No. 154). The veneration
of gemstones, accompanied by the veneration of images and relics, continues for

more than a millenium, from its Constantinian origins to the late Middle Ages. No emperor after Karl IV was able to conceive of the Roman Empire as an allegory and image of the Celestial City of Jerusalem. In 1424, Karl IV's son, Emperor Sigismund, entrusted the custody of the insignia and treasures of the Holy Roman Empire, in exchange for a sum of money, to the free imperial city of Nuremberg, where they were kept until 1796.

The Middle Ages had no concept of a state as such. Concepts such as *regnum, imperium, rîche* signify the personal sovereignty of a king over peoples and lands. The word *rîche* (empire) could mean the territory ruled by either greater or lesser lords: an empire *Ostarîchi (Österreich* = Austria*)*, the territory belonging to the Margrave of the Bavarian Ostmark, as well as the smallest domains. Land is the old German term denoting the 'state', the *Landsleute* the people who live in the *Land*. Unity lay in the commonalty of its law, not in the lord of the land. The old empire was divided into the 'Teutonic lands', originally the five Teutonic-Germanic tribes headed by their stem dukes, and then into the later territories. It was not until the 16th century that the singular form *Deutschland* prevailed over the plural *deutsche Lande* which comprised the Empire. The princes' policies were directed by particularist interests, i.e. towards the formation of self-contained territories (*Länder* = lands) within the Empire. Germany remained an aristocracy (princes of the Empire) with a monarch as its head (King, and mostly also elected Emperor). However, the dualism between Emperor and Empire prevented the development of a unified German state. In contrast to the ideal of unification represented by the Holy Roman Empire — which had dwindled from the idea of Christian-Roman world supremacy to an ardent hope for salvation, and after the Middle Ages had evaporated into little more than an illusory fiction — the desire for national unity gained ground. An early model for the German nation-state that had been vehemently demanded since the wars of liberation in the Napoleonic era, and which did not become a reality until the last third of the 19th century, when the German empire was under Prussian domination, and then only for a few decades, was the well-organised Sicilian-Norman bureaucracy of the Hohenstaufen Emperor Friedrich II († 1250). In the State of the Teutonic Order, and later in the Kingdom of Prussia, it found its successor.   H. T.

Ref.: F. Bock, Die Kleinodien des heiligen Römischen Reiches Deutscher Nation, Vienna 1864; E. Eichmann, Die Kaiserkrönung im Abendland, Würzburg 1942; H. Fichtenau, Zum Reliquienwesen im frühen Mittelalter, in: MIÖG, vol. 60, 1952, p. 60 ff.; H. Fillitz, Die Insignien und Kleinodien des Heiligen Römischen Reiches, Vienna/Munich 1954; P. E. Schramm, Herrschaftszeichen und Staatssymbolik, Stuttgart 1954—1956; H. Wolfram, Constantin als Vorbild für den Herrscher des hochmittelalterlichen Reiches, in: MIÖG, vol. 58, 1960, p. 226 ff.; F. Kempf, Abendländische Völkergemeinschaft und Kirche von 900 bis 1046. Handbuch der Kirchengeschichte vol. III/I, Freiburg 1966, p. 219 ff.; K. Bosl, Staat, Gesellschaft, Wirtschaft im deutschen Mittelalter, in: Gebhardt, Handbuch der deutschen Geschichte, Part 7, 1985 (1970); A. Legner, Wände aus Edelstein und Gefäße aus Kristall, in: exhibition catalogue, Die Parler und der schöne Stil 1350—1400. Europäische Kunst unter den Luxemburgern, vol. III, Cologne 1978, p. 169 ff.; exhibition catalogue, Spätantike und frühes Christentum, Frankfurt 1983/84; G. Duby, Die Zeit der Kathedralen. Kunst und Gesellschaft: 980—1420, Frankfurt/M. 1985 (1976).

**142 THE CORONATION PROCES-
SION ON THE RÖMERBERG**
Studio of Martin van Meytens the
Younger (among others: Johann Dal-
linger von Dalling, 1741—1806)
Canvas; 358 x 412 cms (Inv. No. GG
7466)

This picture derives from a series of six
paintings formerly in Schönbrunn
Palace: 1. The Entry of Emperor Franz
Stephan I and his son Joseph (II) into
Frankfurt on 27. 3. 1764 (exhibited in
the Wagenburg, Schönbrunn Palace);
2. the Coronation Procession on the
Römerberg; 3. The Coronation in the
Church of St. Batholomew (Cat. No.
178a); 4. The Knighting Ceremony after the Coronation (Cat. No. 178b); 5.
The Homage and Performance of the
Hereditary Offices on the Römerberg
(not exhibited, since 1945 in storage —
in a badly damaged condition); 6. The
Coronation Banquet on the Römerberg (exhibited in the writing room of

Archduke Franz Karl in the state apart-
ments of Schönbrunn Palace).

In "Dichtung und Wahrheit" (Poetry
and Truth [Part 1, Book 5]), Johann
Wolfgang von Goethe gives a detailed
account of the preparations and
ceremonies involved in the coronation
of Josef II in Frankfurt:

*"The coronation day dawned at last,
on the 3rd of April, 1764; the weather
was favourable and everybody was in
motion. I, with several of my relations
and friends, had been provided with a
good place in one of the upper stories
of the Römer itself, where we might
completely survey the whole. We be-
took ourselves to the spot very early in
the morning, and from above, as in a
bird's-eye view, contemplated the arrangements which we had inspected
more closely the day before. There was
the newly-erected fountain, with two
large tubs on the left and right, into
which the double-eagle on the post was*

to pour from its two beaks white wine on this side and red wine on that. There, gathered into a heap, lay the oats; here stood the large wooden hut, in which we had several days since seen the whole fat ox roasted and basted on a huge spit before a charcoal fire. All the avenues leading out from the Römer, and from other streets back to the Römer, were secured on both sides by barriers and guards . . . . Now the Emperor is putting on his domestic (sic) robes, we said, a new dress, made after the old Carolingian pattern. The hereditary officers receive the insignia, and with them get on horseback. The Emperor in his robes, the Roman King in the Spanish habit, immediately mount their steeds; and while this is done, the endless procession which precedes them has already announced them.

The eye was already wearied by the multitude of richly-dressed attendants and magistrates, and by the nobility who, in stately fashion, were moving along; but when the electoral envoys, the hereditary officers, and at last, under the richly-embroidered canopy, borne by twelve Schöffen and senators, the Emperor, in romantic costume, and to the left, a little behind him, in the Spanish dress, his son, slowly floated along on magnificently adorned horses, the eye was no more sufficient for the sight."

The second scene in the series shows the coronation procession on the Römerberg (the centre of municipal life in Frankfurt), seen from the north, on the way to the nearby Church of St. Bartholomew. At the head of the mounted procession, front left, are buglers and trumpeters, behind them heralds; then, in pairs, come the electoral ambassadors in full gala dress wearing mantles and wigs, followed by the holders of the hereditary offices with the insignia of the Imperial house. In the first row, one beside the other, the Imperial Hereditary Chamberlain with the Imperial House Sceptre (Cat.

No. 58) (which, according to entries in the diary of the Grand Comptroller of the Imperial Household, Khevenhüller, was always carried by Franz I personally), the Imperial Steward with the Imperial House Orb (Cat. No. 57) and the Imperial Hereditary Treasurer with the Imperial Crown on a golden cushion. Behind them follow, singly, the Imperial Hereditary Cupbearer and the Imperial Hereditary Marshal, Count von Pappenheim, naked on his shoulder the Imperial sword (Cat. No. 160). Beneath the baldaquin borne by the councillors of Frankfurt is Emperor Franz I in the private vestments copied from the old coronation robes (Cat. No. 179) wearing the Crown of Rudolf II (Cat. No. 56). Behind him, Joseph II in the Archducal Habit (Cat. No. 55) wearing the Archducal coronet made especially for this coronation, a slightly different copy of the Austrian Archducal Coronet in the monastery of Klosterneuburg. Alongside and behind the baldaquin are the bodyguards.

In the background of the picture, right, the Römer, the old town hall composed of several houses combined together, the first floor of which is occupied by the Imperial Hall, where the coronation banquets were held. To the left of it, standing on its own, the Gothic Church of St. Nicholas, and in front of it the *Bretterküche*, where an oxen was roasted on a spit for the coronation banquet and afterwards given to the crowd.   K. S.

Sources: Vollständiges Diarium von denen merckwürdigen Vorfällen die sich bey . . . Wahl und Krönung des . . . Herrn Josephs des Anderen . . . ergeben, Mainz 1767—1771 (ed. F. E. Seeger, ph. J. Seitz); Aus der Zeit Maria Theresias, Tagebuch des Fürsten Johann Josef Khevenhüller-Metsch, kaiserlichen Obersthofmeisters, ed. R. Graf Khevenhüller-Metsch u. H. Schlitter, vol. 6, 1764—1767, Vienna 1917, p. 17 ff.; Johann Wolfgang von Goethe, Aus meinem Leben. Dichtung und Wahrheit, Parts 1—3, Tübingen 1811—1813 (Engl. translation by John Oxenford, London 1888).

Ref.: Catalogue, Maria Theresia 1980, nos. 68.01, 150.01—02; Kugler 1986, p. 126 f.

THE CORONATION ROBES OF THE KINGS AND EMPERORS OF THE HOLY ROMAN EMPIRE

The robes which were used at the coronations of the kings and emperors of the Holy Roman Empire do not constitute a homogeneous entity in the sense of having been designed and produced as a complete set of robes as such. Rather, they represent individual pieces or parts of vestments which no longer exist, and although they did indeed serve the representative purposes of a sovereign on ceremonial occasions, their original use was not always connected with a coronation ceremony. When, in 1186, Emperor Heinrich VI married Constance, the daughter of King Roger II of Sicily, the treasure of the Norman kings passed to the House of Hohenstaufen and thence, in 1194, after King Tancred had been expelled from Palermo, to the Empire. Of this treasure, the mantle of King Roger II (1097—1154), and the hose and gown — today referred to as the 'alba' — of King Wilhelm II (1153—1189) have survived, and are attested to by inscriptions. The blue tunicella and the cingulum certainly also belonged to this collection. It is not known exactly when the shoes and gloves, which have generally been associated with Emperor Friedrich II, became part of the vestments, nor when all the pieces were transferred to Germany or first used for a coronation, once they had been assembled as a set. They first receive mention there on 17. 9. 1246 in a document of transfer to King Konrad IV at Castle Trifels in the Palatinate; together with the insignia and relics, they were known as *"the imperial emblems"*. Apart from the *"imperial mantle with precious stones"* we find *"an alba, of whitw samite, with precious stones, two gloves with precious stones, one tunic of samite"* (the blue tunicella?), *"two scarlet hose (stockings), two gilt shoes with stones, three silken girdles."* It is interesting to note how easily a foreign history could be adopted as one's own, something which is especially true in the case of the mantle. The motif of a lion as victor over a camel, which is indeed very strange for the west, together with an inscription in Arabic, which at that time was not read in the north, are features which neither derive from Roman antiquity nor continue the Byzantine tradition, but which have developed from Islamic culture. It is above all the red colour, the particular sumptuousness of the materials, and the admirable way in which they have been worked, that earned this mantle the privileged title of 'imperial' and ensured its further use as such. Yet only one hundred years later — by which time every sovereign kept the Imperial treasures in his own possession — in the document of 12. 3. 1350, transferring the treasure to King Karl IV, it had grown in status from an *"imperial emblem"* to a *"relic and treasure of the holy empire"*. Many of the pieces, including the crown, were now traced back to the Emperor Charlemagne, who had been beatified in 1165: *"a white gown of saint charles, the arms embroidered with precious stones and with pearls"* (alba); *"a red mantle of saint charles with two lions embroidered with precious stones, pearls and gold, two silken gloves with stones, with pearls and with gold, a blue gown, the arms embroidered with gold and with pearls"* (blue tunicella), *"another brown gown with black eagles"* (eagle dalmatic, 1st mention) *"and a cowl"* (lost), *"two gloves and two shoes of the same colour, a stola embroidered with gold, precious stones and with pearls"* (stola, 1st mention) *"and another stola without stones"* (lost). Karl IV at first took the treasure to Prague, but in 1365 he placed it for safekeeping in the sumptuously decorated Chapel of the Cross in the newly-built castle at Karlstein. Every year the relics and insignia were displayed for the veneration of the people, a custom which later developed into the famous Nuremberg ceremony of 'Instruction in the Relics' *(Heiltumsweisung)*. The imperial relics were transferred to Nuremberg on 22. 3. 1424 and remained there until they had to be rescued from Napoleon's troops and taken via Regensburg to Vienna in 1796. According to a document dating from 29. 9. 1423, *"our and the holy empire's relics"* were presented to the council and city of Nuremberg by King Sigismund. From then on the treasure was kept in the

Infirmary Church of the Holy Spirit. The relics hung in an oak chest mounted with silver-plate above the altar, while the robes and the insignia were housed, behind several locks, in a vault above the sacristy. We owe the first authentic pictorial representation of the coronation robes — and, incidentally, also of the imperial crown — to Albrecht Dürer. He received the commission to paint two portraits of the Emperor for the house of the Schopper family in Nuremberg, from where the ceremony of Instruction in the Relics was performed. One of them shows Charlemagne († 814 A.D.) wearing the insignia and coronation robes which then came to be associated with him. For this, Dürer made individual sketches from the originals. One sketch, signed and dated 1510, (today in the Albertina, Vienna) shows a full-length figure of a man wearing the imperial crown, ceremonial sword and imperial orb, adorned with the coronation mantle, eagle dalmatica and stola, and — to judge from the evidence of the cuffs, which are set with gems — also the alba. On the drawing is written: *"This is the habitum of the great emperor saint Charles".* The variety of the records concerning repairs indicates that the costly materials did not always stand up too well to their handling at the annual ceremony of Instruction in the Relics — when private showings were also given to important personages passing through Nuremberg — nor to being transported to the various coronation venues. In 1440, *"26 gulden"* were paid *"to embroider, tack and mend several pieces of the worthy relics, such as emperor charlemagne's cope, stole and a sword's scabbard"* (Schnelbögl 1962, p. 102). Before Karl V's coronation as king in Aix-la-Chapelle in 1520, the alba was *"covered with new white silk, and the cape"* (mantle) *"and knee-breeches"* (hose) *"were lined . . . by the nuns of the Convent of St. Clare"* (Weixlgärtner 1926, p. 64). Repairs to the robes were likewise described in 1619, 1657, 1689, 1711 and 1742 (exhibition catalogue, Nuremberg — Kaiser und Reich 1986, p. 77 f.) The robes used for the royal coronation of Joseph II were in a particularly bad state. In 1763 a *"greatly necessary major repair"* is recorded, for the robes had suffered a great deal during the tracing of the robes for Emperor Franz Stephan I of Lorraine (Cat. No. 179). It is reported that the sleeves of the alba and the mantle lining were torn and that the pearl embroidery was badly in need of repair. The latter was especially vulnerable, as can be seen from the numerous traces of stitching on all the garments set with pearls. Yet even immediately after the coronation of 1764 repairs had to be carried out on the *"imperial robe, returned somewhat damaged from Frankfurt".* Apart from the transportation to the coronation venues, the necessity of adapting them to fit variously proportioned persons in the shortest possible time had also resulted in considerable damage. Recently completed conservation work on the alba, the tunicella and the eagle dalmatica revealed that pieces of fabric from the borders and seam allowances had been quite indifferently cut out in order to use them for sewing on underneath holes or for covering tears. In particular the costly fabric of the lining of the mantle, the outside of which is in exceptionally good condition, has become badly damaged from the frequent re-sewing of the pearls. Christian Gottlieb von Murr reports in 1790 that repairs had to be carried out *"after almost every coronation ceremony, due to the many pearls which are frequently lost when the thread breaks".* The fact that provisions were made for all unforeseen possibilities can be gathered from a detailed description of the Imperial treasures in the Infirmary Church of the Holy Spirit from the beginning of the 18th century, which mentions *"a great box, in it all manner of things, including ribbons, pearls, needles and silk threads, for all eventualities that might come to pass at coronations."* (Weixlgärtner 1938, p. 106).

A complete inventory of the imperial treasures before they were hurriedly transferred to Vienna was drawn up by Johann Adam Delsenbach in his 'Wahre Abbildung der sämtlichen Reichskleinodien', published in Nuremberg in 1790. From this it becomes evident that several objects were lost in the course of the move, such as the humeral (shoulder vestment), a pair of *armillae* (arm bracelets), a pair of spurs, two imperial orbs, a stola, the cowl, two pairs of shoes, two pairs of gloves and a girdle.   R. B.

Ref.: Ch. G. von Murr, Beschreibung der sämtlichen Reichskleinodien und Heiligthümer . . . Nuremberg 1790, p. 33; Deér 1952, p. 75; P. E. Schramm, Kaiser Friedrichs II. Herrschaftszeichen, Göttingen 1955, pp. 131—133; J. Schnelbögl, Die Reichskleinodien in Nürnberg 1424—1523, in: Mitteilungen des Vereins für Geschichte der Stadt Nürnberg 58, 1971, pp. 139—160; B. Bischoff, Mittelalterliche Schatzverzeichnisse, I. Teil, Munich 1967, p. 99 f; A. Bühler, Albrecht Dürer und die Deutschen Reichskleinodien, in: Mitteilungen des Vereins für Geschichte der Stadt Nürnberg 58, 1971, pp. 139—160; F. Gabrieli/U. Scerrato, Gli Arabi in Italia, Milan 1979.

143 THE CORONATION MANTLE

Palermo, Royal workshop, 1133/34
Figured samite (kermes dyed), gold and silk embroidery, pearls, gold with cloisonné enamel, ruby, spinels, sapphires, garnets, glass, tablet weave; 345 cms wide, 146 cms long (Inv. No. XIII 14)

This semicircular mantle of glowing scarlet figured samite (so-called 'incised' silk) displays at its centre like a Tree of Life a stylised palm tree with pendant fruits. On either side of the tree in strict symmetry addorsed lions triumph over camels. These motifs are executed in couched gold embroidery. The internal features of the animals are executed in dark blue silk, most of which has dropped out. The contours of the tree, the animals and the lions' manes, facial features and the tips of their tails are picked out with double rows of pearls. At the lions' knee-joints, and on the brows and bridges of their noses are eight-piece rosettes embroidered in stem-stitch with red, blue, yellow and green silks, which has now partially dropped out. The camels have small circles arranged to form a larger circle on their knee-joints and a smaller circle on their lower legs. The straight side of the semicircle is edged with a border 8 cms wide, which is sumptuously embroidered with a double row of pearls. In this border are 30 small square cloisonné-enamelled plaques, all with ornamental decoration — apart from two which display a hare and a lion respectively — alternating with small palmette-like motifs, originally executed in dark-edged gold embroidery. The hem of the mantle is decorated with a Kufic inscription, bordered on both sides by a double row of pearls, which reads: *This belongs to the articles worked in the Royal workshop,* (which has) *flourished with fortune and honour, with industry and perfection, with might and merit, with* (his) *sanction and* (his) *prosperity, with magnanimity and majesty, with renown and beauty and the fulfilment of desires and hopes and with felicitous days and nights without cease or change, with honour and solicitude, with protection and defence, with success and certainty, with triumph and industry. In the* (capital) *city of Sicily in the year 528.*

The Islamic Hegira date corresponds to the Christian year 1133/34. The monarch thus hymned is the Norman king Roger II, who reigned from 1130 to 1154.

Semicircular mantles of this type were mostly worn assymetrically, so that the opening lay on the right shoulder, thus affording the right arm greater freedom of movement. However, the strictly centralised design on Roger II's mantle can only be fully displayed if it is worn with the opening in the centre at the front. The lion as such — and the lion subduing a weaker animal — is an ancient symbol of power, here possibly accompanied by another: on a celestial globe from Egypt inscribed with the date 1225 (today in the Museo di Capodimonte, Naples), the constellation of Leo is shown. The individual stars outline a lion resembling that on the mantle in several details: a stylised, mask-like face, a mane of short, individually-formed curls, an upright, knotted tail and sharply-contoured ribs. The question arises of whether the rosette medallions on the face and legs of the lion on the mantle are meant to represent stars, and thus refer to the oriental tradition of accoutering a ruler with a celestial mantle. However, the corresponding circles on the camel differ from those on the lion and should be seen as purely decorative motifs, since no camels appear on the celestial globe. Above the heads of each lion is a roundel of cloisonné enamel in a quatrefoil setting, decorated with precious stones and filigree work, the latter patinated in red. The same finish can be seen, albeit somewhat more faintly, on the clasp, and very distinctly on the appliqués of the dalmatica/tunicella (Cat. No. 145).

The clasp consists of three moveable elements overlaid with filigree and set with a ruby and two spinels respectively.

The rich use of threaded pearls to pick out the contours of the individual motifs has a striking parallel in the painted ceiling of the nave of the Capella Palatina in Palermo. Executed by Islamic artists around 1143, these paintings are framed in small panels by rows of 'pearls'. The individual paintings are surrounded by two narrow frames with small beads painted on the blue background between them. (Gabrieli/ Scherrato 1979, illus. 40—96).

Lining fabrics
The mantle is completely lined with a pink linen fabric, which is overlaid with three other materials.

a) Fabric in tapestry technique
Palermo, 1st 3rd of the 12th century
340 cms long, 37 cms wide, tapering to
c. 20 cms at neck and shoulders.

This fabric is the oldest of the three and originates from the time of the mantle itself. It is sewn as a narrow strip to the straight edge of the mantle, so that it was visible when the mantle opened while the wearer was walking. It is woven in tapestry technique using silk thread in red, green, blue, mauve, ochre, white and black, together with gilt membrane (pieces of gilded animal gut cut into narrow strips and wound around a silk core).

Five pieces of fabric, two displaying the same motifs, are sewn together to form a strip. A small number of fragmentary pieces of fabric, which form a group with this piece, has been preserved in various museums. To this group belongs a fabric (of which today only a drawing exists) from the tomb of King Roger I († 1101) in Palermo. Its marked Siculo-Arabic stylistic features and forms makes its origin within the Norman kingdom of Sicily virtually cer-

tain. The fabrics were probably produced by Islamic weavers in Sicily. These three fabrics have up till now been known by the names of the 'Fall of Man' cloth, the 'Dragon' cloth and the 'Bird' cloth, according to the motifs either represented or imagined to be represented on them. The 'Fall of Man cloth', however, should be renamed, since it derives too strongly from a Christian conception of the world. The central motif on this fabric is a stylised tree in a twelve-sided, graduated frame. At various points on its branches grow dragons' heads with pointed ears and out-stretched tongues. Underneath the tree, to either side, stand cloaked figures, accompanied by either a hare or a bird at head height. The pieces of fabric containing the motif are to be found at the beginning and end of the strip of fabric. In view of the motifs, it would seem more useful to give it the name of the 'Tree of Life'.

The second and fourth piece of fabric are divided up by crisscrossing bands, some terminating in dragons' heads. These again have pointed ears and are drinking out of bowls with out-stretched tongues. In the spaces between are human figures, tiny symmetrical trees with three upright pointed oval leaves, birds and four-legged animals. The dominant motif of the dragons' heads gives this fabric its name.

The central piece of the fabric is the longest and tapers around the neck. The crisscrossing, patterned bands, ending at the lower end in snakes' heads, surround the main motif: small,

stylised parasol-shaped trees under which stand symmetrically addorsed birds.

Ref.: Weixlgärtner 1926, p. 63 ff.; Grönwoldt 1977, vol. I, p. 607 ff., esp. Cat. Nos. 781—784, with further references.

The strip of lining fabric woven in tapestry technique was later overlaid with a 'more modern' red fabric. This is in all probability the fabric to be seen in Albrecht Dürer's sketch of 1510 (Albertina, Vienna) of the portrait of Charlemagne wearing the mantle in Nuremberg. The mantle is slightly open, the material showing on the right-hand side.

b) Red lining fabric
Italian, 2nd half of the 15th century
340 cms long; the strip is composed of 8 pieces sewn together and has approximately the same shape as the fabric woven in tapestry technique; i.e. it tapers in the middle around the neck and shoulders from c. 40 cms to c. 10 cms. It is a double-weave lampas. Ground: red satin; pattern: green, blue and white silk twill weave, gold brocaded. Pattern repeat: W 29 cms; the length cannot be fully distinguished; however, graphic reconstructions indicate it was probably 83 cms. Width of weave: 58 cms. Pattern: simple rows of seven-foiled pomegranate rosettes with divided stems. In the centre of the rosettes are thistle flowers, their stems

undulating bands overlaid with vegetable ornamentation; likewise the spaces in between which additionally contain lotus blossoms. The full width of the fabric was used in one length and fitted onto the surface to be covered with four smaller pieces.   R. B.

Ref.: Wardwell 1988—1989, pp. 109 f., fig.48; Wilckens 1987, p. 69.

likewise divided and overlaid with intertwining floral motives. The thistle flowers are surrounded by seven-foiled rosettes, which are decorated with smaller thistle heads, each of these occupying one of the arcs of the pomegranate rosette. Carnations decorate the outside of the rosettes. This motif is accompanied by an offset row of pomegranate rosettes, similar in form to those described above. The outsides of these rosettes, however, are decorated with small posies of flowers. In the centre of each rosette is a pomegranate upon a bed of leaves and flowers, surrounded by a cinquefoiled rosette with a wreath of flowers. The outsides of the rosettes are decorated with pomegranates surrounded by leaves and flowers. A related fabric is to be found in the Deutsche Textilmuseum in Krefeld.

Ref.: B. Tietzel, Italienische Seidengewebe des 13., 14. und 15. Jahrhunderts, Cologne 1984, p. 436.

The sections of the mantle not covered by the two narrow strips are lined with a third fabric.

c) Green lining fabric
Middle East, 13th century
325 cms long, 126 cms wide (segment of circle); lampas; ground: silk, now grey-brown, in modified rep weave; pattern: green silk in modified tabby weave, brocaded in gilt leather strip (tiny gilded leather thongs wound around a silk core). Pattern repeat: H 47 cms, W 11 cms, width of weave 89 cms. Pattern: asymmetric, ascendant

144 THE ALBA
Palermo, royal court workshop, 1181, with later additions
Silk, gold wire embroidery, pearls, emeralds, sapphires, amethysts, spinels, garnets, opals, tablet weave; 154 cms high, 127 cms wide at the hem (Inv. No. XIII 7)

A long, wide gown of yellowed silk in linen weave with an ornamented yoke applied to the breast, and ornamental bands on the forearms, cuffs and hems. The silk of the gown is probably from the 18th century. On the ornamental parts: hammered gold wire embroidery and pearl beading arranged either in straight lines or in decorative shapes. The square ornamental yoke of bright red samite lies over the shoulders and continues for a short distance down the back; together

with a wide inserted piece on the inner side of the cuffs, it is probably an addition made under Friedrich II, some time before 1220. The insertions on the cuffs display crossed bands in gold wire and pearl embroidery. The ground of the resulting sections is covered with bright red silk embroidery and intertwining geometrical motifs in gold wire embroidery alternating with single-headed eagles, none of which, however, are now complete. Obviously, this piece has been cut from a separately embroidered strip, as have presumably the older parts of the cuffs and the borders of the upper arms. On the dark-violet samite are medallions formed of rows of pearls in which figures of addorsed griffons and lions are embroidered in gold wire between small symmetrical trees. The ornamental border at the bottom of the alba consists of four individually worked parts, two of which display the same motif: on the front, on violet samite, three rows with pairs of addorsed griffons — the right part was sewn on upside down, so that the rows of pearls do not join properly; on the back, on natural coloured samite, are pairs of addorsed lions in three rows. On the upper and the lower borders of each of the four pieces of hem

trimming is, respectively, a Latin and an Arabic inscription:

+ OPERATV(M) FELICI VRBE PANORMI XV. ANNO D(OMI)NI W(ILLELMI) D(E)I GR(ATIA) REGIS SICILIE DVCAT(VS) APVLIE ET PRINCIPAT(VS) CAP(VE) FILII REGIS W(ILLELMI) INDICTIO(N)E XIIII.

(Made in the felicitous city of Palermo in the fifteenth year of the reign of William [II], by the Grace of God King of Sicily, Duke of Apulia and Prince of Capua, the son of King Wilhelm [I] in the 14th indiction). The translation of the Arabic Tulut script reads: (This belongs) *to that which was commissioned by the magnificent King Gulyalm (from the French Guillaume = William) the Second, he who is highly esteemed by God, who is supported for his power, who is victorious through his strength, the ruler of Italy, of Ankuburda* (Longobardia = Apulia), *of Qalauria* (Calabria) *and of Siqilliya* (Sicily), *the mainstay of the Imam* (Pope) *of Rumiya* (Rome), *the protector of the Christian faith, in his flourishing, eternally flowering chamber, at the time of ulian* (July?) *the fourteenth, in the year one thousand one hundred and eighty-one in the year of our Lord Jesus the Messiah.*

So much for the external appearance of the alba. Its 'inner life' is composed of many more layers, in the truest sense of the word. Between the material of the gown and the lining, which are both made of the same silk, are three further layers of fabric, the innermost layer of which is sewn between the other two. This innermost layer, which is in very poor condition, is almost certainly the oldest piece of fabric and possibly the 'original' material, dating from the period when the garment was made: unpatterned, badly yellowed samite, which has been covered like a 'relic' with more recent fabric, as is sometimes the case with ecclesiastical vestments which are associated with a particular saint. On top of this 'original' silk is white, unpatterned samite. The wax stains on it indicate that it once formed the outer side. The layer underneath consists of at least three differ-

ent, irregular pieces of silk, one of which corresponds to the one with wax stains on it. It is practically impossible to date silks such as these. Nonetheless, it is known from the records of the Nuremberg State Archive that repairs to the alba were undertaken. In 1520, for instance, it is recorded that the nuns of the convent of St. Clare covered the white dalmatic — *"which was mildewed with age"* — with white silk. And in 1619 it is reported that the tailor Paul Gademann covered the alba with 8¼ ells of white *"double taffeta"*. However, it is not possible to match these reports with the surviving fabrics.

During recent restoration work, linen insertions were discovered beneath the two bands of braiding on the upper arms and beneath one of the cuffs. They bear inscriptions in black ink in Arabic Tulut script. No agreement has yet been reached among linguists concerning their exact reading and the possible existence of a date. However, it is certain that the inscriptions were incorporated during the alteration of a garment which is quite possibly even older. Three embroiderers are mentioned, with the Arabic names of Marzuq, Ali von Malta and Muhsin, all working under the direction of a Chris-

tian called Damyan. Another Christian is mentioned as the master-craftsman Tumas (Thomas). The restoration work also brought to light a discovery in the area of the ornamental yoke. Beneath this is yet another ornamental yoke of the same size, made of purple-violet samite, which certainly constitutes the far simpler predecessor of the richly embroidered panel over it. This is indicated in particular by the gold wire embroidery running beneath the tablet weave border, i.e. in the square at the front and around the neckline.

The question remains as to the original purpose of this garment. As Fillitz established in 1955, it ought not to be compared with a liturgical alba but with an Imperial tunica, such as that worn by the sovereign in the Evangeliar of Otto III, Clm. 4453 of the Bavarian State Library in Munich fol. 24r. It has decorated hem trimmings, the same kind of braiding on the cuffs and upper arms as well as an ornamental yoke. This gown was adopted by the western Emperors from the Byzantine Basileus, who wore it with the loros (see Cat. No. 151). The alba was thus originally an overgarment and worn as such by King William II. When the Norman treasure then passed to the House of Hohenstaufen, those pieces were acquired which were missing from the existing vestments and necessary to make up a complete set of coronation robes, such as the gloves (Cat. No. 148), which were probably for the coronation of Friedrich II as Emperor. In this way, the magnificent overgarment was altered to an alba by the addition of the richly decorated yoke and the trimmings on the cuffs. The costly trimmings may originally have decorated a red gown, since red is the colour of the Basileus.   R. B.

Ref.: H. Fillitz, Die Krönungsgewänder des Heiligen Römischen Reiches und ihr Verhältnis zu Byzanz, in: Jahrbuch der Österrr. Byzantinischen Gesellschaft, vol. IV, Vienna 1955, pp. 128—130; R. Grönwoldt, Miszellen zur Textilkunst der Stauferzeit, in: Die Zeit der Staufer, Stuttgart 1979, vol. V, p. 393 ff.; T. Al Samman, Arabische Inschriften auf den Krönungsgewändern des Heiligen Römischen Reiches, in: Jahrbuch 1982, pp. 10—24; exhibition catalogue, Nürnberg — Kaiser und Reich, Staatsarchiv Nuremberg, 1986, p. 77.

145 THE BLUE DALMATICA (TUNICELLA)

Sicily, Royal workshop, 1st half of the 12th century

Blue samite, figured red samite with gold embroidery, little gold tubes, gold appliqués with cloisonné enamel and filigree, pearls, tablet weave; 141.5 cms long, width at hem 171.5 cms (Inv. No. XIII 6)

This garment is close-fitting to the waist but gains an unusual fullness in the skirt by means of the lateral insets (girons) gathered into folds at the top. The blue samite is dyed with indigo, and not, as was previously assumed, with Tyrian purple. On the hem and sleeves are broad borders of red figured samite ('incised' silk), which does not, however, correspond to the basic fabric of the coronation mantle, as was once claimed. The border round the hem is embroidered with couched gold thread: elongated palmettes, originally outlined in dark blue, with a lily at their

centres, framed with a double row of pearls at the upper and lower edges. On the right-hand side a piece measuring 40 cms has been replaced: the same red samite is embroidered with the same motif but with different gold thread and without the dark outline. The technique of the gold embroidery resembles that of the coronation mantle (Cat. No. 143) so closely that it can be assumed that it was made at the same time or soon after. On the sleeves are palmettes formed by rows of pearls, filled in with small tubes of gold, threaded together, then sewn on and finally beaten flat. This type of embroidery is unique, no other occurrence being known to date. On the cuffs, between rows of pearls, are violin-shaped appliqués with mounted cloisonné enamels which are stylistically related to those on the coronation mantle. The filigree settings correspond technically and stylistically to the two enamel roundels on the clasp of the coronation mantle, right down to the reddish patination (Cat. No. 143). On the right-hand sleeve one of the appliqués differs from the rest: two opposing drop shapes on a common ground in a filigree setting. The enamel work corresponds stylistically to that on the gloves and technically to that of

the square enamel on the mantle and the gloves (Cat. No. 148). On both sleeves two of the appliqués are divided lengthwise down the middle and fitted with interlocking hinge tubes. These can be joined by means of a small pin, thus performing the function of a fastening. Since this was not necessary here, another use for the appliqués must be assumed. The tablet weave sewn with pearls at the neck opening is the same as that on the alba. The first verifiable reference to the dalmatica is in the document of transfer to Karl IV in 1350: *"a blue gown, the arms worked with gold and pearls."*   R. B.

The red silk material of the uppers is richly embroidered with pearls in the form of a foliate pattern with tendrils. The precious stones are framed by two rows of pearls. Parts of a 5.5 cms wide tablet weave band was used on both shoes in four places: from the toes to the instep, on the heel and to the left and right below the ankle.

In 1149, the Pope granted King Roger II the privilege of wearing *"mitram et sandalia".* The tablet weave on the present shoes possibly comes from the very first or somewhat later Norman *sandalia.* It would then have been re-used for alterations made to the shoes in the early 17th century, a dating which is borne out by the construction and cut of the soles. The patterning of the braiding produces, in the narrow edging strips, a stylised tree of life with a pair of birds arranged in heraldic symmetry. In the broad middle strips are oval medallions connected by narrow straps: in those framed in green are griffons, in the red ones sirens, which are covered with pastes and pearl beading at the instep, although they are eas-

146 THE SHOES (SANDALIA)

German, 1st quarter of the 17th century; tablet weave: Palermo, 12th/13th century

Red samite, tablet weave with gold thread, pearls, amethysts, sapphires, emeralds, antique pastes (glass); soles: neat's leather; 10.8 cms high, soles 25.8 cms and 25.6 cms long (Inv. No. XIII 13)

ily distinguishable below the ankles at the side.

The striking decoration, with its double rows of pearls, suggests that it has been taken over — in altered form — from the old shoes from Sicily. There, however, the pearls were always sewn on to strips of parchment or a backing of several linen threads, in order to protect the costly silk fabric. This additional work was dispensed with in the 17th century.   R. B.

Ref.: G. Gall, Die Krönungsschuhe der deutschen Kaiser, in: Tradition und Erneuerung. Erinnerungsgabe für Friedrich Hengst zum 80. Geburtstag, ed. Erwin Stein, Frankfurt/M. 1972, p. 69 ff.

147 THE HOSE
Palermo, Royal workshop, 2nd half of the 12th century
Red silk twill, gold thread, green silk border in tapestry technique with a Tulut inscription in gilt membrane, gold braid; 60 cms long, at the top 17 and 18 cms respectively (Inv. No. XIII 12)

The gold embroidery is formed of several fine gold parallel threads couched with fine, natural-coloured silk threads. Rows of cross-shaped motifs are formed by overlapping quatrefoils, in the centre of which are small four-pointed stars. The gold thread has dropped out in some places. On the upper edge of the hose is a 7—7.2 cms wide green silk band woven in tapestry technique, with a woven Tulut inscription in gilt membrane, which translates as follows: *On the orders of the magnificent and holy King Gulyam, he that is honoured highly by God, protected by his might, victorious through His omnipotence.* The king is simply named 'William', without closer specification. However, since he is accorded the epithet "honoured highly by God", as in the inscription on the hem of the alb, which clearly refers to William II, it seems certain that the hose, too, were made for William II.

The broad, red silk ribbons to secure the hose stem from the 19th century. Delsenbach, writing in 1790, gives short thongs.   R. B.

148 THE GLOVES
Palermo, before 1220
Red samite, gold embroidery, gold appliqués in cloisonné enamel, niello plaques, pearls, rubies, sapphires, amethysts, garnets, spinels, corundums, 26.3 and 27.7 cms long, at the opening 12 cms wide (Inv. No. XIII 11)

The backs of the gloves are closely set with enamel plaques, precious stones and pearls. In between, embroidered in couched work, are tendrils and two birds in heraldic symmetry on either side of the stone below the lily. This restrained decoration creates an impression of extraordinary magnificence. The enamel plaques take various forms and display a variety of motifs. At the base of the fore and ring-fingers are small enamel plaques, each displaying a single-tailed siren, although on the right glove a sapphire has replaced one of the plaques. The fact that this was lost at an early date is confirmed by the copy of a drawing of this glove by Albrecht Dürer, today in the Museum of the Fine Arts in Budapest. Other ornamentation includes cloisonné appliqués, in the form of a fleur-de-lys, two eagle-heads and two so-called Norman shields on each glove. Below the fleur-de-lys on the left glove is a pentagonal plaque with a niello-work angel, most probably a German addition of the 14th century. This same place on the right glove is occupied by a fragment of what was possibly once an enamel star. The area which is not covered because the plaque is so small was filled in with massed pearls. The

palms of the gloves are embroidered with tendrils in couched work, and each bears an appliquéd eagle with an aureole (official symbol of the Hohenstaufen Empire) and outspread wings. In this case the gold embroidery is largely missing, thus revealing the pattern used for drawing the motif. The ends of the gauntlets are enclosed by double rows of pearls, within which, also framed by pearls, alternate enamel plaques and precious stones, together with gold embroidery. It is these enamel plaques, in particular, which stylistically match those on the border of the gown discovered in the tomb of Friedrich II's wife, Konstanze. They also correspond to the decoration on the scabbard of the ceremonial sword (Cat. No. 162) and the crown of Friedrich in Palermo. Thus the gloves may be presumed to have been originally commissioned by Friedrich II, in all probability for his coronation in 1220.

R. B.

Ref.: Deér 1952, p. 66 ff.

149 THE BELT FOR THE IMPERIAL SWORD

Sicily, 12th/13th century, the mounts are a later addition
Woven band, silk and gold, silver-gilt; 189 cms long, 6.3 cms wide (Inv. No. XIII 9)

Strictly symmetrical motifs are woven at intervals of 17 to 20 cms between two raised lines: stylised Trees of Life, with four-legged animals standing underneath and birds sitting in branches which are rolled in on themselves like volutes. Four of the motifs are repeated, two appear only once. The colours — green, red, brown and light blue — have faded almost completely. Woven along both edges at intervals of 4 to 5 cms are the letters CRISTVS RIEGHNAT CHRISTVS INQPARAT DEVS (Christ reigns — Christ rules — God). Between the letters S·I·N·Q·P are four silver-gilt bars fastened with rivets and perforated in the middle for the tongue of the buckle. The buckle is riveted to the belt with a clover leaf-shaped mount, as is the mount at the other end of the belt.

R. B.

Ref.: J. Fingerlin, Gürtel des hohen und des späten Mittelalters, Munich/Berlin 1971, p. 475, no. 545.

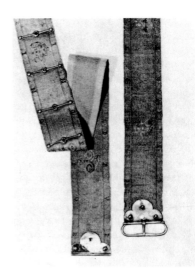

150 THE CINGULUM

Sicily, 12th century
Blue samite, red, yellow, white and blue
threads of silk and gold, garnets,
pearls, gold filigree plaques; 149.3 cms
long, 3.2—3.8 cms wide (Inv. No. XIII
10)

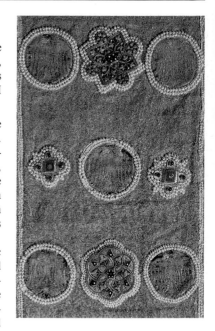

The cingulum served as a girdle for the
garments worn beneath the mantle.
Attached to the left and right of the inside, at intervals of 36.8 and 37 cms,
are red silk cords, by which the girdle
was fastened. The ends of the cingulum
thus hang freely, and for that reason
are decorated on both sides with pearls
and filigree work.

The pattern on the plaques — the basic
motif is an eight-pointed star, inscribed
in a rectangle — is characteristic of Islamic decorative art. At the edges, the
cingulum is embellished with two interwoven cords made of threads of red
silk and gold.   R. B.

151 THE STOLA

Italian, 2nd quarter of the 14th century
Yellow silk: louisine, patterned with
black silk (eagles) and gold thread,
pearls, silver-gilt appliqués with granu-
lation, champlevé enamels in silver,
cloisonné enamels in gold, glass stones;
599—602 cms long, 21—23 cms wide
(Inv. No. XIII 8)

The gold threads form a delicate foliate
pattern. The black silk used for the
eagles has largely dropped out. Alternating with the eagle medallions are
smaller and larger stelliform appliqués,
all of which are edged with a double
row of pearls. It is certain that the appliqués originated in Italy (Venice?) at
the same time as the gold fabric. The
enamels in the appliqués are underlaid
with several layers of paper, cut precisely to shape and covered with writing.
The Latin characters that have been
preserved can be dated to the 14th century, probably to the second quarter.
All the rows of pearls and the greater
part of the appliqués are underlaid
with parchment to protect the costly
silk cloth. Three slender tassels of
green, blue and brown silks, held together with plaited strings of pearls,
are sewn to each of the shorter sides;
traces indicate that originally there
were probably four of these tassels.
The stola is made up of eight pieces of
differing sizes cut from the same
material, whereby the fabric was not always sewn along the warp thread. The
faded red silk lining, which is visible
from the front of the stola, probably
dates from the 18th century.

The form of the stola derives from the
loros, a broad sash, mostly richly ornamented with precious stones, pearls
and embroidery, which the Byzantine
emperors wore over the shoulder and
around the hips, one end falling to the
hem of their robes and the other
draped loosely over the left forearm. In
the Book of Ceremonies of Emperor
Constantine VII, the symbolic significance of the *loros* is explained: it
was wound around the body like the
sindon of Christ and thus symbolised
his Entombment; however, since it also
gleams with gold, it simultaneously
symbolises the glory of his Resurrection. (Deér 1977, p. 24 f.)

The Viennese stola was probably made

in the 14th century and modelled on the Norman *loros,* which had perhaps been badly damaged. The memory of the imperial sash eventually faded and the stola was accorded the same status as that belonging to the liturgical vestments. In the ordo of 1289 dealing with the coronation of King Charles II of Anjou (1285—1309), it is written that he received after his anointment a *"precious robe similar to the dalmatic and over this something richly ornamented similar to the stola".* The 'robe' and *loros* are thus compared to the dalmatica and stola but not accorded the same status. The first attested reference to a stola being worn by the German King is in 1308, at the coronation of Heinrich VII. In 1338, Ludwig of Bavaria wore a stola crossed in liturgical fashion and decorated with 'arms' when he met the English king at Constance. The 'arms' could refer to the eagle medallions. It is not until 1350 that the first documented reference is made to the existence of a *"stola worked with gold, fine stones and with pearls"* in the Imperial Treasury, which could be identical to the one displayed here, as well as *"another stola without stones",* which has been lost. This is likely to be the second stola listed by Delsenbach in 1790. The stola displayed here is without doubt the one referred to in the document of transfer to King Sigismund of 1423 as *"a long stola, golden with eagles and pearls."*

R. B.

Ref.: P. E. Schramm, Von der Trabea des römischen Kaisers über das Lorum des byzantinischen Basileus zur Stola der abendländischen Herrscher, in: Festschrift Adolf Hofmeister, Halle 1955; Deér 1977, p. 24 ff., 44 ff., 52 f.

152 THE EAGLE DALMATIC

Southern Germany, 1330/1340
Fabric: Chinese, c. 1300
Red silk damask twill, silk and gold embroidery, pastes (glass); front 165 cms, back 160 cms long, 138 cms wide at the hem (Inv. No. XIII 15)

Contrary to generally accepted opinion, this Chinese silk damask is not in fact dyed with purple but with archil brightened with madder-lake (plant pigment). The pattern of the fabric here displays a typically Chinese continuous ring of clouds, in between which are double-framed lozenges each with a dot in the centre. 68 eagle medallions have been sewn on over the whole of the gown. The single-headed eagle, embroidered in black silk, in places missing, and the couched gold of the ground are embroidered and appliquéd to the linen. The eagle's eyes, some of which are still extant, consist of black strass. Eagles of a similar design are also found on the stola, which was made around the same time (Cat. No. 151).

Around the neckline, armholes, cuffs and the lower hem, as well as on both of the lateral slits, embroidery in split stitch and couching has been applied to a linen backing: between quatrefoil medallions are foliate designs of acanthus, oak and vine leaves. In the medallions around the neck are six crowned busts of sovereigns, wearing stoles with crosses. The remaining 34 medallions show kings and emperors in three-quarter figures with sceptre and imperial orb. Their insignia, embroidered in gold, stand out in relief from the ground. It is possible that they represent a dynastic series, although no satisfactory interpretation has yet been given. To the dalmatica belonged a capuche-like hood, made of the same fabric, and likewise adorned with eagle medallions and an embroidered border with 7 half-length portraits of crowned sovereigns. Delsenbach, in 1790, still includes a reproduction of it, but since then it has been lost. The dalmatica is first mentioned in the document of transfer, dated 1350, as a *"brown gown with black eagles and a cowl"*. It is not recorded whether it was used for coronations, although in a drawing dating from 1510 Albrecht Dürer depicts Charlemagne dressed in the eagle dalmatic, stola and imperial mantle. It is conceivable that, like the stola, it was made for Ludwig of Bavaria.   R. B.

Ref.: E. Heinemayer, Süddeutsche Stickereien des 13. und 14. Jhs., Diss. Munich 1958, pp. 47—52; D. De Jonghe/M. Tavernier, Maria von Bourgondie, Bruges 1982; De textielresten uit graf 6, p. 216; Wilckens 1987, p. 77.

153 THE IMPERIAL CROWN

Western German, 2nd half of the 10th century; the cross is an addition from the early 11th century; the arch dates from the reign of Emperor Konrad II (1024—1039); the red velvet cap is from the 18th century
Gold, cloisonné enamel, precious stones, pearls; the brow plate 14.9 cms high, 11.2 cms wide; the cross 9.9 cms high (Inv. No. XIII 1)

The inscriptions are arranged according to the depictions on the enamelled plates: on the back right plate REX DAVID bears a banderole with the verse from the psalms: HONOR REGIS IVDICIVM DILIGIT (The honourable king delighteth in judgement). On the front right plate REX SOLOMON bears one of his own proverbs: TIME DOMINVM ET RECEDE A MALO (Fear the Lord and depart from evil). The inscription on the Majestas Domini plate (front left) is also taken from the Proverbs of Solomon: PER ME REGES REGNANT (By me kings reign). The back left plate displays a banderole with the prophecy: ECCE ADICIAM SVPER DIES TVOS XV ANNOS (Behold, I will add unto thy days fifteen years). On the back of the cross in the upper field of the rood is the inscription: IHC NAZARENVS REX IVDEORVM (Jesus Christ of Nazareth, King of the Jews). The eight-lobed high arch bears the inscription in tiny pearls: CHVONRADUS DEI GRATIA / ROMANORV(M) IMPERATOR AVG (VSTVS) — (Konrad, by the grace of God Emperor of the Romans and Augustus).

Eight hinged plates of differing sizes form the octagonal body of the Imperial crown. Two horizontal iron bands reinforce the body on the inside, thus maintaining the regularity of the octagon. The brow plate, although wider than the others, is the same height as the neck plate, while the two temple plates are slightly smaller. These four main plates are closely set with precious stones and pearls. The remaining plates in between, which are clearly lower than the main plates but all of equal size, bear pictorial representations in cloisonné enamel.

The arch spans the crown, mounted in sockets affixed to the brow and neck plates. The arch consists of eight flat lobes in ajouré work with inscriptions on both sides. In its present form it derives from an addition made in the reign of Konrad II. The cross, affixed to the top of the brow plate, dates from the reign of Heinrich II, and was thus also not part of the original crown.

The neck plate and the two temple plates were originally each set with three club-shaped pearls attached to

tiny horizontal tubes (still extant) on the inside of the plates. In addition to this, pendant chains, known as pendilia, which were set with precious stones, were attached to the lower edge of the temple plates. Originally, a mitre would have been worn under the octagon of the crown, a sign of sovereignty deriving from the vestments of the Jewish high priests. It was probably made of white material and indented above the crown to accomodate the metal arch.

The brow and neck plates of the crown are both set with twelve large gemstones in raised settings arranged in three vertical rows. Probably in order to allow more light to reach the stones and thus increase their luminosity, perforations were made in the bedplates. Held by three-toed claws, the cabochon stones seem to float, suffused with light, on the surface of the bedplate. Their raised settings comprise two parts: a base of tiny cylindrical columns supports an airy 'basket' of gold wire beading which encloses the irregular stones.

18 large pearls on tiny turrets of gold wire beading form a continuous pattern around the stones, rather like the five points on a die, a formal motif deriving from late antique tradition. The colour combination of green blue and white on the other hand, had from time immemorial been the exclusive preserve of the Byzantine Emperor and his next of kin. To the primary gemstones in each plate are added 14 smaller stones, together with four gold beads on cylindrical shafts, an ornament which had been adopted from Carolingian art. The remaining surface of the ground is covered with a pattern of gold filigree. On each temple plate, 72 stones and pearls of varying size are arranged around a single large emerald, the more important stones being mounted over perforations.

The cloisonné enamel plaques on the four intermediate plates are interrelated in terms of symbolic content. The figures are named in the inscriptions and banderoles explain their significance.

David — both King of Israel and prophet, like his son and successor, Solomon — symbolises justice; King Solomon stands for wisdom and the fear of God; Isaiah prophesies a further 15 years of life to King Hezekiah who has prayed to God as he lies on his deathbed. The ruler trusts in divine mercy, and his long life vouchsafes to his people peace and justice. Christ, portrayed as the Ruler of the Universe and flanked by two seraphim, the highest beings in the hierarchy of the angels, here represents the Holy Trinity. He is the "King of kings", the celestial Emperor, represented in the earthly empire by the emperor until the Day of Judgement. The sovereign rules, chosen by the grace of God in the sign of the Cross. All of the Bible texts in the inscriptions are quotations from the coronation liturgy. The wearer of the crown was chosen to rule by God; this was due neither to his own merits nor to the hallowed right of blood-lineage. The most important qualities of a good ruler are emphasised by means of exemplary models. The artistic influence at work in the enamel images of the Imperial Crown is almost certainly Byzantine. The technique of cloisonné enamelling itself had in all probability been taken over directly from the East. Besides the use of the cloisonné technique where both subject and background are shown in enamel, the goldsmiths also took over another cloisonné technique consisting of an enamelled representation on a gold ground. It is this technique that was used for the plaques of the Imperial crown.

Because of its intrinsic value, gold has always enjoyed an exceptional status. As well as its qualities as a rare, non-corroding and immutable precious metal, it also possesses a spiritual dimension: a gold ground has always been seen as a symbol of transcendental light. In the radiance of the gold, divine light is tangibly transmuted into light that is immediately perceivable to the senses. Apart from the Carolingian gold mosaics, the cloisonné enamel plaques of the Imperial Crown are perhaps the earliest evidence of the momentous appearance of the ceremonious gold light of Byzantine art north of the Alps. From this time onwards, gold light became indigenous in the West and the gold ground remained a means of conveying the sacral sphere of images until the end of the Middle Ages.

The master who created these cloisonné enamels also attempted to continue the Byzantine conception of the relation between the body and the drapery covering it. This assumes the greatest importance here. It was the Greeks who had discovered the art of draping figures while simultaneously suggesting the body behind them.

The principle of 'wet drapery' was continued in Byzantine art, whereby the drapery assumed a predominant life of its own. From then on the folds and hems of the drapery form a linear system which only permits isolated parts of the body to appear. In the cloisonné enamelling of the Imperial Crown, the folds of the garments form the cloisons; this simultaneously results in the surface of the figures being divided into a decorative segmental pattern.

What in fact constituted the independent achievement made by this Western artist to the art of cloisonné enamelling? In the Christian world, it was the book, i.e. the Bible, which alone counted as the witness of the promise of redemption. In the use of the word bible, which in its original sense simply meant scroll, the equating of book and Holy Scriptures becomes apparent. The prominence given to the scrolls on the enamels proclaims the veneration of the message of salvation. The creative impulse lay in the interaction of word and image, letter and figure, the interpenetrating elements of image and script. Thus the banderoles held by the Kings and Prophets of the Old Testament supply the conceptual aspect, i.e. that which is not immediately perceivable to the senses. In contrast to the identifying titles, the 'scripture' is not simply letters on a gold background; the motto, in the pictorial form of a banderole, is conceived as a tangible and concrete object. This concretisation derives from an antique concept. Similarly, the idea of the biblical kings and prophets as a type of authorial 'portrait' also derives from ancient traditions. What is new and specifically mediaeval here is the idea of making the figures quite literally the bearers of their own words. One could say that in the enamel plaques a sort of speaking image arises, an effective merging of image and word.

Ottonian art soon freed itself from the perspective of late classical and Carolingian illusionism which we encounter in its purest form in the images of the Evangelists in the Coronation Evangeliary. What now develops is a treatment of the representation in a pattern of interposed layers. On the pictorial plaques of the Imperial Crown the figures stand out clearly against the blank purity of the gold ground as isolated areas of colour. This is reinforced by the new structural principle, the figures themselves combining into blocks.

Ceremonial representations tend of themselves towards frontality. The ceremonial display seen in the representations of King David and King Solomon is surpassed by the representation of the Godhead itself, the Majestas Domini. Flanked by the six-winged seraphim, the Almighty sits enthroned in strict frontality, his right hand raised in blessing, his left hand supporting the Holy Scriptures. Of all these figures, only that of God bears no banderole. The motto on this plate occupies the space where the figures in the other enamels are named. Even in the plaque with Isaiah and Ezekiah, where the scene could have been translated into a composition that unfolds laterally, the frontal impact of the image is immediate. Comparison with the small number of other Ottonian enamels that have survived shows that the cloisonné enamels of the Imperial Crown were heavily influenced by Byzantine models. Taking into account the subsequent history of the Ottonian style, these enamels can be placed at the beginning of its development. The portrayal of the figures of Christ's forefathers and their juxtaposition with the Ruler of the Universe himself emphasise the typological and allegor-

ical aspects. Thus a dense complex of salvational concepts are given pictorial expression. The exemplary figures of the divinely-chosen kings and prophets of the Old Testament represent a theocratic concept of sovereignty, in the sense of divine sovereignty. The Roman Empire *(imperium Romanum)* was regarded as the imperfect image of the celestial empire. Finally, the emperor appears with the universal claim to exercise his office as Christ's proxy by the grace of God. The sovereign subordinates himself to the dual kingship of Christ, the eternal High Priest and eternal Ruler of the Universe.

All emperors were accorded apostolate dignity, following Byzantine tradition. This is symbolised in the disposition of the gemstones on the brow plate, discussed below.

As Vicar of Christ, the emperor embodied sovereign dignity *(regnum)* and sacral priesthood *(sacerdotium)*. When sovereign office is conceived as divine mission, the distinction between the office of ruler and that of priest disappears.

The typological interpretation refers to the relationship between the ideal figures chosen to God and to the ruler. By juxtaposing these prototypes of God-given sovereignty with Christ himself, the nexus of salvational and temporal history in the divine act of redemption is given vivid pictorial expression. The key to a true understanding of the doctrine of salvation lies in the cross; thus it stands above the brow of the ruler. On the outside, it takes the form of the triumphal *crux gemmata,* the jewelled Cross of Victory. On the back the Redeemer is depicted with his wounds bleeding, and yet with his eyes open as a sign of his victory over death. The programmatic conception of the crown thus forms the fundament of the ruler's claim to universal temporal power by the grace of God and to his unique position in the history of salvation.

The programmatic, theological conception of the crown is developed in the more prominent of the stone-encrusted plates. The twelve precious stones on the brow plate correspond to the number of the apostles. The twelve stones on the neck plate refer to the pectoral of the Jewish High Priest, the stones of which were engraved with the names of the Twelve Tribes of Israel. The Ottonian emperors not only elevated their status by placing themselves in the succession of biblical kings and prophets, as it were incorporating them into their genealogy as ideal, exemplary models.

They also saw themselves as successors to the office of High Priest and thus as equals of the apostles. Previous interpretation of the programmatic significance of the stones, including the temple plates, has construed the Imperial Crown, according to its number symbolism and the mystic attributes of the stones, both as an allegory of the Celestial City of Jerusalem and as a symbol of redemption. The allegorism of gemstones is always polyvalent. Previous theories relating to the number symbolism have suffered from the flaw that there was always one part of the crown that was excluded and the fact that we have no evidence as to the original number of stones.

In place of the heart-shaped sapphire at the top of the arch of the brow plate, there was once the 'Waise' (Orphan; the word derives from the Byzantine state jewel, called the *orphanos*), the fabled 'guiding stone' of the Imperial Crown. This stone was last mentioned in an inventory of 1350, and subsequently lost. A pen-and-ink drawing of around 1510 by Albrecht Dürer already shows the sapphire. Another interpretation of the word *'Waise'* as the 'stone of wisdom' first occurs in the poetry of Walter von der Vogelweide in 1198. In this context the *'Waise'* is made to stand for the crown itself. In the epic of Duke Ernst, also written around 1200, the legend is related of how the Duke presents to Emperor Otto that miraculous gem, the "Orphan", which one could see in his *"rîches krone"* (Imperial Crown). This is also the first mention of this crown as the Imperial crown.

The *'Waise'* was probably a precious opal, a stone highly prized since antiquity. It was valued both for its luminosity and for its property of uniting the colours of all precious gems and thus their qualities. Judging by allegorical allusions made to it, the 'Waise' seems to have been regarded as a symbol of Christ. It must therefore have had dual significance in order to fulfil the apostolic correspondence of the brow plate.

In summary, it can be said that the Imperial Crown is the realisation of a programmatic, christological conception. The interpretation of its symbolic significance remains problematic, on the one hand since mystic or allegorical interpretations always risk assuming content and motives which had no validity when the piece was made. On the other hand, historians attempting to establish concrete parameters for a dating have written of *"the rather pro-*

pagandistic symbolism of the Imperial crown'', which would seem to suggest that it was made at a time of conflict. However, there is no reason why it should not have been made for the coronation of Otto the Great as Emperor in 962, or for the coronation of his son, Otto II as co-emperor, which took place in Rome at Christmas in the year 967, to mention only the most likely occasions. There is, however, no reliable evidence for any particular ac-

Coin depicting Emperor Constantine, 313 A.D
(Staatliche Münzsammlung, Munich)

tuality or concrete historical situation. In conclusion, the question arises of to what extent the theological interpretation, which derives its arguments mainly from the relation of the emperor to his perfect ideal, Christ the Ruler of the Universe, overlays the pre-Christian, antique origin of this 'symbol'.

As an insignia, the crown is in itself the highest sign of human elevation. Even though the roots of some forms of insignia and their original purpose were no longer known, the traditional forms of the 'symbol' speak their own, unmistakeable language. The form of the crown can be traced back to the types of headcovering worn in times of peace and war by the Roman emperors from late antiquity onwards. The circlet of the crown developed out of the jewelled diadem worn in times of peace. The armour of the Emperor-General included a helmet: its decoration survives in the arch of the crown, here signifying universal dominion. The pendant pen-

dilia probably also derive from the diadem of the ceremonial armour. At least according to pictorial evidence, crowns bearing crosses have existed ever since the 8th century. And yet a coin from 313 — minted one year after his victory ''under the sign of the Cross'' — depicts Constantine the Great wearing a helmet with a christogramme above the brow. The coin also displays the helmet ornament which eventually developed into the eight-lobed arch of the Imperial Crown.

As a crown consisting of plates with accentuated ornamentation at the brow and high arch, the Imperial Crown is the oldest crown combining all the imperial elements. It is the only extant crown to combine plates decorated with cloisonné enamels and those set with gemstones.

The basic form of the octagon goes back to numerous works of imperial ceremony. For the classical world, the number eight signified perfection. The early Christian Church took this perfect interpenetration of two squares as a symbol of Rebirth in Baptism and of the Resurrection. Emperor Charlemagne had the Palatine chapel at Aix-la-Chapelle, which was destined to be his place of burial, built in the form of an octagon. It was there, on his marble throne, that all the Roman-German kings from Otto I onwards were to be enthroned. In its octagonal form consisting of four large and four smaller plates, the Imperial Crown recalls one of the shapes used for the imperial Byzantine crowns.

It has become clear that kingly sovereignty (regnum) and priesthood (sacerdotium), the dual mission of the divinely protected earthly empire (imperium), attain in the Imperial Crown a formal and symbolic synthesis. Thus it is truly a 'symbol' of the empire. However, the claim, based on its underlying spiritual concept, that it was profounder and more significant than other works of art from the Ottonian period cannot be sustained.

Much remains unclear, ambiguous, even contradictory, in particular with regard to the significance of the gemstones. Thus it is difficult to overlook

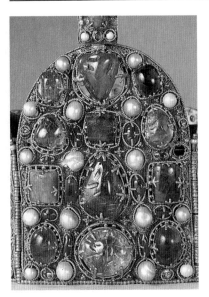

the fact that in a work of art rooted in a hierarchically based view of the world the representation of God appears merely on a subordinate plate. In its formal position of rank it is by far surpassed by the jewelled brow plate. The *'Waise'* would then have stood in dual function for Christ, who appears a third time on the back of the cross, again in figural representation. The symbolism and hierarchy of the stones was given precedence over the representational world of images.

Contemporary chroniclers have attested to the hierarchy of the insignia. In the Ottonian and Salian periods, the Imperial Crown was by far surpassed in importance as an insigne by the Holy Lance and later the Particle of the Cross. It has not yet been possible to localise the workmanship of the crown convincingly.   H. T.

Ref.: Weixlgärtner 1926, p. 18 ff.; Schramm-Mütherich 1962, no. 67; R. Staats, Theologie der Reichskrone. Ottonische ''Renovatio Imperii'' im Spiegel einer Insignie, in: Monographien zur Geschichte des Mittelalters, vol. 13, Stuttgart 1976; G. Wolf, Der ''Waise''. Bemerkungen zum Leitstein der Wiener Reichskrone, in: Deutsches Archiv, Jg. 41, 1985, p. 39 ff.: Fillitz 1986, no. 1; Kugler 1986.

154 THE IMPERIAL CROSS
Western German, c. 1024/25
Oak foundation, covered with red fabric and plated with gold foil, precious stones in raised mountings, pearls; back and side walls: niello, iron pin for use as a processional cross; 77.5 cms high, 70.8 cms wide (Inv. No. XIII 21)

Base of the Cross: Prague, 1352
Silver-gilt, enamel; 17.3 cms high, overall height of the standing cross: 95.2 cm

This cross potent with square beam-ends originally served as a receptacle for the Imperial relics. Parts of the front, which is set with precious stones, could be lifted as plates and at one time revealed the relics hidden in recesses in the wooden foundation: in the cross-beam was the Holy Lance, in the shaft were particles of the Cross and in the two compartments of the beam-ends were further relics.

Along the side walls of the Imperial Cross runs the inscription: ECCE CRVCEM DOMINI FVGIAT PARS HOSTIS INIQVI. HINC, CHVONRADE, TIBI CEDANT OMNES INIMICI. (May the supporters of the Evil One take flight before this Cross of Our Lord. Hence may all adversaries [also] yield before thee, Konrad).

At the base of the cross is the inscription: ANNO MILLENO TERCIO QVINQVAGENO SECVNDO KAROLVS AVGVSTVS ROMANVS REXQVE BOHEMVS HOC LIGNVM DOMINI TALI PEDE SIC DECORAVIT. (In the year 1352, Karl, Roman Emperor and King of Bohemia, ordered the wood [of the cross] of Our Lord to be embellished with this pedestal).

At first glance, it might seem strange that implements of the passion and their reliquary have come to be part of the Imperial Treasure and, moreover, that the reliquary itself is in the form of a cross. However, the reasons for this will become clearer if we attempt to visualise the historical situation.

Veneration of the relics of the suffering and death of the Lord goes back to early Christian times. The relics were

interpreted as a sign of Jesus Christ's accession to power: *"His suffering became his triumph"*, preached Pope Leo the Great; the conqueror of death emerges as the *"God who terrifies the world"* (Paulinus of Nola). The redemptory aspect therefore provides one reason for the luxurious design of the reliquary case and its transformation into a sign of victory. Another is that, according to the traditional conception of Christian sovereignty, only the Emperor was entitled to possess a bejewelled cross, because it symbolised Christ's rulership of the Universe and thus absolute sovereignty, which was not simply bestowed by divine right, as in the case of the temporal ruler.

Just as the imperial relics were certainly regarded as a pledge of 'salvation' and the sovereign's power of victory *per se,* so the powerful appearance of the Imperial cross was intended to express, with the same force of conviction, a sacral correspondence between the immanent power of the relics and their protective case.

The distinct form of the cross derives from the harmonious relationship of the square ends of the beams to the larger area in the middle. Each of the square beam ends forms a many-layered decorative shield, heightening the composition as a whole. They are subdivided into circular plates upon arched tendril-structures. The stones themselves — mystical powers and virtues were attributed to them in the Middle Ages — are raised on translucent arcades of beaded filigree wire, together with their frame mountings, creating the effect of little domed structures when seen from an angle. Down the middle of the limbs of the cross are four continuous rows of pearls, flanked on either side by precious stones and larger pearls in raised settings.

Symbolic concepts of sovereignty determine every part of the form, as can be seen in the hierarchical gradation of the formal composition of the mounted stones. The resulting tension between the clarity of the whole and the sumptuous wealth of its parts remained unsurpassed. The inventive-

ness of Ottonian goldsmithery attains its peak in the jewellery on the *crux gemmata* side of the Imperial cross.

Also discernible in the Imperial cross is the emphasis on the christological idea of victory which sees Christ as the divine king and priest who returns to judge the world, for whom the emperor is called upon to be the representative in the temporal realm. On the side walls we encounter the monumental inscription, written as a couplet in hexameters, which names the donor and makes reference to Constantine's promise of victory, a traditional dedicatory concept (see below). As a variation of the text referring to the raising of the cross in the antiphony at vespers, we find written: *"May the supporters of the Evil One take flight before this Cross of Our Lord. Hence may all adversaries"* (also) *"yield before thee, Konrad"*. The name refers to Konrad II, early in whose reign the case of the cross was added as his donation to the imperial treasure. The old idea of the shimmering, escatological cross had obviously lost none of its fascination, for even the nielloed pictorial programme on the shimmering gold back announces the cosmic world supremacy of Christ Resurrected. For the purpose of illustration, individual motifs have been adopted from St. John's divine visions of the apocalypse: the Lamb of God stands on the sealed scroll which only *It* is capable of reading, holding staff of the cross as its victory symbol. This symbol contains a distinct reference to Christ's sacrificial death as a precondition for being elevated to his place at the right hand of the Father and to the office of Judge at the Last Judgement. With the opening of the seal on the scroll, the end of the world will begin; with the return of Christ the promise of the life to come will be fulfilled. Four winged beings extol the *agnus dei* as a symbol of glory and present *It* with their books. As symbols for the Evangelists, the four beings signify at the same time the Evangelium; this extends in all four directions of heaven, towards which the symbols of the evangelists at the end of the

beams of the cross are also pointing. The apostles appear on thrones, as assistant judges at the Last Judgement and co-regents in the realm of God. However, under the leadership of the Princes of the Apostles, Peter and Paul, they also represent the community of the redeemed in its entirety.

As early as 348 A.D., St. Cyril, Bishop of Jerusalem, mentions that *"the whole world is now full of pieces of the Holy Cross, which exists here with us and from which Christians detach particles by reason of their belief."* From reports of pilgrimages to the Holy Land, which first occur in the middle of the 6th century A.D., we know that *"the lance with which Christ was pierced in the side was placed in a wooden cross in the atrium of the Basilica of Constantine."* This served as the model for the Imperial cross.

Before the decisive battle against his rival Maxentius at the Milvian Bridge in A.D. 312, a cross of light appeared to Constantine the Great with the promise that he would be victorious under this sign; and on the day after the vision Constantine did in fact achieve victory beneath a banner bearing the monogramme of Christ *(labarum)*. After that, soldiers fighting under the protection of the cross achieved their victories in the name of Christ; from this event a Christian-imperial cult of the Emperor developed in both the east and the west of the divided *imperium Romanum.* Furthermore, the idea of the reverence of the cross in general also goes back to the holy Emperor Constantine, for it was through him and his mother, St. Helen, that the True Cross was rediscovered. Thus at the tomb of St. Peter in Old St. Peter's Emperor Constantine donated, among other things, a monumental gold cross with a dedicatory inscription referring to himself and his mother and the victory he had achieved with divine help. This tradition of the Constantinian inscription was still alive at the time when the Imperial cross was made.

Sometime before 450 A.D., on the place on the hill of Golgotha near Jerusalem where the crucifixion of Christ had taken place, Emperor Theodosius II ordered the restoration of the great jewelled Constantinian (?) gold cross which had been erected in memory of the Lord's victory. Since it was distinguished as a *crux gemmata,* or jewelled cross, this cross was regarded as being a symbol of divine power, a monument representing the power and sovereignty of the emperor in an exemplary way. The *crux gemmata* originated from the fusion of the late-Roman imperial *idea triumphans* with the Christian symbol of victory, the cross.

In the 6th century, Justinian II and his wife Sophia donated a jewelled cross with a round capsule inserted at the point of intersection of the beams, containing a particle of the True Cross (St. Peter's, Rome). In the dedicatory text, which refers to the fact that the relics themselves were an assurance of victory through the victory of Christ on the cross, the donors are also named. As in the case of the Imperial cross, the representation of the Lamb of God, the *Agnus Dei,* decorates the back of the central capsule; the symbol of the lamb stands for the Passion of Christ.

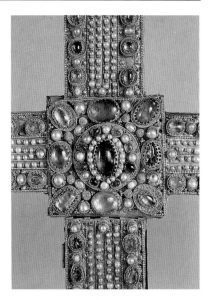

The Constantinian tradition lasted well into Carolingian times. During the *renovatio romani imperii,* the 'Carolingian renaissance', Charlemagne regarded his emperorship as a sovereign office in the succession of Constantine: as the invincible conquerer of the heathen — as which he was always ready to take to the field against the infidels under the standard of the Cross which had even conquered death — and as a worshipper of the cross in accordance with his religious orientation. In the *libri Carolini,* a polemical treatise with political implications, it is written: *"With the standard of the cross the ancient Evil Fiend was vanquished . . . the cross is the insigne of our king, which the legions of our army behold continuously. Our host follows the cross into battle."*

Another jewelled cross which also once contained a particle of the Cross, but which has long since disappeared (only the elaborate pedestal is known from reproductions), must have had the same significance as a state monument for the Carolingian concept of empire. Its inscription relates that one Einhard donated the (triumphal) arch to serve as the bearer of the pledge of eternal victory. This Einhard, a learned clergyman and Charlemagne's historian, also seems to have worked as an artist himself, because he was compared to Beseleel, the architect of the Tabernacle and maker of the Ark of the Covenant in the Old Testament. The style and christological iconography of the Einhard cross must have been close

to that of the Viennese coronation evangeliar. What makes this even more significant is the fact that it was supposed to have been Einhard who summoned to the court of Charlemagne the foreigners who created the miniatures for the coronation evangeliar (Cat. No. 157).

The continuity of the Carolingian link to Constantine can be traced further to Spain. On all the gold crosses from Asturias dating from the 9th century, the Constantine assurance of victory by the grace of God is repeated using the same Latin formula. Through Charlemagne's exceptional achievements and successes, fundamental questions were decided in advance even for his successors.

Convincing localisation of the Imperial cross has not yet been established. As the inscription informs us, Emperor Karl IV commissioned a plain, smooth pedestal for the cross in 1352, in Prague, his city of residence. On its long sides is the escutcheon with the Imperial eagle, on its narrow sides the heraldic shield with the Bohemian lion.

H. T.

Ref.: Weixlgärtner 1926, p. 32 ff.; Schramm/Mütherich 1962, no. 145; Hauck 1974, p. 143—205, especially p. 170 ff.; Schramm/Fillitz 1978, no. 37; Schwineköper 1981, p. 237 f.; Fritz 1982, p. 221; Fillitz 1986, no. 2. ff.: Fillitz 1986, no. 1; Kugler 1986.

155 THE HOLY LANCE

Carolingian, 8th century
Steel, iron, brass, silver, gold, leather;
50.7 cms long (Inv. No. XIII 19)

Inscription on the (covered) silver band: CLAVVS DOMINICVS †
HEINRICVS D(E)I GR(ATI)A TER-
CIVS ROMANO(RVM) IMPERA-
TOR AVG(VSTVS) HOC AR-
GENTVM IVSSIT FABRICARI AD
CONFIRMATIONE(M) CLAVI
D(OMI)NI ET LANCEE SANCTI
MAVRICII.SANCTVS MAVRITIVS.
(Nail of the Lord † Heinrich by God's
grace the Third, Roman Emperor, Au-
gustus, ordered this silver (band) to be
made in order to strengthen the Nail of
the Lord and the Lance of St. Maurice.
Saint Maurice.)
Inscription on the gold sleeve: † LAN-
CEA ET CLAVVS DOMINI (Lance
and Nail of the Lord).
The Holy Lance is a Carolingian
winged lance with perforated work of
incomparable execution: a pointed,
oval aperture has been chiselled out of
the centre of the blade and a forged

ornamental iron pin inserted. The so-
called 'knotted pin' was further embellished by the insertion of a piece of
metal. Half-moon-shaped segments of
this are visible between the 'knots' of
the pin. At the lower end of the blade
of the lance are two blades which were
added to the lance later and which extend to the wings of the lance and are
tied to it with narrow leather thongs.
Peter Paulsen has identified them as
two knives dating from the 7th or 8th
century.
As such, the Holy Lance belonging to
the Imperial insignia is very likely identical to the Holy Lance in the possession of Otto I described by Luitprand
of Cremona in his History, completed
in 961. The probability that they are
identical is increased by Luitprand's
description of the Holy Lance as having *"on its blade crosses* (formed) *of
the nails which were driven through the
hands and feet of Our Lord Jesus
Christ."* The Treasury Holy Lance does
indeed have crosses inlaid in brass on
the knots of the pin and additionally
on the wings of the lance. Tiny reliquary particles of the Nails of the
Cross could have been forged into the
lance in the shape of a cross for identification.
Luitprand's description is more con-
sonant with the actual data than the
mention of a Nail of the Cross in the
inscription on the silver band which
Heinrich IV had made a century later.
A Nail of the Cross of this kind is not
present here. A tradition must have
grown up over the centuries — obviously determined by the wishful thinking of the lance's owners — whereby
the particles of various Nails of the
Cross became the one *clavus domini*
that the iron pin was held to be. Furthermore, the mention of the spear of
St. Maurice in the Salian inscription
could be connected with the character
of the Holy Lance as a dual relic and
the two flanking knife blades connected to the increasing veneration of St.
Maurice as patron saint of the empire.
There is evidence that relics were transferred as early as the 8th century from
the Burgundian seat of the Theban
order, St. Maurice d'Agaune, to the old

Frankish lands. The size of the relic or particles thereof was of relative unimportance for the mediaeval mind; much more important were the proofs of its power to perform miracles. Luitprand himself, who had spent some time at the Byzantine court as ambassador, and the court prelates of Otto I knew perfectly well that the Lance of Longinus was in the possession of the Byzantine emperors. This was the lance that had pierced the side of the Lord and been bathed in the Blood of Christ and was thus revered as one of the most precious relics of the Redeemer's Passion. The Byzantine emperors possessed an incomparable treasure of holy relics, which they kept in the Pharos palace chapel in Constantinople, as a guarantee of their victories. In Byzantium, as in antiquity, imperial power was regarded as divinely sanctioned if it had been proved by victory in battle.

It would seem that the Ottonian dynasty, which was at this time beginning to consolidate its power, felt the urge to set up the victory-bringing insigne of the Holy Lance as a state relic of equal status to those believed to guarantee the supremacy of the imperial Byzantine monarchy. The grounds for this impulse correspond to the concept of sovereignty which springs from the ancient god-kings and priest-kings of the Old Testament, while simultaneously regarding the lance as the true weapon and insigne of the Germanic stem dukes and also moving towards the Christian concept of the divine right of kings.

As an experienced courtier, Luitprand gives in his History several intimations of the correct view of the Holy Lance, i.e. that desired at the court of Otto I, inserting, for example, the phrase *"it is said that this lance once belonged to Constantine the Great."* He also gives an account of its history, according to which in 921/22, Count Samson and his partisans entrusted dominion over the *regnum Italicum* to Rudolf, King of Burgundy with the Holy Lance, begging him to drive out Emperor Berengar. However, since the reliquary lance was a *"treasure by which God binds*

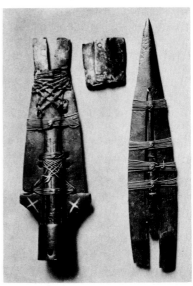

The Holy Lance, dismantled and without its gold and silver bands

the earthly and the celestial and to ensure victory over visible and invisible foes," the German king Heinrich secured its possession by bestowing lavish gifts on the Burgundian king, and eventually entrusted it on his deathbed to his son, Otto, as a symbol of Imperial power. For Luitprand, the decisive point is reached when he represents the defeat of the insurgents at the Battle of Birten in 939 (in which Otto was unable to intervene but watched from across the Rhine), as a victory achieved by Otto on account of his piety. Since the kings and prophets of the Old Testament prefigure in exemplary fashion the Imperial monarchy (as Moses on his hill top, separated from Joshua and his warriors, had to endure the onslaught of the Amalekites, his staff raised in his hands in prayer) so Otto held the Holy Lance and prayed. For the medieval reader, the spiritual meaning of the lance, strengthened by the 'Nails of the Cross', as the contemporary variant of the *virga Dei,* the miraculous, budding rod of Moses, was immediately established through the biblical reference to the renewal of the miracle. However, this also implied the setting up of the Holy Lance as an equal to the *virga Moysi,* one of the most important state relics of the Byzantine Empire. Through this miraculous victory, Otto was celebrated as a divinely-blessed victor and new Moses. He had shown himself to be chosen by God, and, like Constantine, accoutered with the sign of his sovereign dignity. The man in whose hands the Lance of Constantine displayed the same miraculous power as the virga Dei of Moses must have seemed chosen by God to be Holy Roman Emperor. In the year of Otto's holy victories, that of 955 over the Hungarians at the Battle of Lechfeld, and against the Slavs, Otto I proved himself to be the new Constantine and future emperor, elected by divine Providence. The miraculous power of the Holy Lance was from then on regarded as indisputably proven.

As Karl Hauck has shown, there was a definite purpose behind Luitprand's exaltation of the political events and the glorification of the Holy Lance: the significance of this theological stylisation was the promulgation of the divine right of the Ottonian dynasty.

There is no evidence as to whether the Holy Lance was in Carolingian possession, but the arguments in favour are very convincing. In contrast to other historical sources, Widukind von Corvey relates that the Holy Lance was presented to Heinrich I by the heirs of his predecessor, Konrad I. Reliquary weapons with 'Constantinian' reliquary nails of the Cross seem to have been a familiar concept in Carolingian times. According to a well-known legend, St. Helena had particles of the nails of the Cross forged into the lance and other parts of the imperial armour of her son, Constantine, as a guarantee of everlasting victory.

In a representation of the Apocalypse from the second quarter of the 10th century, Christ appears as the King of Kings, mounted on a horse and bearing a winged lance with a perforated blade. This extremely simplified representation seems to be the earliest of the surviving representations of the Holy Lance as the virga Dei.

One of the main characteristics of monarchical ideology since the time of Charlemagne had been the orientation towards ideal ages and memorable precedents which provided morally binding examples.

Thus Constantine the Great served as the model of the ideal ruler for Charlemagne's renewal of the imperium Christianum in the spreading of the faith and the conquest of the heathen. It appears all the more significant when Charles, the future emperor, as Protector of the Roman Church and of the Pope, on the occasion of the apostolic reliquary donation from the year 774, received from the Pope, as a parting gift and divine guarantee of victory, a reliquary lance, the rompheam victoriae. Romphea is a rare loan word from the Greek, which Luitprand uses almost two hundred years later as an interchangeable term for the Holy Lance as the Lance of Constantine. In this connection, Peter Paulsen's opinion that the Holy Lance is a Carolingian lance gains all the more in significance. At once an outstanding weapon and an insigne of power, it is probably the lance belonging to Charlemagne himself.

It was perhaps Princess Theophano, who, having ascended the throne as the consort of Otto II and later as regent for her infant son, Otto II, provided the impulse for the blade of the Holy Lance to be embellished with a jewelled sheath surmounted by a cross. The Lance of Longinus in the Imperial Treasury at Constantinople had a sheath with a cross of this kind, fitted with a tiny particle of the True Cross. The first mention of a cross fitted to this triumphal lance is on the occasion of Otto III's departure for Italy in 996, where *"according to ancient custom, the Holy and Imperial Lance bearing the cross"* was carried before him.

We can form an idea of what this lost sheath must have looked like from the portrait of the monarch in Heinrich II's sacramentary (Regensburg, between 1002 and 1014). This representation, perhaps based on an earlier model, combines the celebration of the heavenly investiture of Heinrich II with his glorification as pious worshipper, like Moses. Two bishops support his arms, spread out in prayer, just as Aaron and Hur supported the arms of Moses, the worshipper elected by God, during the battle against the Amalekites. The shaft of the lance is depicted as the miraculous budding rod of the *virga Dei*. The motif of the supporting of the arms, however, is also rooted in ancient tradition, and is similarly based on the concept of the ruler supported and accompanied by heavenly beings on the way to salvation, and thus able to perform superhuman feats. This motif of *sustentatio* or support, is to be seen in a relief representing the Roman Emperor Domitian in the company of the gods, the goddess Roma herself supporting the Emperor's elbow.

Sacramentary of Heinrich II, *The Coronation of Heinrich II by Christ* (Staatsbibliothek, Munich)

On the assumption of power by Heinrich II, the Holy Lance was for the first and last time included in the rituals of the coronation ceremony. It was handed over as a vicarious symbol for all the other insignia to King Heinrich, representing the responsibility for the empire. Probably influenced by Byzantine court ceremonial, where it was the custom to keep the most important state relics from the public gaze, either Heinrich II, the last of the Saxon dynasty, or his successor, Konrad II, the first Salian emperor (of the dynasty of the Frankish dukes) decided to have the most important Imperial relics concealed in a reliquary cross, namely the Imperial Cross. A case-like compartment for the lance was hollowed out in the cross-beam, but no provision was made for the jewelled sheath surmounted by a cross as described above.

At an unknown date, the blade of the lance was broken, probably during the making of one of the several copies of this most important Imperial insigne, whereby small particles of the metal were chiselled off and incorporated into the copy. It is held together at the point of fracture by a narrow band of iron and the blade secured as a whole by lashing with silver wire. The socket below the wings of the lance was also reinforced by forging a piece over it, also at an unknown date.

The simple iron band is covered by a silver band with an inscription on a gilded strip, ordered by Emperor Heinrich IV (1084—1105). In it the lance is described as the Lance of St. Maurice with a Nail of the Cross. The elevation of the knotted pin fitted with particles of the Cross into a fully-fledged Nail of the Cross as a result of pious wishful thinking has already been mentioned, as has the increasing importance of the patron saint of the Empire, St. Maurice, which emerges at the beginning of the 11th century. The Salian coronation *ordo* from the second half of the 11th century decreed that the Imperial Cross, together with the particle of the True Cross and the Lance of St. Maurice, were to be carried in front of the Emperor. The status of the Holy Lance as the symbol of Imperial power was preserved, but it was St. Maurice as the patron saint of the Empire, and no longer Constantine, who was the object of the Emperor's veneration.

During the course of the 13th century, the significance of the lance gradually underwent another change, possibly because much had been forgotten or misunderstood. The Holy Lance was superseded by the Imperial Crown as the most important insigne of the Empire, and by the Particle of the Cross as the most important relic of the Passion. Since the Battle of Lechfeld had been fought on the Day of St. Longinus in 955, and this day had been entered in the medieval state records as a holy day, the wish to emphasise the connection of this relic to the Passion, the relic that had for so long been venerated as the victory-bringing weapon of the Empire, was acquiesced to and it was duly reinterpreted as the Lance of Longinus.

The gold sleeve visible today (with the inscription naming it as the Lance and Nail of the Lord), was ordered by Emperor Karl IV around the middle of the 14th century, and the venerated relic placed in an ostensory, which has since been lost.   H. T.

Ref.: Weixlgärtner 1926, p. 54 ff.: Schramm-Mütherich 1962, no. 62; H. L. Adelson, The Holy Lance and the Hereditary German Monarchy, in: The Art Bulletin Vol. 48, New York 1966, p. 177 ff.; P. Paulsen, Flügellanzen. Zum archäologischen Horizont der Wiener "sancta lancea", in: Frühmittelalterliche Studien. Jb. f. Frühmittelalterforschung d. Universität Münster, vol. 3, 1969, p. 289 ff.; K. Hauck, Erzbischof Adalbert von Magdeburg als Geschichtsschreiber, in: Mitteldeutsche Forschungen 74/2, Cologne/Vienna 1974, p. 304 ff.; Deèr 1977 (1958), p. 62 ff.; Schramm-Fillitz 1978, no. 36; Schwineköper 1981, p. 207 ff.; K. Hauck, Die bildliche Wiedergabe von Götter- und Heldenwaffen im Norden seit der Völkerwanderungszeit, in: Arbeiten zur Frühmittelalterforschung vol. 1, Berlin/New York 1981, p. 248 ff.

156 PARTICLE OF THE 'TRUE' CROSS

Pinewood; 25.3 cms long
Reliquary in the form of a processional cross:
Prague (?), after 1350
Gold, painted black; 31.3 cms high, 20.2 cms wide (Inv. No. XIII 20)

Ever since the time of Constantine, special veneration had been accorded to those remains and relics which testified to the life and suffering of Jesus Christ on earth. It was the conviction of all believers that the most precious part of his earthly nature which Christ left behind when he ascended to heaven was his blood, which, according to the Christian doctrine, he had sacrificed for the salvation of mankind. Eucharistic connections to the blood of the New Testament in the sacrifice of the ceremony of the Mass deepen the symbolic significance of the holy blood.

The wood of the cross — this much was believed to be certain — had soaked up the blood that had flowed from the wounds of the saviour; so that, after a time, the sacred wood had become saturated with salvific blood, especially at the places where Christ had been nailed to the cross.

What is important here is not the genuineness or spuriousness of those particles of the cross to be found among the Imperial treasures, but rather — since belief creates reality — what they signified for people in the Middle Ages. The relics of the Passion, for which the compartment in the lower shaft of the Imperial cross was designed in the second quarter of the 11th century, was venerated as a particle of the 'True Cross'. Its unusual size alone distinguished it from the other particles of the cross that were known in the West. In addition, the crucifixion relic displays one of the nail holes, into which a nail of the cross had been hammered. The piece of wood is thus a piece from one of those places on the cross which came into direct contact with the wounds of the crucified Christ, and which became soaked with his blood. With this particle of the cross, the Roman emperor possessed a sacred object, a relic and a ruler's insigne in one, thus placing him on the same level of importance as the Byzantine emperor. From now on, the ruler of the Western empire, too, was visibly protected by Christ himself, since according to the belief of the times, the saviour was personally present in the form of his blood, with which the piece of wood from the cross had been soaked.

A relic of the cross of this degree of sanctity could only have been presented as a gift by the Byzantine emperor himself. For by the time Jerusalem was being threatened by the Arab conquerers, all the most important pieces, with one Roman exception, had already been transported to Constantinople. And since then, no-one other than the Byzantine emperor had had access to them. In the West it was believed that alone in the Emperor's palace chapel there were preserved three particles of the cross which were all of considerable size. Only the Basileus was entitled to carry in ceremonial processions both the most important relics of the Passion, which proved him to be the representative of Christ on earth, and those connected with the Old Testament, such as the ring of Solomon or the above-mentioned blossoming branch of Moses, the *virga Moysi* (see Cat. No. 155). In these state processions, the continuity between the great biblical figures and the Eastern Roman emperors was visibly demonstrated to the people. The proud feeling of being in possession of these relics of inestimable value which guaranteed victory, enabled the Byzantines to look down on the rulers in the West, who had no such concrete proofs of their legitimacy.

We know a great deal about the veneration of the cross. The cult blossomed in the Empire even in Carolingian times, and after the 10th century underwent a marked increase in popularity, which reached its peak in the 13th century. However, it has so far not been possible to provide sound evidence for the provenance of the Particle of the Cross prior to its concealment in the Imperial Cross.

While there are no clues to the earliest possible dating of its introduction into the Imperial treasury, it can at least be affirmed that only the reign of Konrad II (1024—1039) comes into consideration as a possible period of its acquisition. There is reason to believe that a connection exists between Konrad II's

commission for the manufacture of the Imperial cross and his acquisition of the Particle of the Cross. It has furthermore been proposed that the Particle of the Cross is identical with the gift brought back by the returning legation of Konrad II from Emperor Romanos III Argyros, which was so generous and unusual that the precious gift served to distract from the failure of the negotiations. Should it become possible to corroborate this hypothesis, then the dating of the manufacture of the Imperial Cross would have to be altered to the last decade of the reign of Konrad II. The Particle of the Cross has probably been kept in the tree of this golden processional cross ever since the third quarter of the 14th century, the time of Karl IV. The simple mounting exposes as much as possible of the piece of wood from the cross, displaying the nail hole at the point of intersection of its beams. The gold of the cross-beams has since been painted black, so that the relic is no longer encased by the majestic form and sparkling jewels of a victory cross. It is now the hallowed wood alone which inspires the believer to compassion with the Saviour.   H. T.

Ref.: Hauck 1974, p. 157 ff. and 217 f.; Schramm/Fillitz 1978, p. 33, 37, 40; Schwineköper 1981, p. 224 ff. and 270 f.

157 THE CORONATION EVANGELIAR

Codex: Court of Charlemagne, Aix-la-Chapelle, shortly before 800
236 purple-dyed vellum leaves, gold and silver ink, body colour; one column of text and 26 lines per page; 32.4 x 24.9 cms
Binding: Hans von Reutlingen, Aix-la-Chapelle, c. 1500
Silver-gilt, precious stones; 34.5 x 24.9 cms (Inv. No. XIII 18)

On the four incipit pages of the Gospels all three types of writing common to valuable late antique illustrated manuscripts are represented: the first line is in *capitalis rustica,* followed by a line of monumental *capitalis quadrata* and the Latin text of the Gospels is written in continuous uncials, without spaces between the words or punctuation, in gold ink. The initial letters alone betray Carolingian taste and in their intertwining patterns the formal ornamental imagination of the Hiberno-Saxon illuminated manuscripts lives on.

The Viennese Evangeliar is the principal work in a small group of manuscripts which were produced at the court of Charlemagne after it had moved to Aix-la-Chapelle in 794. It is court art of a higher level than the products of the court school as such. This scriptorium, which was formerly termed the 'Palace School', is characterised by a particular style that can perhaps be described by the term 'cool classicism'. The book is embellished with a series of 16 canon plates and four representations of the Evangelists, one at the beginning of each Gospel. All but two of the canon plates are of the arcaded type, spanned by an arch, which is typical for the court school. The two exceptions belong to the entablature type, resembling the fassade of a classical temple, a type created by the Theodosian renaissance around 400. A gospel manuscript from late antiquity was doubtless available to the artists at Charlemagne's court; in later manuscripts of the Palace School its series of canon plates was used in its entirety.

In contrast to the abstract, formal pattern of the manuscript pages and canon plates, with their shimmering silver and gold, the representations of the Evangelists, composed according to visual and physical logic, represent a radically different solution in the relation of frame to pictorial content. Here, in the most classicistic of all medieval images of the Evangelists, the illusion of a framed panel painting is striven for. The purple of the pages becomes a dark wall, its sombre hue contrasting with the light of the picture. The illusion is created of a view into a light-filled space, the border again assuming the function of the frame. In the representation of John the Baptist, the footstool of the Evangelist overlaps the frame, as if the imaginary pictorial space behind the page of the book continued out into the space of the onlooker. A bright strip of sky over the landscape catches the eye and conveys the impression of depth.

The enthroned figures dominate the pictorial space, their origins in the ancient representations of poets and authors obvious; two of the Evangelists are portrayed frontally, the other two in profile. In each picture, the pictorial concept derives from the character of the narrative mis-en-scène of the authorial image.

Mark, his arms spread out in a dynamic diagonal gesture that fills the frame of the picture, unrolls his scroll. In contrast, John, enclosed in the block of an exhedra-like niche, holds his scroll rolled up. His stylus raised, he seems to pause in his writing, sunk in contemplation, and poses, like Mark, as if he were having his portrait painted, in a frontal appeal to the onlooker.

In the representations of Matthew and Luke, the scribes' hunched posture articulates the composition of the fig-

Coronation Evangeliar, Mark the Evangelist and the beginning of the Gospel according to St. Mark

ures: the line of the back is curved into a closed circle, imbuing the figures with an air of intense concentration.

All the Evangelists are clothed in the classical white of Greek garb. The composition of the drapery is organised from the movements of the body as a counterpoint of tensions and as such illustrates the classical duality between body and drapery. The latter seems made of fluid light, the white contrasting with the more substantial gold, in particular that of the haloes. At the cost of atmospheric vividness, it contributes to the cohesion of the surfaces. The athletic appearance of the three Synoptists who resemble one another is difficult to reconcile with their role as intellectuals, Matthew in particular rather resembling a pugilist. However, even the artists of late antiquity had already fallen into the habit of depicting saints and martyrs as triumphant heroes. Of more decisive importance is the formal link with the art of late antiquity, namely in the illusion of plasticity created by extreme painterly means, all the forms dissolving in dimensionalised sections of light and shade.

In short, only works of art from late antiquity can be taken for purposes of stylistic comparison. This kind of retrospective mentality was alien to the age of Carolingian art. Slavish imitation of revered models was something that — devotion to classical ideals notwithstanding — not even the scriptorium of the neighbouring Palace School could bring themselves to. Their independent contribution to the art of the Carolingian renaissance and the character of their reappraisal of ancient art remained unmistakeable.

Wilhelm Koehler has attempted to explain the circumstances of the unheralded origin of the Imperial Evangeliar by the appearance of foreigners at the Carolingian court. Otto Pächt holds that this foreigner must have been a Greek, a theory supported by the fact that the paint flakes off in the same way as in Byzantine codices. It may further be concluded that the sought-after, but lost prototype must have existed in the East, perhaps in Constantinople itself. It remains a mystery that there was somebody around the year 800 who still employed the artistic idiom of the post-Justinian era around 600 as if it were his own language. As a survivor of an otherwise extinct artistic tradition, he appears at the court at Aix-la-Chapelle, there for the first time encountering motifs and ideas that had originated in Italy. The real miracle here is, however, that he did not remain alien in the sphere of Carolingian

John the Evangelist

art, but was rather able to implant the living seeds of classical form into the medieval pictorial tradition and thus contribute to the *renovatio Romani imperii* of Charlemagne.

On the cover of the book, chased in high relief, God the Father appears as the paragon and ideal of all rulers in front of the richly-profiled architecture of the canopy of his throne, his right hand raised in blessing. The slight turn of the head mitigates the hieratic severity of the tectonic composition, and it is obvious that His gesture of blessing is meant for Mary, here depicted in the Annunciation group. On

another level of illusion, this Annunciation could almost be a group of sculptures occupying the lateral niches of the extensive architecture of the throne, which encompasses the whole surface of the book cover.

Symbols of the Evangelists in medallions occupy the corners. The raiment of God the Father resembles the vestments of an emperor, and he wears a mitre crown which corresponds to the personal crown of Emperor Maximilian I. The facial features of God the Father seem to derive from an ideal portrait of the canonised Charlemagne, in whose succession all the emperors of the Holy Roman Empire saw themselves.

At the coronation, the future emperor took an oath on this Evangeliar, placing three fingers of his right hand on the incipit page of the Gospel of St. John.   H. T.

Ref.: W. Koehler, Die karolingischen Miniaturen, vol. 3: Die Gruppe des Wiener Krönungsevangeliars. Metzer Handschriften, Berlin 1960, p. 57 ff.; Schramm-Mütherich 1962, no. 13; F. Mütherich, Die Buchmalerei am Hofe Karls des Grossen, in: Karl der Grosse, Lebenswerk und Nachleben, vol. III; Karolingische Kunst, ed. W. Braunfels and H. Schnitzler, Düsseldorf 1965, p. 45 ff.; Grimme 1972, no. 5, no. 113; F. Mütherich and J. E. Gaehde, Karolingische Buchmalerei, Munich 1976, p. 11 and 48 ff.; Fritz 1982, no. 950; O. Pächt, Buchmalerei des Mittelalters. Eine Einführung, Munich 1984, p. 140 and 177.

Binding of the Coronation Evangeliar

158 THE BURSE OF ST. STEPHEN

Carolingian, 1st decade of the 9th century, with later additions
Gold foil over a wooden foundation, the back made of silver-gilt, precious stones, pearls, glass; 32 cms high (Inv. No. XIII 26)

The wooden foundation contains hollow recesses, in which relics were probably once kept; according to one tradition, the reliquary was supposed to have contained earth soaked with the blood of the archmartyr St. Stephen. The largest relic compartment leads into the inside of the wooden core from the bottom and conceals the remnant of a small piece of fabric which, although it cannot be identified in more detail, is authenticated as a relic by the seal of the Cathedral Chapter of Worms, dating from the first half of the 12th century.

The reliquary takes the shape of a 'burse', an old pilgrim's purse, whose form, embellished with precious metals, was imitated for use as a reliquary as early as pre-Carolingian times.

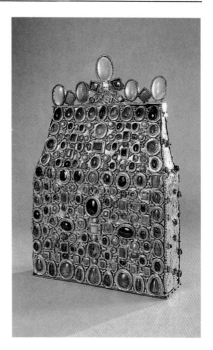

The mass of decoration on the display side consists of pearls and precious stones, the latter varying greatly in colour, shape and size; the unequal height of their sunk settings contributes to the lively modulation of the surface. Small, tri-radiate gold bosses occupy the spaces between the rows of roughly arranged stones. The reflecting grooves of the rings encircling the hollows intensify the gleam of the stones, at a casual glance accentuating the impression of randomly dispersed riches. Upon closer examination, however, the original formal intention of the order of the stones becomes clear: closed bands of stones en cabochon surround the whole of the front, as well as dividing it into box and roof. The horizontal row can at the same time be seen as the crossbeam of a large cross, although its shaft stands out less distinctly. The role of the cross as the supreme symbol is emphasised by virtue of its being a *crux gemmata,* or jewelled cross, whose significance derives from the fusion of the imperial symbol of sovereignty with the Christian symbol of victory. Recurring several times on the sides are medallions, stamped in gold foil, depicting a fisherman, a falconer, bird-hunters and a goddess of revenge (designated MALIS VINDICTA). Due to the restiveness of the reflected light, the elongated figures, whose postures exhibit a lissome, feathery quality, appear weightless. The models on which they were based have been sought in book illustrations from that time, although the question still remains as to whether the figures reflect the atmosphere of the court school of Charlemagne (early 9th century) with its closeness to the traditions of antiquity, or whether the presence of the Reims style (816—835), the vital nerve of which was the spas-mic, vibrating line, is already making itself felt here.

The back of the reliquary burse was originally decorated in the same style as the sides. Presumably around 1827, it was replaced in Vienna by the present, neo-Classical back, made of gilded silver foil, which nevertheless does essentially correspond to the old covering. The crowning element at the top of the reliquary seems to have been added in the 15th century.   H. T.

Ref.: M. Rosenberg, Das Stephansreliquiar im Lichte des Utrechtpsalters, in: Jahrbuch der Preußischen Kunstsammlungen vol. XLIII, Berlin 1922, p. 169 ff.; Schramm/Mütherich 1962, no. 24; K. H. Usener, Zur Datierung der Stephansbursa, in Miscellenea pro Arte, Hermann Schnitzler zur Vollendung des 60. Lebensjahres, Düsseldorf 1965, p. 37 ff.; V. H. Elbern, Das Engerer Bursenreliquiar und die Zierkunst des frühen Mittelalters, in: Niederdeutsche Beiträge zur Kunstgeschichte, vol. 10, 1971, p. 52 ff.; Grimme 1972, no. 6; E. Zwierlein-Diehl III 1991, no. 2538 ter.

"the sword of Attila", "part of the booty from the Avars" from 796, or *"gift of Haroun al Rashid"* to Charlemagne have no historical authenticity. Since the sabre was held to be a relic of Charlemagne, the monarch was girded with it at the coronation.   H. T.

Ref.: Z. Toth, "Attilas Schwert". Studien über die Herkunft des sogenannten Säbels Karl des Grossen in Wien, Budapest 1930; Schramm-Mütherich 1962, no. 163; Grimme 1972, no. 10; A. Kirpicnikov, Der sogenannte Säbel Karls des Grossen, in: Gladius 1973, p. 69 ff.; I. Erdély, Über die Zusammenhänge der Grabfunde bei Martan-Cu, in: Acta archaeologica academiae scientarium Hungaricae 1983, p. 207 ff.

159 THE 'SABRE OF CHARLEMAGNE'

Eastern Europe (Hungary?), 1st half of the 10th century
Sabre: steel blade with partially gilded copper inlay; Hilt: wood, fish-skin, gold, silver-gilt with precious stones; 90.5 cms long
Scabbard: Wood, leather, gold; 86.5 cms long (Inv. No. XIII 5)

The sabre was a favourite weapon among the peoples of the horse in combat with enemies on the steppe. This ceremonial sabre, executed in costly materials, is an eastern European piece and probably dates from the 1st half of the 10th century. Its ornamentation can be compared with finds excavated in southern Russia, the settlement area of the Hungarians before the conquest, and also in the newly-conquered area of the future Hungarian kingdom.

Supported by findings from recent excavations, the connection between the Hungarian people at the time of the conquest and the Alanian tribes becomes evident. In the northern Caucasus, near the early Alanian capital Magas, a sabre was excavated from a catacomb grave which bears the closest resemblance by far to the so-called 'Sabre of Charlemagne', and is dated to the same time. However, among the finds from the northern Caucasus, this sabre is an exception. Other, similar sabres have been found in the Carpathian basin and at scattered sites over the eastern European steppes.

It is also unclear when the ceremonial weapon was brought to Aix-la-Chapelle and included in the Imperial insignia. Legendary descriptions such as

160 THE IMPERIAL SWORD (SWORD OF ST. MAURITIUS)

Scabbard: German, 2nd third of the 11th century; Byzantine or in Byzantine style enamels
Olive wood encased in gold foil, enamel plates, garnets, the pearl beading contours have been lost
Sword: German, between 1198 and 1218
Blade of steel, pommel and quillons faintly gilded; hilt bound with silver-wire; 110 cms long (Inv. No. XIII 17)

On the pommel of the sword are the arms of King Otto IV (1198—1218), together with the Imperial eagle and the inscription: BENEDICTVS DO (MINV)S DE(V)S · QVI · DOCET MANVS. (Blessed be the Lord and God who teaches the hand [to wield]). Inscription on the quillons: †
CHRISTVS : VINCIT : CHRISTVS REINAT and CHRISTVS VINCIT : CHRISTVS REIGNAT : CHRIST(VS) INPERAT. († Christ triumphs · Christ reigns · and Christ triumphs · Christ reigns · Christ rules.) The first, shorter inscription is to be read when the blade is pointing downwards, the second when it is pointing upwards.

From the inscriptions on the sword itself, which was restored in 1200, and from the representations on its scabbard, which was made in the middle of the 11th century, it may be concluded

gians despite two intervening changes of dynasty. Heinrich III considered himself to be the rightful successor of Charlemagne, although he was the 14th sovereign to come to the throne since the reign of the latter.

The transverse banding with Byzantine enamel plaques (in later times partially replaced) provides the interconnecting substructure of the individual embossed gold-foil plates. The worship of Christ in the inscription on the pommel of the sword, which bears the arms of King Otto IV, repeats the concluding *trikolon,* the three-part hymn of praise, or ceremonial paean, with which allegiance was sworn to the newly-crowned Roman king.   H. T.

Ref.: Schramm/Mütherich 1962, no. 159; P. E. Schramm, Die deutschen Kaiser und Könige in Bildern ihrer Zeit: 751—1190, Munich 1983 (1928), no. 160; Fillitz 1986, no. 3.

that the Imperial sword was primarily designed to be carried by the sword-bearer with the tip pointing upwards. None of the seven figures of sovereigns depicted on either side of the scabbard carries a sword in his baldric. Standing in hieratic frontality before a plain gold ground, the sovereigns — who are not named in the inscription — are depicted with the insignia of their office, each holding in his hands the Imperial orb and sceptre, the latter sometimes appearing in the form of a long staff-like sceptre. On their heads they wear mitre crowns, sometimes with, sometimes without pendilia, which had been missing from the Imperial crown for a long time.

The Imperial Sword was actually made for Heinrich III, although in the Imperial treasury it was soon regarded as the erstwhile weapon of St. Maurice (the prototype of all warriors). With its series of 14 kings and sovereigns, it testified to the awareness of that 'legitimistic' tradition which still linked the Salians with the Carolin-

161 THE IMPERIAL ORB

Cologne (?), c. 1200

Gold, precious stones and pearls; 21 cms high (Inv. No. XIII 2)

The sphere consists of a resinous mass covered with gold foil. The rows of pearls belonging to the equatorial band have been lost. On one side of the cross there is a sapphire intaglio (Byzantine, 2nd half of the 6th-7th century), at the point where the arms of the cross intersect. The Imperial orb of the Hohenstaufen is characterised by intersecting bands set with precious stones, the symbolism of which derives from cosmological concepts of late antiquity. Individual insignia such as this remained heavily influenced by Byzantine artistic concepts. A precious Byzantine gold enamel icon in the treasury of San Marco in Venice displays Archangel Michael robed as an emperor. As the insignia of his power, he bears the imperial orb and sword, which are formed three-dimensionally and seem separate from the surface of the icon. They could almost have been

zantine *kosmokrator,* the Ruler of the Universe.

After the victory of Christianity, the *sphaira* as an insigne of power was surmounted by a cross. *"For the Emperor rules over the world by virtue of his faith in the Cross,"* confirms a chronicler from the early Byzantine era. Christ himself is from then on the *kosmokrator;* the emperor rules as his representative. The cross symbolises the victory of the Redeemer over death, and is interpreted as a victory-bringing emblem. Thus the Christian rulers borrowed an image of the cosmos and the Earth from the pagan past, as a concrete insigne reinterpreted for their own purposes. Although, in the Middle Ages, it had been concentrated into a three or four-part symbol for the world, the belief that the universal *Roma aeterna* would endure for ever lived on. Thus with its concept of universal rule among much else, the ancient world bequeathed a heritage of almost indestructible power, which was, with varying intensity, to hold the following centuries in its thrall.

This orb, as an Imperial insigne, belongs to a long tradition which, as Josef Déer has indicated, remained unbroken, at least in Byzantium. The Carolingian dynasty had already placed themselves in this tradition, in conscious imitation of the Basileus, the Greek emperor. On the occasion of the coronation of Heinrich II in 1014, the Pope had exhorted the last emperor of the Ottonian dynasty to rule such that he be worthy of the protection of the Cross, and just as the orb was adorned with precious stones, so must the emperor be adorned with virtues.   H. T.

Ref.: P. E. Schramm, Sphaira, Globus, Reichsapfel, Stuttgart 1958, p. 87 ff.; Schramm-Mütherich 1962, no. 185; Deér 1977 (1961), p. 70 ff.; E. Zwierlein-Diehl III 1991, no. 2538 bis.

the models for the pieces belonging to the Imperial insignia. Common stylistic features with works produced by goldsmiths in Cologne indicate that it was probably made in that city around the year 1200. The fleur-de-lys-shaped extremities of the cross are typical of the artistic taste of the time.

In the ancient world, the form of the sphere had three functions: it was an image of the cosmos and as such bore the heavenly constellations on its surface, rather like our celestial globes. It was also an image of the Earth, analogous to our terrestrial globes, and displayed what the ancient world already knew of the Earth. Thirdly, the sphere symbolised even at this time the idea of universal power.

Ever since the foundation of the *imperium Romanum,* the world seemed predestined to be subject to imperial omnipotence. Even after the capital was moved from Rome to Constantinople, thus entailing the division of the empire, the *sphaira* or globe still expressed the confluence of the power of East and West in the hand of the By-

162 THE CEREMONIAL SWORD

Palermo, sometime before 1220

Sword: blade of steel, hilt and quillons of wood, covered with gold foil and decorated with enamel and filigree; the pommel of silver-gilt with the imperial eagle and Bohemian lion added for Karl IV: Prague, 3rd quarter of the 14th century; 108.5 cms long

Scabbard: parchment on glued wood, linen covering; overlaid with gold foil, partially decorated with enamel (champlevé), partly with 'vermicular filigree', pearls in between; four rubies on the top locket; 92.5 cms long (Inv. No. XIII 16)

The ceremonial sword belongs to the set of vestments which were used for the coronation of Friedrich II as Roman Emperor in 1220. An accompanying spherical helmet-type crown, closely related to the sword both technically and stylistically, was a burial gift of the Emperor to his wife Constance; today it is to be found in the Cathedral treasury in Palermo.

The sword's name is probably connected with the fact that, from the 15th century onwards, it was used by the newly-crowned Roman king in the ceremony of dubbing his knights, a ceremony which at the coronation of Karl V had to be performed three times on account of the great throng of candidates for knighthood. The envoys from Nuremberg, who, after 1423, brought the imperial insignia for the coronation, were always knighted.

In biblical times the sword, wielded in the name of God, was regarded as a holy weapon. In the *imperium Romanum* the sword formed part of the armour of the Emperor as a military commander and thus also part of his insignia. From an ecclesiastical point of view the weapon was intended to instill fear rather than to kill. It is not an end in itself, but a means to peace. *"For the saints did not conquer kingdoms with the sword but with faith,"* the Pope admonished Friedrich II at his coronation. The only person allowed to enter a house of God carrying a sword was the king, his sword constituting the exception as a weapon of justice, serving to protect the Church. In Carolingian times the emperor was presented with the sword 'for Church and Empire': it was his duty to expand the Empire and spread the faith. An extension of the power of the empire entailed at the same time an augmentation of Christendom. Thus the Pope could call the Emperor an ''image of the saviour of the world''.

In the German coronation ceremony, the sword conferred on the king sovereignty over all the Teutonic tribes. Thus by Ottonian times, the sword had already taken over the original function of the lance.

At the emperor's coronation, the Pope and the Emperor combined to present the world with an example of the relationship between the two supreme authorities. The Carolingian idea of the 'saviour of the world' who was destined for world dominion had long since been superseded by the time Friedrich II was crowned emperor in 1220. Nothing could alter the precedence of the Pope, and the concept of shared authority had been rejected. Coronation ceremonial, the proceedings of which included written prayer formulas, was laid down in the *ordines,* although the ordinances for the papal coronation of the Roman emperor differed from those for his coronation as king in the German kingdom.

In the Imperial ordinance for the papal coronation of 1220, the sword was given a greater role and preeminent status. In this can be discerned a sweeping change in the conception of church policy. In earlier times, after the sword had been presented, it had been declared in the prayers that God himself championed the Emperor's cause with the heavenly weapon. However, in later times there was mention of another sword besides that of the Emperor, a spiritual one: the sword of anathema. In times of trouble, such as during the Investiture Controversy, those emperors who were excommunicated by the Pope came to feel the compelling force of the anathema, which was originally combined with the ban of the empire. The altered balance of power was revealed in extreme fashion when Friedrich II, upon being presented with the Imperial sword, was told that, legally, the sword belonged to the Pope, who, although he did not actually wield it himself, entrusted it to the emperor solely for the purposes of administration.

It might appear at once noteworthy and contradictory that the title of *sacrum imperium Romanum,* Holy Roman Empire, with which we are so familiar, first originated under the Hohenstaufen, and remained the accepted title until the Empire came to an end in Napoleonic times.

The resemblance of the ceremonial sword to a work of textile craftsmanship seems to be connected with the fact that in the royal workshops in Palermo the goldsmiths' art took second place to that of textile manufacture. In addition, it allowed for a reduction in weight, which seems to have been important to Friedrich II, who commissioned the regalia. To provide the lozenge-shaped enamel pla-

ques at the top with a surrounding double row of pearls is a typical feature of textile decoration.

The cloisonné work of the enamel decoration consists of staff-shaped tendrils and quadrifoliate forms. The distinctly Byzantine origin of the cloisonné work can be seen in the abstract, geometrical patterning of the enamel on the top locket. The thick walls of the individual cloisons, on the other hand, may be a technical characteristic of the royal workshop in Palermo. Likewise the bud-shaped rivets covered by filigree wire. They rest on triangular fields set with small-scale vermicular filigree.   H. T.

Ref.: Deér 1952, p. 66 ff.; Schramm/Mütherich 1962, no. 197.

163 THE SCEPTRE

German, 1st half of the 14th century
Silver-gilt; 61.5 cms long (Inv. No. XIII 3)

This plain, Gothic sceptre has a slender, hexagonal shaft with four boss-rings. Crowned with leafwork formed from six intertwined oakleaves, the point of the sceptre ends in the form of an acorn.

Although sceptres have always been counted as belonging to the supreme insignia, no examples from the High Middle Ages have survived in their original form. Iconographic evidence survives from the ancient civilisations of the Near East, showing kings bearing both mace-like sceptres and long staves. Starting from the oldest written sources available in the Middle Ages, the sceptre in the Bible signifies sovereign power itself: the king is the shepherd of his people, his staff points their way forward. At the same time, the ruler's staff is the instrument of punishment: if need be, he must rule with a rod of iron, as the psalmist says. Staff and sceptre thus became the symbol of stern justice.

It was the supreme duty of the ruler to sit in judgement and make the law.

However, the sceptre can also be seen as a symbol of benevolence, of pardon and of peace. In the Christian era, symbolic links were sought with the Old Testament. The bishops at the Council of Aix in 816 chose the long staff as the emblem of their pastoral office and the sceptre as a symbol of their power of punishment and discipline. However, Charlemagne subsequently refused to accept this.

From the 3rd century onwards at least, the sceptre was an integral part of the Imperial regalia of the Roman Empire. The emblem of Jupiter's power, the long staff surmounted by an eagle stands for the felicitous union of victory and Roman consulship. Well into the Ottonian era, when supreme power had long stood under the sign of the cross, the eagle surmounting the long sceptre still clearly indicates the consular provenance of this insigne. According to a legend, when Constantine the Great moved the seat of empire from Rome to Byzantium (Constantinople), he presented Pope Sylvester with the gift of his armour, made 'firm' with relics, together with the insignia of his imperial omnipotence, among which was a sceptre.

In contrast to the Greek Basileus, who from the very beginning claimed supreme powers over both temporal and spiritual concerns alike, in the western half of the Empire secular and spiritual power were officially in separate hands. A power conflict developed between the secular territorial power of ecclesiastical office (Imperial Church system) and the emperor's prerogative of investiture, which made the division of powers increasingly problematic. At times, the claim to mutual participation in power resulted in open hostility.

Representations of the emperors at the beginning of the Salian era carrying either the long staff or the short sceptre, as in the reliefs of the line of monarchs on the Imperial Sword, should be understood as an image of the imperial concept of their universal office as sovereign.

In the 12th century, the long staff was abandoned as an Imperial insigne and

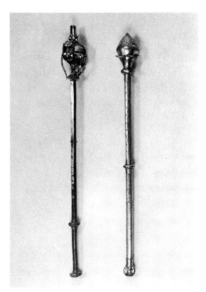

163, 164

was then reserved exclusively for bishops and abbots in the form of the crozier. The sceptre on the other hand, which Charlemagne had objected to the clergy carrying, disappeared as an emblem of ecclesiastical dignity. The settlement of the Investiture Controversy (1075—1122) must have been responsible for this, resulting as it did in a clearer division between ecclesiastical office and temporal concerns.   H. T.

Ref.: E. Eichmann, Die Kaiserkrönung im Abendland, II., Würzburg 1942, p. 82 ff.; Schramm-Fillitz 1978, no. 16.

164 THE ASPERGILLUM
German, 1st third of the 14th century
Silver, 58.5 cms long (Inv. No. XVIII 4)

The circular shaft, with its three bosses, opens out into a vessel with a finely perforated watering rose, in the form of flower-buds enwreathed in leaves.

The aspergillum was used for sprinkling the altar with holy water and for consecration. The reason for its presence among the imperial treasures is connected with the emperor's spiritual status.

In the High Middle Ages, the emperor-to-be was first ordained as a priest by the Pope before being actually crowned in Old St. Peter's in Rome. A similar rite was also performed when he was later crowned Roman-German king in the empire. No obligations accompanied his clerical rank, although it did entail certain ecclesiastical honours. Among the latter were his acceptance as a canon in several cathedral chapters and the right to wear liturgical garments. The old idea of the participation of the emperor in Christ's priesthood and kingship nevertheless continued to recede into the background as the strength of the Papacy increased. The 'Christus Domini', or 'Lord's annointed' was demoted to a layman, and this, in its turn, led to the emperor's emphasis on the grace of God. The aspergillum, mentioned as a *"silver sceptre"* in the inventory drawn up for the transfer of the Imperial treasure to Karl IV in 1350, testifies to the dogged persistence of ceremonial conventions.   H. T.

Ref: Schramm/Fillitz 1978, no. 17.

165 THE PORTRAITS OF EMPEROR CHARLEMAGNE AND EMPEROR SIGISMUND

Copies from the late 16th or early 17th century after the portraits of the Emperors executed by Albrecht Dürer in 1512/13 for the *Heiltumskammer* in the Schopper House in the market place in Nuremberg.

a) Ideal portrait of Charlemagne
Oil on canvas; 209 x 119.5 cms (Inv. No. GG 2771)

In the background to the left and right of the Emperor's head is the inscription: KAROLUS MAGNUS IMP(ER) AVIT ANNIS 14 (Charlemagne reigned as Emperor for 14 years). Above this, on the left, is a coat of arms with the German (single-headed) eagle, on the right the French arms with fleurs-de-lys. On the painted frame (also copied from the original) is the inscription: DIS IST DER GSTALT UND BILTNUS GLEICH / KAISER KARLUS DER DAS REMISCH REICH DEN TEITSCHEN UNDERTENIG MACHT / SEIN KRON UND KLAIDUNG HOCH GEACHT / ZAIGT MAN ZU NURENBERG ALLE JAR MIT ANDERN HALTUM OFFENBAR (This is the form and likeness / of Emperor Charles who subjugated the Roman Empire to the Germans / his crown and raiment highly revered / are shown every year with other relics at Nuremberg).

b) Portrait of Emperor Sigismund
Oil on canvas, 209 x 119.5 cms (Inv. No. GG 2770)

In the background to the right and left of the Emperor's head is the inscription: SIGISMU(N)D(US) IMP(ER) AVIT ANNIS 28 (Sigismund reigned as Emperor for 28 years). Over this are the arms of Sigismund's territorial possessions: the Imperial double-headed eagle, the Bohemian lion, Old and New Hungary and Luxemburg. On the painted frame, also copied from the original, the inscription: DIES BILT IST KAISER SIGMUNDS GESTALT / DER DISER STAT SO MANIGFALT MIT SUNDERN GNADEN WAS GENAIGT / FIL HALTUMS DAS MAN JARLICH ZAIGT / DAS BRACHT ER HER GAR OFFENBAR DER KLAIN ZAL FYER UN(D) ZWAINZIG JAR. MCCCC (This picture is Emperor Sigismund's form / who so graciously favoured this city, / many holy relics that are shown every year / he brought them here in the year four-and-twenty MCCCC).

After Emperor Sigismund had entrusted the Imperial regalia to the safekeeping of the City of Nuremberg in perpetuity, the Imperial Relics were displayed to the public annually on the Feast of the Holy Lance, the second Friday after Easter, an occasion marked by a solemn mass and the granting of indulgences. The exhibiting of the Holy Relics took place in the Hauptmarkt (main market place) at Nuremberg, where a wooden scaffolding platform was erected in front of the house belonging to the Schopper and Behaim families, opposite the Frauenkirche. This platform, called the *'Heiltumsstuhl'* (lit. 'See of the Holy Relics'), was several metres high and was reached through one of the windows of the Schopper house via a bridge. The Imperial insignia were kept

in the *Kirche des Heiliggeistspitals* (Infirmary Church of the Holy Spirit), which was under the administration of the city: the relics in a shrine suspended by chains high above the choir, the insignia and vestments in the upper vestry.

The day before they were exhibited, the Imperial insignia were taken to the *'Heiltumskammer'* (Chamber of the Holy Relics) the room behind the platform in the Schopper house. From here, after high mass had been celebrated, the clergy brought them out onto the platform and paraded them to the crowd. A 'crier' was appointed to read out explanations in a loud voice, while the respective object was indicated with a staff. A select company of people were allowed into the *Heiltumskammer* during the exhibition. In 1512/13, when the chamber was refurbished, the Council of the City of Nuremberg commissioned Albrecht Dürer to paint the larger than life-size portraits of Charlemagne, from whom the Imperial treasure was then supposed to have originated, and Emperor Sigismund, who had first entrusted it to the City of Nuremberg.

With this painting of Charlemagne, Dürer created an idealised portrait of the Emperor that was to determine the idea of his appearance throughout the following centuries. Dürer was permitted to view the Imperial treasure in order to make preliminary watercolour studies for the accurate representation of the coronation vestments and insignia. Emperor Sigismund is portrayed in a set of private vestments and wearing a crown with an arch. This strongly individualised portrait goes back to a contemporary portrait, which has come down to us as a miniature copy in the Book of Portraits of Hieronymus Beck von Leopoldsdorf (Kunsthistorisches Museum, Picture Gallery) K. S.

Ref.: Anzelewsky 1971, p. 233 f., nos. 123, 124; Strieder 1981, p. 68 ff.; Catalogue, New York, The Metropolitan Museum of Art 1986 (Gothic and Renaissance Art in Nuremberg 1300—1550); Kugler 1986, p. 90 f.

166 RELIQUARY WITH CHAIN-LINKS

Pictorial representations on the casket by an Italian engraver in Rome or Prague c. 1368
Gold, engraved; enamel, semi-precious stones, iron; 12.5 cms x 5.1 x 2.8 cms (Inv. No. XIII 29)

To all three of the iron chain-links are fastened other, smaller chains with inscribed banderoles and gold rings. Similar rings on the relic of St. Paul (with an intaglio probably dating from the 2nd half of the 4th century, depicting St. Paul wearing the *corona vitae* of a martyr) and of St. John the Evangelist (Byzantine cameo with a bust of the Mother of God); from the relic of St. Peter hangs a plain gold ring, with a portrait of a saint engraved on its bezel. The inscription is identical on both rings: IEXVS AVTEM TRANSIENS PER M(ARE) (Jesus, who walks upon the water); on the reverse of one of the rings: M(I)S(ER)IATVR (May he have mercy).

The casket's smooth form, which is untypical for the Gothic style, derives from considerably older examples. Here, however, it becomes the vehicle of pictures executed with a sense of spatiality, an innovation for this time. On its lid appear the Apostles John the Evangelist, Peter and Paul in chains, depicted using the technique of engraving with a filling compound rubbed into the lines.

With extremely sparing use of the pictorial means used to represent spatiality, the artist creates the impression that the three Apostles have been brought together in captivity in the same place at the same time, which was not, of course, the case. This is achieved by the continuity of the ground, the axial symmetry of the figures, the way they crouch within the frame, yet overlap its edges, and the eye-contact between them. Translated into the terms of goldsmithery, the suggestive pictorial power of emergent Italian realism, with its earthly, heavily-modelled figures, here celebrates its first triumph. Just how intent upon its object realism can be, is demonstrated by the obsessively detailed depiction of the Apostles' chains.

With the portrait-like reproduction of the facial features of Pope Urban V and Emperor Karl IV on the front of the casket, the breakthrough to a more life-like representation of a historical event is achieved. The subject depicted is the Pope presenting the chain relic of John the Evangelist to Karl IV, the two other relics having already been in his possession. The event depicted occurred in Rome in 1368. The ruler indicates the chain relic in veneration, although his gesture and glance probably also hint at covetous desire. H. T.

Ref.: Fritz 1966, p. 259 ff.; G. Schmidt, Malerei bis 1450. Tafelmalerei-Wandmalerei-Buchmalerei, in: Gotik in Böhmen, ed. K. M. Swoboda, Munich 1969, p. 218; Schramm/Fillitz 1978, no. 51; Otavsky 1978, p. 704; Fritz 1982, p. 99; Fillitz 1986, no. 19; E. Zwierlein-Diehl III 1991, no. 2538.

167 RELIQUARY CONTAINING A FRAGMENT OF THE ROBE OF JOHN THE EVANGELIST

Pictorial representations on the casket by an Italian engraver in Rome or Prague, c. 1368
Gold engraved and blackened with a filling compound; cameo, rock crystal; 26.1 x 12.3 x 2.2 cms (Inv. No. XIII 25)

The front of the casket bears the inscription: DE TVNICA S(ANCTI) IOHANNIS EWA(N)GEL(ISTE) — (from the tunic of John the Evangelist).

This cloth relic was given to Emperor Charles IV by Pope Urban V in 1368. To allow the relic to be seen, a cruciform aperture was made in the centre

and there is a richer use of graphic media than in the chain reliquary, where, despite being more idiosyncratic, the representations are considerably more two-dimensional.   H. T.

Ref.: Schramm-Fillitz 1978, no. 54; Otavsky 1978, p. 705; Fritz 1982, p. 222f.; Fillitz 1986, no. 20.

168 RELIQUARY WITH A PIECE OF WOOD FROM CHRIST'S MANGER

Rome or Prague, the mounts on the lid most likely from Prague, sometime after 1368

Gold, precious stones, pearls; 49 x 4.1 x 3.9 cms (Inv. No. XIII 24)

On the glass cast is the signature of an intaglio: ΘAMYPOY (of Thamyras).

Pope Urban V presented the relic as a gift to Emperor Karl IV in Rome in 1368. Its case is mounted with smooth gold foil. The lid can be raised as a whole, and through a little window in its central section the piece of wood from the manger can be seen. This ajouré window reveals an engraved and blackened depiction of the Infant Jesus in his manger. 13 precious stones are mounted in lozenge-shaped settings. The spandrels are filled with trefoils bearing pearls in their centres. The outermost stone on the right is a glass cast after a classical intaglio depicting a mythological scene.

No decisive arguments can be found for its localisation, since the fact that this type of setting was very widespread precludes closer stylistic classification. Most revealing is the fact that the relic was presented in a box which has been deliberately kept plain after the fashion of earlier models.

of the lid and fitted with a pane of rock crystal. This is surmounted by a late antique cameo of an eagle, which is the symbol of John the Evangelist.

On the lid of the casket are eight scenes from the life of John the Evangelist: in the first of these Mary Salome entrusts her sons, John and James the Great, to Christ; the second depicts the Last Supper; in the third John is being martyred in a cauldron of boiling oil; in the fourth scene he drinks the poison which has killed three miscreants; in the fifth he restores them to life by waving his tunic; next he is abandoned on the island of Patmos; in the seventh scene he reveals his visions of revelation to his disciples; in the final scene he dies in an open grave.

By means of cross and parallel hatching, the engraver has masterfully brought out the half-tones between light and dark in the modelling of the figures, imbuing them with corporeality.

The individual scenes are given only as much dimensionality as is absolutely necessary to accomodate figures, objects and indications of location. That there was already a considerable urge in the 14th century towards dimensional representation is clear from the accumulation of figures with their backs to the viewer; these serve to create the narrative links between fore and back ground.

Stylistic comparisons with the representations on the reliquary containing the chain links reveal the difference in the hands, and that the images of the Evangelist are much more closely related to the mainstream of Italian art. There is more dimensionality in the scenes, the figures are more organic

Thus the settings for the gemstones could just as easily have been mounted subsequently in Prague or in Rome at the outset. The quality of the representation of the manger is nonetheless too modest to have satisfied the standards required of papal goldsmiths. H. T.

Ref.: O. Kurz, An Engraved Gem signed by Thamyras, in: Album amicorum J. G. van Gelder, Den Haag 1973, p. 211 ff.; Schramm/Fillitz 1978, no. 53; Otavsky 1978, p. 706; Fillitz 1986, no. 21; E. Zwierlein-Diehl III 1991, no. 2537.

169 RELIQUARY WITH THE TOOTH OF JOHN THE BAPTIST

Prague, 3rd quarter of the 14th century
Silver-gilt, rock crystal; 41 cms high
(Inv. No. XIII 27)

The reliquary contains a scrap of parchment with the inscription: DENS DE MENTO S(ANCTI) JOH(ANNIS) BAPTISTE SV(M)TVM IN TAVRINO (Tooth from the chin of St. John the Baptist, acquired in Turin).

A reliquary tooth belonging to this saint was already listed as belonging to the holy relics concealed in the Imper-

ial Cross in 1246 and again in 1350, without, however, any mention of its provenance. The relic is suspended in the cylindrical crystal vessel of a 'tower' reliquary, and is thus visible from all sides. Emperor Charles IV commissioned several of these reliquaries, which were known as monstrances. The structure of the stand is typically Gothic: over the quatrefoil foot with triangular sections between the foils is an octagonal chapel-like knop, its eight facets corresponding to the shaft with its boss, which bears eight quatrefoil rotuli. The vessel is surmounted by a conical roof crowned with a cross on a square plate. H. T.

Ref.: Schramm-Fillitz 1978, no. 39; Fillitz 1986, no. 23.

170 RELIQUARY WITH THE ARMBONE OF ST. ANNE

Prague (?), 3rd quarter of the 14th century
Casket with sliding lid: silver-gilt; 20.8 x 3.4 x 3.6 cms (Inv. No. XIII 28)
Mounting of the relic: gold; 18.2 cms long. The inscription on the mounting: † ISTVD EST BRA(CH)IV(M) S(AN) C(T)E ANNE M(AT)RIS B(EA)TE MARIE (This is the arm of St. Anne, mother of the Blessed Virgin Mary).

This relic of an armbone of St. Anne is first noted in the inventory of 1350, as one of the relics concealed in the Imperial Cross. Yet the present piece does not fit in as an extra object in the compartment provided for the particle of the cross, and no other compartment comes into consideration. For this reason it can be assumed that Emperor Karl IV had a smaller piece exchanged for the armbone that we have here.

The tubular mounting for the relic, with its large display-window, was assembled from two parts. By mistake, the goldsmith engraved the two halves of the inscription the wrong way round. In order to correct this, he chiselled out the inscribed area on the smaller part, turned it through 180 degrees and then soldered it on again. This is evident from the abbreviation marks, which have been left as they were and are now wrongly placed. The character of the hand matches that of the inscription on the pedestal of the Imperial Cross.   H. T.

Ref.: Schramm/Fillitz 1978, no. 35

171 TWO RELIQUARIES BY HANS KRUG THE YOUNGER (?)

a) Reliquary with a piece of the Tablecloth from the Last Supper

Hans Krug the Younger (?), Nuremberg, 1518
Silver-gilt, precious stones, pearls; 55.9 cms high (Inv. No. XIII 22)

On the underside of the foot is the inscription: † ANNO 1518 HER ANTHONI TVCHER HER IERONIMVS EBNER VND HER MERTENI GEVDER DER ZEIT LOSSVNGER VND OBERSTE HAVBTLEVT. The reliquary was commissioned by the persons named in the inscriptio-den, who were invested with the administration of the Imperial insignia by the City of Nuremberg.   H. T.

b) Reliquary with a piece from the Apron of Christ

as above (Inv. No. XIII 23)

This pair of identical reliquaries displays a richness of formal expression combining both the modification of traditional late Gothic elements and the introduction of the newly-developed forms of Renaissance art. Pieces from the workshop of Ludwig Krug are in general closely related to the designs for goldsmith's work and altars produced by Albrecht Dürer.

The sweeping curves of the six-foiled foot lead into an engraved shaft bounded at each end by a plate. The boss on the shaft is overlaid with scrolling leafwork. Scrolled and arching tendril motifs veil the transition from the three-dimensional stand to the two-dimensional framed structure of the reliquary itself. The architectural tracery surrounding the frame and the flanking statues of the patron saints of Nuremberg, SS. Sebaldus and Laurence, recall the idiom of late Gothic forms. Although executed at a time of change, on the eve of the Renaissance, the combined effect of the elements from architecture, sculpture, and jewellery work recalls the stylistic principles of late Gothic. Surmounting the square structure enclosing the relic, a round arch terminates the piece, crowned by three lively putti, an element deriving from the new style. They pull playfully at strictly symmetrical twining tendrils which end in trumpet-shaped flowers. While the plasticity of the display side seems to be built up of different layers, the smooth back is dominated by engraved scenes. The scenes of Jesus washing the feet of his disciples and the Last Supper are engraved on the reflecting gold surface as a vivid commentary on the two relics.
                    H. T.

Ref. Fritz 1966, p. 553 f.; Kohlhausen 1968, nos. 404, 405; Fritz 1982, no. 792.

172 CASE FOR THE IMPERIAL CROWN

Prague, after 1350
Container made of leather, sewn in layers, decorated with blind-stamping and leather carving, partially dyed, lined with blue velvet; clasps and lock made of iron; 25 cms high, 30.8 cms diameter (Inv. No. XIII 30)

On the left part of the top of the lid appear the Imperial arms, with the black eagle on a yellow ground. This is matched on the right by the arms of the Kingdom of Bohemia, with a white lion rampant on a red ground. In the gyrons are trefoils, while the ground is filled by embossed beading. 12 mythological beings occupy the sides of the the lid. The lower part of the case, which is fastened to the lid by iron clasps, is decorated with panels of foliate tendrilling.

Emperor Karl IV had leather cases made for some of the objects of the Imperial regalia — he had come into possession of them in 1350 — in a Prague workshop.

Apart from its great decorative potential, leather lent itself to the manufacture of cases on account of its flexibility of form and material toughness. It was always worked to fit specific objects. The case for the Imperial Crown provides a good example of the extent to which decoration and technical so-

lutions concide. The individual pieces of leather, sewn together, correspond to the panels into which the decoration is divided. On the sides, carrying-loops, through which a strap can be drawn, were intended to facilitate transportation.

The oldest method of decorating leather was blind-stamping, whereby metal punches are hammered or impressed into the leather. The beaded ground, with provides an effective contrast to the smooth decoration, is also embossed, as are the rows of detailed ornamentation on the framing bands and the bodies of animals.

In order to achieve the desired network of freely drawn lines for the ornamental forms, the technique of leather carving was employed. This allows the leather-worker considerably more scope than the use of a stamp. Using three-edged knives, the surface of the leather was embellished with a carved linear decoration.

The division of the surface by the framing bands is accentuated by contrasting colours, although the effect of these colours was originally far more intensive.   H. T.

Ref.: Gall 1965, p. 49 ff.; Schramm/Fillitz 1978, no. 38a; Fritz 1982, p. 77.

173 THE CASE FOR THE CEREMONIAL SWORD

Prague, after 1350
Brown leather with rich leather carving, lined with red velvet, iron mounts; 115 cms long (Inv. No. XIII 33)

The sword-case was probably made in the same workshop as other leather cases commissioned by Karl IV. However, compared to the case for the Imperial Crown, its ornamentation is considerably more modest. Neither in delicacy of execution nor in the wealth of the decorative motifs does it approach the same level. However, in the pattern of acanthus leaves interrupted by two horizontal bands, striking use is made of a further medium of leather ornamentation: relief work. This was achieved by chasing or die-pressing the

wet leather. As with the case for the crown, parallel carving was used for the ribs of the leaves, while the ground was stamped.   H. T.

Ref.: Gall 1965, p. 54 f.; Schramm-Fillitz 1978, no. 34.

174 CASE FOR THE IMPERIAL CROSS

Nuremberg, dated 1495
Brown leather, blind-stamp and blind-tooling, leather-carving, iron mounts; 97.3 x 76.9 x 13.8 cms (Inv. No. XIII 36)

The decoration, which is typical for Nuremberg cases from the late Gothic period, is restricted to the date of the year, and the *'Jungfernadler'* and *'Schwabenfeld',* which are the arms of Nuremberg. The fine diagonal lattice pattern, made of continuous blind-tooling, is an invariable feature of such cases.

It has not been possible to identify individual case-makers working in Nuremberg at this time.   H. T.

Ref: Gall 1965, p. 136.

175 THE CASE FOR THE SMALLER RELICS

Nuremberg, c. 1500
Blackish leather, blind-stamped, lined with red parchment, iron mounts; 57.2 x 20.6 x 17 cms (Inv. No. XIII 40)

The continuous blind-stamped pattern was achieved using one stamp only.
H. T.

176 CASE FOR THE RELIQUARY WITH THE PARTICLE OF THE CROSS

Nuremberg, 1517 (dated on the back)
Brown leather, leather-carving, lined with red parchment, brass mounts; 35 x 24 x 3.5 cms (Inv. No. XIII 35)

The convoluted coiling of a single, continuous leaf tendril here conveys the impression of feathery elasticity; its technical design shows that it was a product of traditional leather-carving methods. This always allowed great scope to the creativity of the craftsman. The effect of the tendril decoration is heightened by the delicate relief work which stands out from the embossed ground.   H. T.

Ref.: Gall 1965, p. 136.

177 RELIQUARY CASES

a) Case for the Tablecloth reliquary
Nuremberg, 1518
Brown leather, leather carving, blind-stamp and blind tooling, lined with red parchment; 61 x 24 x 18.8 cms (Inv. No. XIII 37)

b) Case for the Apron Reliquary
Nuremberg, 1518
Brown leather, leather carving, blind-stamp and blind tooling, lined with red parchment; 62 x 24 x 18.8 cms (Inv. No. XIII 38)

These cases for the two frame reliquaries display a motif frequently found in Nuremberg leather work: a diagonal lattice of blind-tooled lines with additional blind-stamping.
Repeated with almost monotonous invariability, this ornamental Renaissance motif occasionally risked descending to the decorative level of mass-produced objects. Both cases display the *'Schwabenfeld'* (the arms of Nuremberg) in leather carving technique, together with the date 1518.

H. T.

Ref.: Gall 1965, p. 134.

178 THE CORONATION OF JOSEPH II AS ROMAN KING IN FRANKFURT AM MAIN ON 3. 4. 1764
Studio of Martin van Meytens the Younger (among others: Johann Dallinger von Dalling, 1741—1806) (cf. Cat. No. 142)

a) The Coronation in the Church of St. Bartholomew
Oil on canvas; 362 x 295 cms (Inv. No. GG 7468)

The coronation altar stands in the crossing of the Church of St. Bartholomew. Joseph II kneels on the top step of the altar, wearing the coronation robes (Cat. No. 143—151), and is being crowned with the Imperial Crown (Cat. No. 153) by the Archbishop of Mainz, who is assisted by the Archbishops of Cologne and Trier. Capitulars from Mainz Cathedral, as well as bishops and abbots from the diocese of Mainz provide clerical assistance. The ambassadors chosen as the representatives of the other prince electors have taken up position immediately behind Joseph II. (Ever since the Reformation, the Protestant secular prince electors no longer attended the coronation personally but were represented by their chosen ambassadors).

By the northern pillar of the crossing the throne has been set up, from which Emperor Franz Stephan I witnesses the coronation ceremony, surrounded by the holders of the Imperial hereditary offices (bearing the dynastic insignia), the holders of the supreme court offices and by the commanders of the Guards. For this occasion, as in the procession to the church, the Emperor is wearing the newly-made personal robes (Cat. No. 179) and the Crown of Rudolf II (Cat. No. 56). On the insignia table in front of him lie the Imperial Evangeliar (Cat. No. 157), the Burse of St. Stephen (Cat. No. 158), and the so-called Sabre of Charlemagne (Cat. No. 159). Of the many participants at the ceremony, conversing animatedly among themselves, a large number are characterised as if in a portrait.

b) The Knighting Ceremony after the Coronation

Oil on canvas; 363 x 212 cms (Inv. No. GG 7470)

Immediately after the coronation, the Roman king performed his first official act: the knighting of a number of selected candidates, chosen partly by the king himself and partly by the prince electors. The ceremony took place on the proclamation platform at the entrance of the southern transverse of Frankfurt Cathedral. Joseph II, surrounded by the ambassadors of the prince electors, is here seen knighting Franz Heinrich, Baron von Dalberg, who kneels in full armour before the king. The honour of being the first to be knighted was traditionally the priviledge of a member of the Dalberg family, holders of the office of Treasurer of Mainz. The list of candidates is here being read out by the Captain of the Household Guard, Lieutenant Field-Marshal Count Hamilton, seen standing to the right of the throne.   K. S.

Sources: Vollständiges Diarium von denen merckwürdigen Vorfällen die sich bey . . . Wahl und Krönung des . . . Herrn Josephs des Anderen . . . ergehen, Mainz 1767—1771 (ed. F. E. Seeger, Ph. J. Seitz); Aus der Zeit Maria Theresias, Tagebuch des Fürsten Johann Josef Khevenhüller-Metsch, kaiserlichen Hofmeisters, ed. R. Graf Khevenhüller-Metsch and H. Schlitter, vol. 6, 1764—1767, Vienna 1917, p. 17 ff.; Johann Wolfgang von

Goethe, Aus meinem Leben. Dichtung und Wahrheit, Parts 1—3, Tübingen 1811—1813.

Ref.: Catalogue, Maria Theresia 1980, no. 68.01, 150.01—02; Kugler 1986, p. 126 f.

179 THE VESTMENTS OF EMPEROR FRANZ STEPHAN I OF LORRAINE

(Baroque copies of the Coronation Vestments of the Holy Roman Empire) Vienna, 1763/64

The individual pieces belonging to the set of vestments are copies of the corresponding items from the Coronation Vestments of the Holy Roman Empire. Paper tracings of the originals were made by Wolfgang Nikolaus Reif in Nuremberg in 1763, which were then used in Vienna to make the copies. Emperor Franz Stephan I of Lorraine wore these vestments at the coronation of his son, Joseph (II), as Roman-German King in Frankfurt on 27. 3. 1764, also availing himself of the dynastic insignia, i.e. the Crown of Rudolf II, together with the sceptre and imperial orb that Emperor Matthias had commissioned to go with it (Cat. Nos. 56-58). The young king wore an *archducal habit* (Cat. No. 55) and a new archducal coronet during the mounted procession to the Church of St. Bartholomew. For the coronation, he was clothed in

different vestments. On leaving the church he wore the original coronation vestments (Cat. Nos. 143-152). Johann Wolfgang von Goethe describes this moment in the fifth book of 'Dichtung und Wahrheit': *Finally both their Majesties came up. Father and son were altogether dressed like Menaechmi. The Emperor's robes, of purple-coloured silk, richly adorned with pearls and stones, as well as his crown, sceptre, and imperial orb, struck the eye with good effect. For all in them was new, and the imitation of the antique was tasteful. He moved, too, quite easily in his attire, and his true-hearted, dignified face, indicated at once the emperor and father. The young king, on the contrary, in his monstrous articles of dress, with the crown-jewels of Charlemagne, dragged himself along as if he had been in disguise, so that he himself, looking at his father from time to time, could not refrain from smiling.* The copies are made of considerably lighter materials. Small silver platelets were used in place of the thousands of tiny pearls on the originals. On 27. 6. 1764 the *imperial habit* was entrusted to the Treasury. The emeralds missing from the mantle and alba were removed in 1879 and used in two bracelets.

a) The mantle

Atlas, gold embroidery, gold, silver paillettes, silk embroidery, gold braid, champlevé enamel, rubies, sapphires, spinels, lining of green silk; 318 cms wide, 151 cms long (Inv. No. XIV 104)

b) The alba

White silk, red atlas, gold embroidery, silver paillettes, rubies, sapphire; 122.5 cms long (Inv. No. XIV 105)

On the hem in place of the Latin inscription (cf. Cat. No. 144) a row of letters. The Arabic inscriptions have been transformed into an ornamental pattern.

c) The dalmatica
Blue silk, red atlas, enamelled gold platelets, silver paillettes, gold braid; 135 cms long (Inv. No. XIV 106)

d) The stola
Gold lamé, eagles embroidered in black silk, gold appliqués, enamelled, silver paillettes; 380 cms long, 25.7 cms wide (Inv. No. XIV 107)

e) The cingulum (girdle)
Silk, gold platelets, rubies; 165 cms long, 3.5 cms wide (Inv. No. XIV 108)

f) The sword-belt
Gold lamé, silver and silk embroidery, clasp and mounts of gold; 160 cms long, 6.6 cms wide (Inv. No. XIV 109)

The characters along the edges have been incorrectly copied (cf. Cat. No. 149): CHRISTVS RIEGNAT VOINQ-PARAT DEVG. (sic!)

g) The gloves
Atlas, gold embroidery, gold enamel appliqués, silver paillettes, rubies, spinels, sapphires; 27 cms long (Inv. No. XIV 110)

h) The hose
Atlas, gold embroidery; 64 cms long (Inv. No. XIV 111)

i) The shoes
Atlas, gold embroidery, silver paillettes, emeralds, sapphires, ruby, spinels; 25.5 cms long (Inv. No. XIV 112)

k) The sabre
Gold, partially enamelled, emeralds, rubies, one diamond backed with red foil; blade of steel; scabbard: velvet, gold enamelled; 75.5 cms long (Inv. No. XIV 114)

Modelled on the 'Sabre of Charlemagne' (Cat. No. 159). The missing emeralds were removed in 1879 and used in an emerald clock.   R. B.

THE BURGUNDIAN INHERITANCE
King John II (the Good) of France, and of the House of Valois, invested his two younger sons with the great seignioralties of his kingdom. In the last third of the 14th century, the royal court in Paris, and, above all, the residences of the two royal princes attracted many artists in search of commissions. Belonging to the princely household, they were bound to the person of their patron, but possessed enough independence to be able to move from one court to the other, thus facilitating the exchange of new ideas. At Bourges, Jean de France, the Duke of Berry, presided over a court of princely magnificence, and it is to his patronage that we owe supreme achievements in the art of book illumination. In 1363, John the Good invested his youngest and most-loved son, Philip, with the Duchy of Burgundy. Philip the Bold established his court at Dijon, and as Duke of Burgundy laid the foundations of a flourishing dynasty.

In the "autumn of the Middle Ages", as Johan Huizinga has termed the social and intellectual forms of the era of transition from the 14th to the 15th century, when dream and play were discovered as cultural concepts, courtly art owed much to the Dukes of Burgundy. Their patronage provided the impulse for a flourishing of creative talent, which produced a wealth of supremely important works in all branches of art. Philip the Bold was adept at attracting all the most talented artists of the age to his court. His largest commissions were for the work on the Carthusian monastery at Champmol near Dijon, which he had built as a tomb for himself and his successors. It was begun in 1383, and for nearly a century the most distinguished sculptors north of the Alps, among them that master of genius, Claus Sluter († 1406), worked on the monumental project, in particular on the tombs. His style is characterised by pathos, an inner grandeur and a solid plasticity of form. His realism contains a characteristic element which reappears in Netherlandish art: the faithful reproduction of concrete objects. Burgundian panel painting, which was preeminent in Europe around 1400, followed similar aims. In 1384, besides the County of Burgundy (Franche Comté), Philip the Bold acquired the County of Flanders and the Artois, to which in 1390 he added the County of Charolais, whose title and revenues rightfully belonged to the hereditary prince. The expansion of power in the complex of territories of the so-called 'Nether'-lands (lowlands) — as opposed to the Burgundian heartland which lay at a higher elevation — which had been achieved in 1384, represented a crucial objective of Burgundian policy. The Netherlands comprised a multitude of territories, duchies and counties and also included the independent bishoprics of Liège and Utrecht. The greater part of this disjointed patchwork of territories belonged to the Holy Roman Empire, the rest was under the seignioralty of the French crown. The Dukes of Burgundy concentrated all their efforts on uniting the Netherlands under their rule and were prepared to disregard the ancient feudal boundariés of the Empire. The complex of lands gradually grew into a new whole. However, the Burgundian realm was never anything more than an association of lands held together merely by the person of a common ruler.

Duke Philip the Good (reigned 1419—1467) extended his northern possessions by skilful diplomatic manoeuvering, acquiring the County of Namur in 1429, the Duchies of Brabant and Limburg in 1430, the Counties of Hainault, Holland and Zeeland in 1433, and the Duchy of Luxemburg in 1443.

The focus of Burgundian interests thus shifted to the Netherlands. While the political impulse originated in Burgundy, the actual nucleus of crystallisation for the development of the Netherlands was Flanders. Here, uniform organisation of the administrative districts and strictly organised administration of the domains were established early on. Flanders owed its prosperity to the achievements of the cloth-weaving industry. Its economic prosperity was based on extensive foreign trade: merchants, in particular from the modern Italian trading houses, came from abroad to buy at Ghent and Bruges thanks to the flourishing textile industry, and a bourse was eventually established. The Netherlands represented the most productive, economically sound region in Europe at this time, whereby the economic fulcrum shifted gradually from Flanders to Brabant.

With Philip the Good, the 'Great Duke of the West', a new protagonist had entered the arena of European politics. As sovereign prince, Philip strove to achieve the transition from a personal to an institutional sovereignty with the aim of establishing a permanent administrative unit. He achieved his discharge from feudal fealty to France, which was entangled in the Hundred Years' War with England. However, Duke Philip's hope that Emperor Friedrich III would grant him the title of king and thus full sovereignty, was not to be fulfilled.

His son and successor, Charles the Bold, who had even more ambitious plans, was likewise unable either to create a bridge between the two parts of his realm, Burgundy in the south and the Netherlands in the north, or to gain the crown he so desired and which seemed at one point to be almost within his grasp, during the negotiations with Emperor Friedrich III in Trier in 1473. In the event, his occupation of the Duchy of Lorraine in 1475 proved to be the prelude to his downfall. In the war against the Swiss Confederation and finally against the Duke of Lorraine, whom he had previously defeated, Charles the Bold was routed in three battles, and lost his life during the last of these at Nancy in January 1477. King Louis XI of France, sworn enemy of Charles the Bold, repossessed the Duchy of Burgundy as a vacant male feoff. Crises also arose for various reasons in the Netherlands. Mary of Burgundy, Charles' legal female heir, had been betrothed to the future Emperor, Maximilian I, and the wedding took place later the same year. Maximilian was able to avert the threat from the French, the idea of the Netherlands proving stronger than its internal feudal borders. What remained corresponded approximately to the area today covered by Belgium and Holland. Thus the House of Austria came into an unusual inheritance, which faced the Habsburgs with the necessity of making far-reaching political decisions. Karl V grew up in Flanders, and the Netherlands soon represented the fulcrum of his mighty empire, on which, it was said, the sun never set. During the reign of his son, Philip II of Spain (1556—1598), the terrors of the Inquisition and above all the sanguinary justice excercised by the Spanish military authorities under the Duke of Alba, led to the collapse of national unity. In the Netherlandish struggle for liberation (1568—1648), the 'Seven Provinces' of the north (States General) led by Holland achieved independence from Spain, thus effecting a lasting separation.

H. T.

Ref.: Burgund und seine Herzöge in Augenzeugenberichten, ed. C. Dericum, Düsseldorf 1966; J. Huizinga, Herbst des Mittelalters. Studien über Lebens- und Geistesformen des 14. und 15. Jahrhunderts in Frankreich und in den Niederlanden, Stuttgart 1969 (1919); R. L. Wyss, Zur Kunst am Hofe der Herzöge von Burgund, in: exhibition catalogue, Die Burgunderbeute und Werke der Burgundischen Hofkunst, Berne 1969, p. 318 ff.; R. L. Wyss, The Dukes of Burgundy and the encouragement of textiles in the Netherlands, in: The Connoisseur vol. 194, 1977, p. 168 ff.; exhibition catalogue: Charles le Témeraire: 1433—1477, Brussels 1977; W. Prevenier and W. Blockmans, The Burgundian Netherlands, Cambridge (Mass.) 1986.

THE OFFICERS OF ARMS AND THE CHAMBER OF HERALDS OF THE NETHERLANDS

All courtly ceremonial was determined by the armorial and emblematic insignia of the House of Burgundy. The most frequent emblem is that of the St. Andrew's cross, a cross decussata, attribute of the patron saint of the House of Burgundy. Duke Philip the Good chose the fire steel together with the spark-emitting flint as his personal emblem, adding the motto *ante ferit quam flamme micet* (First strike, then the flame flashes). His personal device was transferred to the Order of the Golden Fleece: the neckchain of the Order consists of stylised fire steels with stones emitting fiery sparks in between. The actual symbol of the Order, the Golden Fleece, hangs from the middle of the chain. The neckchain surrounds the escutcheons of the members of the Order. From 1430 onwards, the arms of Duke Philip the Good appear unchanged. From 1453, the Duke bore a second emblem, a pair of heraldically symmetrical miniscule 'e's, which, however, his son, Charles the Bold, never used himself.

The original task of the heralds was to identify the participants in battle and at tournaments by their arms. This was only possible because people and information could circulate freely among the officers of arms, a free brotherhood which was not bound by state borders. Thus they came to assume the highest authority in questions of heraldry. Heralds and kings-at-arms (the higher rank in the College of the Officers of Arms) functioned as messengers in time of peace and war. As envoys, they were entrusted with important missions by their lords. The king-at-arms wore the arms of his lord on a tabard. These were displayed on the breast and the back and in reduced form on the shoulder-pieces. The heralds bore the name of the lord whose arms they wore. As a matter of principle, the heralds did not carry arms, but a sceptre-like herald's staff.

When Philip the Good of Burgundy established the statutes regulating the Order of the Golden Fleece, he also reorganised the College of Heralds. In 1431 he appointed the First King-at-Arms with the official name of Toison d'Or (Golden Fleece), to whom all the heralds in the Duke's service were subordinate. However, apart from his official functions as herald of the Order, the First King-at-Arms had few additional duties, because his competence had been only very vaguely designated. Within the hierarchy of the officers of arms, after the Toison d'Or came the kings-at-arms of all the duchies, counties and domains belonging to Burgundy. The kings-at-arms and the subordinate heralds, who were empowered to represent them, had to travel to the provinces whose arms they bore and attend to all heraldic matters.

The distinction between kings of arms and heralds gradually disappeared, and by the beginning of the 17th century the two functions had merged into one. This had occurred primarily because many of the heralds' duties had become obsolete and the majority of the permanent offices had not been filled again for reasons of economy. Thus only ten mandates for kings-at-arms and heralds were left in the Southern Netherlands, which were ruled by Spain. In the 18th century, when the southern Netherlands had passed to the Austrian line and were ruled from Vienna, two further mandates were dispensed with. On ceremonial occasions the King-at-Arms and Herald of Brabant, who since time immemorial had had precedence over all other kings-at-arms, wore the tabard of Lower Lorraine, because the monarchical ambitions of Charles the Bold survived in the titular claim to Lorraine. At certain ceremonies, court officials were chosen at random to wear the tabards of the vacant heralds' offices.

The College of Officers of Arms gradually came to be called the Chamber of Heralds. This name derives from the chambers once allocated to the College in the ducal palace in Brussels. The college archives, together with the tabards and heralds' staffs were counted among the most precious possessions of the Chamber of Heralds.

The Chamber of Heralds served three masters: the sovereign himself, the Order of the Golden Fleece and, to an ever greater degree with the increasingly centralised politics of administration, the Privy Council, since this supervised the administration of the patents of nobility.

After the removal of the Court to Spain, the vivifying effect of the Order of the Golden Fleece on the heraldic system weakened. The officers of arms of the Netherlands participated in the ceremonial when the chapter of the Order had last taken place in 1559. Since this time many of the ceremonies previously provided for the rulers residing at Brussels had lapsed.

In addition to this, the obligation of the Toison d'Or to be with the ruler at all times had meant that the First King-at-Arms had been absent for long periods during the reigns of Karl V and Philip II. To remedy this state of affairs, a representative was appointed, called the Stadholder-First King-at-Arms and vested with the same authority and privileges. He was also called the Toison d'Or and later at official ceremonies of state even wore the splendid Chain of Office of the Herald of the Order, the Potence, which had remained in Brussels together with the Order's treasure.

Under the regency of Archduke Albrecht, who from 1598 to 1621 ruled not as Governor but as Sovereign of the Netherlands, the first Officer of Arms of the Netherlands was accorded the higher rank of First King-at-Arms. However, he was not called Toison d'Or during this period, because at that time the King-at-Arms of Brabant was invested with the representative function of the Herald of the Order. Later, when the Habsburg Netherlands were again ruled by governors, the supreme herald again became the Stadholder-First King-at-Arms, and was called the Toison d'Or. After the invasion of the revolutionary French army in 1794 the Chamber of Heralds ceased to exist.   H. T.

Ref.: Luc Duerloo, Privilegies uitbeelden de Zuidnederlandse wapenkonigen en wapenkunde in de eeuw van de verlichting, Doctoral thesis, Catholic University of Löwen, 1986. (On the tabards and heralds' staffs cf. esp. pp. 137—152.)

180 TABARD FOR THE FIRST KING-AT-ARMS OF ARCHDUKE ALBRECHT, SOVEREIGN OF THE NETHERLANDS 1598—1621

Brussels, between 1598—1621
Velvet, gold and silver lamé, gold, silver and silk embroidery; 86 cms long, 130 cms wide (Inv. No. XIV 97)

Front and back: arms divided horizontally. Above: divided vertically: right, divided into Hungary and Bohemia; left, divided vertically: right, quartered, Castile and Leon; left, divided vertically into Aragon and Sicily. Charged with the arms of Portugal, in a concave-sided triangle Granada. Below, quartered: 1. Austria, 2. New Burgundy, 3. Old Burgundy, 4. Brabant; charged with an inescutcheon divided vertically: left Flanders, right Tyrol. Arms rotated through 90 degrees on the shoulder-pieces. Appliqué work. Red silk damask lining. A similar herald's tabard is to be found in the Museum van de Bijloke, Gent.   R. B.

181 a) TABARD FOR THE KING-AT-ARMS AND HERALD OF THE DUCHY OF LUXEMBURG

Brussels, 17th century (Repaired 1715)
Silver lamé, velvet; 84 cms long, 124 cms wide (Inv. No. XIV 83)

Front and back: nine quarterings, silver and blue. Charged with a rampant, double-tailed, red lion, crowned and armed. Arms laterally rotated through 90 degrees on the shoulder-pieces. Appliqué work, partially embroidered. Crown in raised work. Red silk damask lining.

b) Herald's staff

Brussels, 1735
Marc Rimbout, goldsmith
Wood, silver lamé, rep, velvet, silver, parcel-gilt; 80.5 cms long (Inv. No. XIV 84)   R. B.

182 a) TABARD FOR THE KING-AT-ARMS AND HERALD OF THE ARCHDUCHY OF BRABANT

Brussels, 1715
Louis Aimé, embroiderer
Velvet, gold lamé; 84 cms long, 129 cms wide (Inv. No. XIV 79)

Front and back: rampant golden lion on black ground, armed in red. Arms laterally rotated through 90 degrees on the shoulder-pieces. Appliqué work, partially embroidered. Pile of the black velvet largely dropped out. Yellow silk damask lining.

b) Herald's Staff

Brussels, 1737
Marc Rimbout, goldsmith
Wood, velvet, gold lamé, silver, parcel-gilt; 81 cms long (Inv. No. XIV 80)   R. B.

183 a) HERALD'S TABARD FOR THE KING-AT-ARMS AND HERALD OF THE DUCHY OF BURGUNDY
Brussels, 17th century
Velvet, silver lamé; 85.5 cms long, 130 cms wide (Inv. No. XIV 75)

Front and back: Old Burgundy, divided into five diagonal bands, alternately gold and blue, with a red border. Arms laterally rotated through 90 degrees on the shoulder-pieces. Blue silk damask lining.

b) Herald's staff
Brussels, 18th century
Attributed to master goldsmith Marc Rimbout
Wood, gold lamé, silver, parcel-gilt; 82.5 cms long (Inv. No. XIV 76). R. B.

184 TABARD FOR A HERALD OF MARIA THERESIA
(In the function of the First King-at-Arms)
Brussels, 1742
Master embroiderer Eydens
Velvet, silver lamé, gold, silver and silk embroidery; 81.5 cms long, 126 cms wide (Inv. No. XIV 99)

Front and back: arms twice divided horizontally. Above: quartered heraldically right: 1. Castile, 2. Leon, 3. Aragon, 4. Sicily; in the middle divided twice vertically into Old Hungary, New Hungary and Bohemia; quartered heraldically left: 1. Brabant, 2. Styria, 3. Carinthia, 4. Carniola. Centre: divided vertically four times into Transylvania, Flanders, Habsburg, Tyrol, Gorizia. Below: twice horizontally into Lorraine, Tuscany, Bar. Charged with crowned inescutcheon: left Austria, right Old Burgundy. Arms laterally rotated through 90 degrees on the shoulder-pieces.
Appliqué work. Red silk damask lining.   R. B.

185 a) HERALD'S TABARD FOR THE DUCHY OF LOWER LORRAINE
Brussels, 17th century (Repaired 1715)
Velvet, silver lamé; 82 cms long, 119.5 cms wide (Inv. No. XIV 69)

Front and back: a silver fesse on a red ground. Arms laterally rotated through 90 degrees on the shoulder-pieces. Red silk taffeta lining.
At the ceremony of the swearing of the Oath of Fealty to Karl VI as Count of Flanders in 1717, the herald appeared for the first time as Herald of Austria in this tabard. From then on the tabard was used in both functions.

b) Herald's staff
Brussels, beginning of the 18th century
Wood, velvet, silver lamé, silver, parcel-gilt; 80.5 cms long (Inv. No. XIV 70)   R. B.

186 a) TABARD FOR THE KING-AT-ARMS AND HERALD OF THE DUCHY OF LIMBURG
Brussels, 17th century (repaired 1715)
Velvet, silver lamé; 82.5 cms long, 127.5 cms wide (Inv. No. XIV 81)

Front and back: rampant double-tailed red lion, crowned in gold and armed in gold on silver. Arms laterally rotated through 90 degrees on the shoulder-pieces. Appliqué work, partially embroidered. Red silk damask lining.

b) Herald's Staff
Brussels, 1717
Master-goldsmith Grondoni
Wood, silver lamé, velvet, silver, parcel-gilt; 80.5 cms long (Inv. No. XIV 82)
R. B.

188

187 a) TABARD FOR THE KING-AT-ARMS AND HERALD OF THE DUCHY OF GUELDERS
Brussels, 1717
Louis Aimé, embroiderer
Velvet, gold lamé; 84 cms long, 127 cms wide (Inv. No. XIV 92)

Front and back: crowned rampant gold lion rampant, armed in red on a blue ground. Arms laterally rotated through 90 degrees on the shoulder-pieces. Appliqué work, partially embroidered. Yellow silk damask lining.

b) Herald's staff
Brussels, 1735
Marc Rimbout, master goldsmith
Wood, velvet, gold lamé, silver, parcel-gilt; 80 cms long (Inv. No. XIV 93)
R. B.

188 HERALD'S TABARD FOR THE MARGRAVIATE OF ANTWERP
Brussels, 17th century
Velvet, silver lamé; 84 cms long, 128 cms wide (Inv. No. XIV 89)

Front and back: four-towered castle and two hands, silver on red. On gold escutcheon the Imperial double-eagle. Arms laterally rotated through 90 degrees on the shoulder-pieces. Appliqué work, partially embroidered and painted. Red silk damask lining.
R. B.

189 TABARD FOR THE KING-AT-ARMS AND HERALD OF THE COUNTY OF ARTOIS
Brussels, 17th century
Velvet, gold lamé; 86 cms long, 130 cms wide (Inv. No. XIV 96)

Front and back: blue ground strewn with golden fleurs-de-lys. Charged with a red triple-bibbed tilting collar. Each bib charged with three gold towers. Arms laterally rotated through 90 degrees on the shoulder-pieces. Appliqué work, partially embroidered. Yellow silk damask lining.
R. B.

189

190 a) TABARD FOR THE KING-AT-ARMS AND HERALD OF THE COUNTY OF FLANDERS
Brussels, 1715
Louis Aimé, embroiderer
Velvet, gold lamé; 83 cms long, 126 cms wide (Inv. No. XIV 87)

Front and back: rampant black lion on gold, armed in red. Arms laterally rotated through 90 degrees on the shoulder-pieces. Appliqué work, partially embroidered. Pile of the black velvet largely dropped out. Yellow silk damask lining.

b) Herald's Staff
Brussels, 1737
Marc Rimbout, goldsmith
Wood, gold lamé, velvet, silver, parcel-gilt; 77 cms long (Inv. No. XIV 88)

R. B.

191 a) TABARD FOR THE KING-AT-ARMS AND HERALD OF THE COUNTY OF HAINAULT
Brussels, 1715
Louis Aimé, embroiderer
Gold lamé, velvet; 82.5 cms long, 128 cms wide (Inv. No. XIV 85)

Front and back: quartered; on the 1st and 4th a black rampant lion armed in red. On the 2nd and 3rd, a red rampant lion, armed in blue. Arms laterally rotated through 90 degrees on the shoulder-pieces. Appliqué work, partially embroidered. The pile of the black velvet has largely dropped out. Red silk damask lining.

b) Herald's staff
Brussels, 1737
Marc Rimbout, goldsmith
Wood, gold lamé, velvet, silver, parcel-gilt; 76.5 cms long (Inv. No. XIV 86)

R. B.

192 a) TABARD FOR THE KING-AT-ARMS AND HERALD OF THE COUNTY OF NAMUR
Brussels, 1715
Louis Aimé, embroiderer
Gold lamé, velvet; 84 cms long, 125 cms wide (Inv. No. XIV 90)

Front and back: rampant black lion on gold, armed in red, with supplementary red diagonal band. Arms laterally

rotated through 90 degrees on the shoulder-pieces. Appliqué work, partially embroidered. Pile of the black velvet almost completely dropped out. Red silk damask lining.

b) Herald's Staff
Brussels, 1737
Marc Rimbout, goldsmith
Wood, gold lamé, velvet, silver, parcel-gilt; 77 cms long (Inv. No. XIV 91)

R. B.

193 a) TABARD FOR THE KING-AT-ARMS AND HERALD OF THE SEIGNORY OF MECHLIN
Brussels, 1715
Gold lamé, velvet; 84 cms long, 126.5 cms wide (Inv. No. XIV 94)

Front and back: divided into six vertical bands in gold and red. Inescutcheon with black double-headed eagle. Arms laterally rotated through 90 degrees on the shoulder-pieces. Appliqué work, eagle embroidered in black and red silks and gold thread. Red silk damask lining.

b) Herald's staff
Brussels, 17th century
Wood, velvet, gold lamé, gold; 75.5 cms long (Inv. No. XIV 95)

On the staff a crowned helmet surmounted by a dragon; lambrequin of gold.

R. B.

vertically divided inescutcheons: right, Flanders; left, Tyrol. In the border a continuous palm trunk, to which are attached bunches of fruit and flowers. The weaver's mark of Willem de Pannemaker can be seen on the blue edging below right.   R. B.

195 PHILIP THE BOLD, DUKE OF BURGUNDY (1342—1404)

Copy c. 1500 after an early 15th century original
Oil on wood; 36 x 27.5 cms. Inscription on upper edge: PH(ILIPP)E FILZ · DE · FRANCE · D(UC) · LE · HARD(I). From a series of portraits of the Dukes of Burgundy. (Inv. No. GG 4442)

Duke Philip the Bold, born in 1342 as the youngest son of King John the Good of France, was invested with the Duchy of Burgundy by the French crown in 1363. By his marriage to Margaret of Flanders he laid the foundations of the Burgundian possessions in the Netherlands.
Besides a well-attested series of portraits showing the Duke in profile (among others those in the museums at Dijon, Versailles and Cincinnati), another, less well-documented transmission exists. To this tradition belong the original of this copy, (which, at least at the time of its execution around 1500, was considered to be authentic, as the inscription attests) and a Burgundian portrait medallion from around 1400 (in the Treasury of the Residenz in Munich). However, the person portrayed is shown wearing the Order of the Golden Fleece, which was not founded until 1430, and has traditionally been held to be Duke Philip the Good. More recent opinion believes it to be a portrait of Robert de Masmines.   K. S.

Ref.: Meiss 1967, p. 378, note 52; Catalogue, Porträtgalerie 1976, no. 188.

194 TWO TAPESTRIES WITH THE ARMS OF EMPEROR KARL V

Brussels, c. 1540
Weaver: Willem de Pannemaker
Wool, silk, gold and silver thread; 205 cms high, 127 cms wide, 8—10 warp threads per cm (Inv. No. T XXXIII/7 and 8)

The pictorial field is densely set with flower and leaf sprays. These wall hangings, which were also called 'verdures' are in the tradition of the *millefleurs* tapestries. One series of verdures, which comprises six hangings with the weaver's mark of Willem de Pannemaker, is in the Louvre in Paris. The Vienna series, which originally consisted of eight pieces (two of them are today in the Rijksmuseum in Amsterdam), display this verdure ground with the Imperial double-headed eagle, crowned and haloed, and charged with the arms of Emperor Karl V, which are quartered as follows: 1. quartered again into Castile and Leon, 2. horizontally divided into Aragon and Sicily, with the pomegranate of Granada in a concave-sided triangle 3. horizontally divided into Austria and Old Burgundy, 4. horizontally divided into New Burgundy and Brabant. In the

196 JOHN THE FEARLESS, DUKE OF BURGUNDY (1371—1419)

Copy c. 1500 after Netherlandish original from the early 15th century
Oil on wood; 35.6 x 27.8 cms. Inscription on the upper edge of the picture: LE DUC · JEH(AN) · DE · BOURGONGNE. From a series of portraits of the Dukes of Burgundy (Inv. No. GG 4443)

As son of Duke Philip the Bold and Margaret of Flanders, John the Fearless was able, through his marriage to Margaret of Hainault-Holland, to further extend Burgundian dominance in the Netherlands. Favouring the English party in the war between France and England, Duke John arranged in 1407 for the murder of his cousin Louis of Orleans, the Regent of France. He subsequently suffered the same fate himself, during peace negotiations with the Dauphin on the Yonne Bridge in Montereau in 1419, when he was murdered by the latter's partisans, the Armagnacs.

The panel painting is based on a portrait from around 1415, which has only survived in copies of it painted some decades afterwards in the studio of Rogier van der Weyden, and in still later copies. The best of these versions is in the Museum of Fine Arts in Antwerp.   K. S.

Ref.: Catalogue, Porträtgalerie 1976, no. 189.

197 PHILIP THE GOOD, DUKE OF BURGUNDY (1396—1467)

Copy c. 1500 after Rogier van der Weyden (c. 1400—1464)
Oil on wood; 30.8 x 19.5 cms (Inv. No. GG 4445)

Philip the Good, the son of Duke John the Fearless, became Duke of Burgundy after his father was murdered in 1419. Under his rule, the Burgundian domains were considerably extended through the acquisition of Namur, Holland, Zeeland, Hainault, Brabant, Limburg and Luxemburg. This complex of lands thus became an autonomous state, virtually independent of its feudal seignors, France and the Roman-German Empire. On 10. 1. 1430, on the occasion of Philip's marriage to Isabella of Portugal, his third wife, he founded the Order of the Golden Fleece.

The painting is a copy from the early 16th century after a lost original by Rogier van der Weyden, of which several versions are still extant, among others in the Groeninge Museum, Bruges, at Windsor Castle, in the Louvre, Paris and in the Museum at Dijon.   K. S.

Ref.: Catalogue, Porträtgalerie 1976, no. 190.

198 CHARLES THE BOLD, DUKE OF BURGUNDY (1433—1477)

Copy c. 1500 after Rogier van der Weyden (c. 1400—1464)
Oil on wood; 33.8 x 26.8 cms. Inscription on the upper edge of the picture: LE · DUC · CHARLES · DE · BOURGONGNE.
From a series of portraits of the Dukes of Burgundy (Inv. No. GG 7011)

Charles the Bold was the issue of Duke Philip the Good's third marriage, and his sole legitimate heir, following his father to power in 1467. His ambition knew no bounds, and he planned to unite the territories of Burgundy and the Netherlands by the acquisition of Lorraine. However, he was unsuccessful in the wars that he overhastily waged to this end against the French king and the Swiss Confederation, and fell in 1477 at the siege of Nancy.

The picture is a reproduction of a half-figure portrait by Rogier van der Weyden from the period around 1460, the original of which is possibly the painting preserved in the Staatlichen Museen Preußischer Kulturbesitz in Berlin-Dahlem.   K. S.

Ref.: Catalogue, Porträtgalerie 1976, no. 192.

199 MARY, DUCHESS OF BURGUNDY (1458—1482)

Ascribed to Niclas Reiser (active from 1498 for Maximilian I, resident in Schwaz, Tyrol)
Wood; 79 x 46 cms (Inv. No. GG 4402)

As the only legitimate female heir of Charles the Bold, Maria inherited Burgundy and the Netherlands following the death of her father in 1477. According to the agreement made between Duke Charles and Emperor Friedrich III, she was married later the same year to the latter's son, Maximilian I, the future Emperor.

The painting is a copy with variations after a Netherlandish original. The original head and shoulders portrait is here extended to a half-length portrait. The spatial composition suggests it might have been painted as a companion piece to one of the portraits of Maximilian by Strigel.

The Styrian Regional Museum of the Joanneum in Graz possesses a version that is relatively close to the original, and a copy, of which only fragments have survived, is preserved in the Depot of the Picture Gallery of the Kunsthistorische Museum.

The portrait was formerly ascribed to Hans Maler but is more likely to have been painted by an earlier court painter, perhaps by Niclas Reiser, also documented as working in Schwaz around 1500. A version with the subject facing the other way is currently on display at Castle Ambras.   K. S.

Ref.: Catalogue, Porträtgalerie 1976, no. 193.

200 KING PHILIP I THE HANDSOME (1478—1506) OR KING FERDINAND I (1503—1564)

Southern German, beginning of the 16th century
Oil on wood; 25.7 x 18.4 cms. Inscribed, top centre: REX.PHILIPVS. (Inv. No. GG 6914)

The picture portrays either King Philip I, the Handsome, the sole male progeny of the marriage between Maximilian I and Mary of Burgundy, or else Philip's second-born son Ferdinand, who later became Emperor. An identical version of the portrait was used as that of Philip on the backgammon board made in 1537 by Hans Kels the

Elder for Emperor Ferdinand I (Kunstkammer, Kunsthistorisches Museum, Vienna). Since the other portraits on the board are based on reliable sources and are appropriately designated, it would seem safe to say, with the added support of the inscription, that the portrait is that of Philip the Handsome. However, while the similarity of the portrait with other pictures of Philip is marginal, it is that much greater with other portraits of Ferdinand; as can be seen, for example, by comparing it with the watercolour portrait dating from 1521/22, in the Christchurch College Library in Oxford (perhaps Hans Maler, though formerly attributed to Bernhard Strigel). K. S.

Ref.: Catalogue, Porträtgalerie 1976, no. 25.

201 EMPEROR MAXIMILIAN I (1459—1519)
Bernhard Strigel (Memmingen 1460—1528 Memmingen), c. 1500
Oil on limewood; 60.5 x 41 cms (Inv. No. GG 922)

Maximilian I is here depicted as Emperor and victorious general; he wears a suit of gilded armour of unknown provenance, although the style indic-

ates that it dates from the last decade of the 15th century. Over this he wears a mantle with a broad border embellished with pearls and precious stones. The mitre crown, which corresponds to the type worn by Emperor Friedrich III as a personal crown, does not appear in any of the other portraits of Maximilian by Strigel and differs in any case from the Imperial crown to be seen in another, privately-owned portrait of the Emperor (exhibition catalogue: Maximilian I, Innsbruck 1969, No. 550). Probably painted around or shortly before 1500, the painting is the earliest in a chronological series of portraits painted by Strigel of which several copies exist, and which were obviously felt to be a representative likeness by Maximilian and his contemporaries. K. S.

Ref.: Catalogue, Porträtgalerie 1976, no. 11.

202 BROOCH
Burgundian-Netherlandish, c. 1430/1440
Gold, enamel en ronde bosse, precious stones and pearls; c. 5 cms diameter (Inv. No. Pl 130)

Depicted is a fashionably dressed young couple from the nobility in a little love-garden enclosed by a fence. The jewelled crown of the tree behind the bridal pair has been broken off.
Gold enamel sculpture including little figures made of cast gold and fully enamelled, was one of the most sophisticated developments in courtly art around 1400. This new technique produced pictorial effects which please the eye — today as then — with an immediacy derived from a close observation of nature.
In the Burgundian Netherlands, Bruges — which at that time was a prosperous centre of world trade — was also important for the production of luxury goods. It was there that the art of diamond-cutting was supposed to have been invented, in order to bring out the stones' intrinsic brilliance. H. T.

Ref.: Steingräber 1972, p. 318.

202

203 THE THRONE-OF-GRACE TRINITY

Burgundian-Netherlandish, c. 1453—1467
Ivory; 14.6 x 11.1 cms (Inv. No. Pl. 10.078)

Inscription around the edge of the relief: VERI ADORATORES ADORABVNT PATREM IN SPIRITV ET VERITATE IHOIS 4° (The true worshippers shall worship the Father in spirit and in truth — John 4, 23)

The relief displays the Holy Trinity in the form of the Throne of Grace: God the Father, seated on his throne, holds in his outstretched arms the cross with his crucified Son; the Holy Ghost, the third person of the Trinity, appears in the shape of a dove on the cross-beam.

The cross itself rests on the globe, which signifies both the universe and the world, whose redemption is promised through Christ's sacrifice. Similarly, the baldachin signifies the Tent of Heaven.

The Throne-of-Grace Trinity is flanked by the archangels, with Gabriel holding the Lily of Mercy and Michael bearing the Sword of Justice, both attributes of the Judge of the World at the Last Judgement.

The emblems of the fire steel, together with the spark-emitting flint and the pair of heraldically symmetrical minuscule 'e's identify this sumptuous devotional plaque as the possession of Duke Philip the Good of Burgundy.   H. T.

Ref.: U. Panhans-Bühler, Eklektizismus und Originalität im Werk des Petrus Christus, Vienna 1978, p. 46; G. Török, Beiträge zur Verbreitung einer niederländischen Dreifaltigkeitsdarstellung im 15. Jahrhundert, in: Jahrbuch vol. 81, 1985.

204 THE 'AINKHÜRN' SWORD

Burgundian-Netherlandish, 2nd third of the 15th century
Steel, 'Ainkhürn' (unicorn horn = narwhal tusk), gold, enamel; the replacements: silver-gilt, ruby, pearls; 106 cms long (Inv. No. XIV 3)

The sword has a four-edged blade, and the remaining original mounts are made of gold. Its name and high esteem are due to the peculiarity that the hilt and scabbard are made of 'unicorn horn', i.e. a narwhal's tusk. (Regarding the miraculous powers attributed to the unicorn, see Cat. No. 138). The quillons and the hilt display a recurring pattern of the fire-steel and the spark-emitting flint on gold bands with an engraved matt ground. The fire-steel with its golden sparks also occurs twice on the chape of the scabbard. Restoration of the chape, based on the damaged original, was probably undertaken in the 19th century, likewise that of the locket clasps on the scabbard; only the bottom pair is still original and made of gold. In an inventory drawn up for Charles the Bold in 1469, the C-shaped decorative motif on

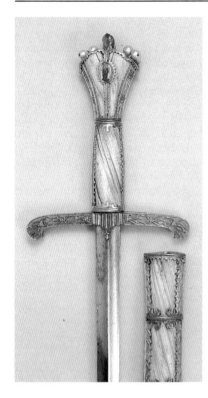

either side of the locket clasps has obviously been wrongly interpreted as the initials of a name, perhaps because one of the ends finishes in an ornamental trefoil. Furthermore, the same inventory records a representation of Christ crucified and the Mother of God on a gold plaque in translucent en basse taille enamel, and the pearls on the pommel, but neglects to mention the ruby between the groups of pearls.

This magnificent sword can be traced back with certainty to Duke Philip the Good († 1467), Charles' father, as this is recorded in the inventory of his estate, made in February 1469. The *'Ainkhürn'* sword passed from the estate of Charles the Bold to his son-in-law, Maximilian I, who was forced to pawn it, along with other treasures, in 1486. Negotiations for the sword dragged out over decades, failing time after time, and it was only in 1630 that it returned into imperial hands — as a gift.   H. T.

Ref.: Weixlgärtner 1928, p. 267 ff.; Schramm/Fillitz 1978, no. 126; U. Jenni und D. Thoss, Das Schwarze Gebetbuch, Frankfurt/M. 1982, p. 136.

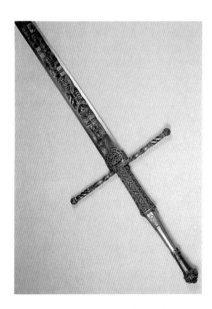

205 CEREMONIAL SWORD OF EMPEROR MAXIMILIAN I

Hans Sumersperger, Hall/Tyrol, 1496
Steel, blued and gilded, chiselled iron, brass, silver, mother-of-pearl (replaced); 139 cms long (Inv. No. XIV 4)

On the 'George' side of the blade is the supplicatory inscription of the 'Blessing of the Sword': HILF HEILIGERR RITTER S SANDT JORRG HILF UN(S) and MARIIA HILF UNS AUS (Help us, Holy Knight St. George, and: Maria, help us); on the heel of the blade: MAISTER (master). On the 'Mary' side of the blade: HILLF MARIA MVETER RAINE MAIDT MICH PEHVDT VOR L(EID) and HILF RITER SAN IORG (Help us

Mary, Mother, stainless maid, protect me from harm; and: Help us, Knight Saint George); on the tang, just legible: MAISTER NS VON H (Master Hanns of Hall).

On the quillons the date .496 IAR (in the year 1496). On the arciform 'flaps' of the quillons on the 'George' side, a royal crown in ajouré leafwork and the letters MR (Maximilianus Rex); on the 'Mary' side an M (Maximilianus) below the archducal coronet.

This sword of investiture has a two-edged blade along its whole length. Both surfaces are facet-ground and completely covered in fire-gilt patterning on a blued ground. Before the cutting edges were worn down with repeated sharpening, the blue-gold ornamentation originally extended to the outer edge of the blade. Since it is unclear which side of the sword is the front, the two sides are called the 'George' and 'Mary' sides respectively. On each side of the blade, above the single-headed royal Roman eagle and the emblems of the Order of the Golden Fleece, are 23 coats of arms arranged in pairs with their corresponding inscriptions, 46 in all. The quillons and the pommel also display a combination of the same 46 coats of arms. The power and prestige of a prince was expressed in the number of heraldic emblems he bore. Emperor Maximilian ruled over two dominions of different provenance; the 'Domains of Austria' and the complex of lands of the House of Burgundy, the 'Netherlands'. After the early demise of his wife, Mary, he possessed as head of the united House of Austria-Burgundy the right to bear the emblems and titles of these lands. The decorational heraldic scheme is based on the ranking of these titles of possession in order of precedence. The scheme also included the arms of lands which Maximilian did not at that time possess, but which he counted on inheriting.

This ceremonial sword was apparently carried in front of the ruler with both hands and with the tip pointing upwards at the swearing of oaths of fealty and at investitures, ceremonies and festivities of all kinds. It is part of a set of three identically decorated ceremonial swords commissioned by Emperor Maximilian and made by the Tyrolean master swordsmith Hans Sumersperger.   H. T.

Ref.: B. Thomas, Die Prunkschwerter Kaiser Maximilians I. in Wien und Copenhagen, in: Vaabenhistoriske Aarboger 1950/51, p. 156 ff.; Bauer/ Haupt 1976, no. 685; Schramm/Fillitz 1978, no. 139.

206 THE BURGUNDIAN COURT GOBLET

Burgundian-Netherlandish, between 1453 and 1467

Rock-crystal, gold enamelled, pearls, diamonds, rubies; 46 cms high (Inv. No. Pl 27)

Goblet, lid, knob, shaft and base are all made from clear, masterfully cut rock-crystal. On its outside wall, the high, slim, conical goblet has 16 facets, and these are decorated with round hollows cut into the quartz in four rows, one on top of the other. The calotte-shaped lid is also facetted on sixteen sides, each

facet having three decorative hollows. The decagonal base displays spherical motifs too, here cut into both the inside and the outside of the crystal. It is joined to the smooth cylindrical shaft and decoratively cut decagonal knob. Set in rich gold and sumptuously decorated with gemstones and pearls, it is a superb example of medieval hardstone carving. The edges of the base, lip and lid, as well as the magnificent decoration surmounting the lid, with its sumptuous leafwork, all bear the emblems of Duke Philip the Good, and testify to his ownership of the goblet. The two emblems of the fire-steel and the symmetrical double minuscule 'e', with its two halves knotted together by a cord, were borne by the Duke of Burgundy from 1453 until the end of his life, providing us with an approximate date for the goblet. The heraldic fleurs-de-lys composed of five diamonds, belonging to the House of Valois, are also to be seen.

The diamonds in the vessel-mounts display early table, point, rose and dodecahedral cuts. Accompanied by cords and wreaths, precious stones alternate on jewelled friezes together with pearls in bunches of three and enamel emblems on a pounced ground. From the estate of Charles the Bold, the goblet entered the French crown treasure. In 1570, King Charles IX presented the 'Court Goblet', together with the 'Salt Cellar' of Benvenuto Cellini, the 'Goblet of St. Michael' and the 'Onyx Ewer' (all in the Kunsthistorische Museum, Vienna), to Archduke Ferdinand II (of Tyrol), who acted as proxy for the French king at his marriage to Archduchess Elisabeth of Austria.   H. T.

Ref.: M. Leithe-Jasper, Der Bergkristallpokal Herzog Philipps des Guten von Burgund, das »vierte Stück« der Geschenke König Karls IX. von Frankreich an Erzherzog Ferdinand II., in: Jahrbuch 1970, p. 227 ff.; H. Tillander, the Burgundian Court Goblet, in: The Journal of Gemmology, April 1970, p. 44 ff.; F. Salet, Objets d'art, in: Bulletin Monumental vol. 130/II, 1972, p. 159 f.; Steingräber 1972, p. 319; H. R. Hahnloser and S. Brugger-Koch, Corpus der Hartsteinschliffe des 12.—15. Jahrhunderts, Berlin 1985, p. 179, no. 335.

THE ORDER OF THE GOLDEN FLEECE

On 10. 1. 1430, during the marriage celebrations for Duke Philip the Good and his third wife, Princess Isabella of Portugal, the Herald of Flanders stepped out in front of the lists after a joust and announced to the guests that his master, His Most Serene and Powerful Prince and Lord, the Duke of Burgundy, Count of Flanders, and Artois, and Palgrave of Namur, had founded an order, called the Order of the Golden Fleece. The first ceremonial meeting of the chapter of the Order and the formal acknowledgement of its regulations took place on 30. 11. 1431, at Lille, on the feast day of the Apostle Andrew, the patron saint of the House of Burgundy and also of the new Order, in the presence of the Duke himself and the first 24 knights nominated by him. The Order of the Golden Fleece was intended as a knightly brotherhood and a friendly alliance of noblemen. The number of knights was originally limited to 31, and new members were thereafter to be elected at chapters of the Order. They had to be noblemen 'in name and arms' and 'truly devoted' to the sovereign of the Order, the respective bearer of the title of Duke of Burgundy. Membership was awarded once only and was lifelong.

The principal aims of the Order were to promote the glory of God and to defend the Christian faith. Churchgoing and mass still play a large role in the rites of the Order even today: the knights sit in choir stalls and the remembrance service for deceased members is held in strict church style.

A spiritual meaning is still inherent in the word *ordre* (order), for which the word *religion* was also used by knightly orders. Membership was thus experienced as a strong, holy bond which pledged one to loyalty to the sovereign of the order. One of the reasons which prompted Philip the Good to found the Order of the Golden Fleece may well have been the political motive of binding in loyalty to himself and his dynasty the highest-ranking nobles in his realm as knights of the Order. The realm of the Burgundian dukes had grown considerably through inheritances and acquisitions, and the loose coexistence of greatly differing dominions was held together solely by the person of the common ruler.

The reason why the Order of the Golden Fleece outshone all other orders lay in the wealth, splendour and standing of the Burgundian dukes. The Golden Fleece claimed pride of place among the Christian orders, and the Habsburgs later endeavoured to consolidate this position.

Philip the Good took as his starting point the well-known Greek myth, according to which Jason stole the Golden Fleece from Colchis and brought it home; and in his sermon on the occasion of the Order's first chapter, the chancellor of the Order made reference to a biblical miracle: as a sign that he was really chosen to save Israel from her enemies, Gideon asked the Lord to moisten an outspread ram's fleece with dew, while the ground around it remain dry. When this happened, Gideon asked God to perform the same miracle again, except that the ground should be moist and the fleece dry, and this also occurred. The image of the fleece covered in dew was regarded as the symbol of the immaculate conception, foreshadowing the Annunciation. The biblical theme of the fleece, which had long been popular in typological depictions in the *Biblia Pauperum,* was widespread in the printed Netherlandish block books of the 15th century. Duke Philip and the members of the Order warmly approved of their spiritual chancellor's hermeneutics.

The newly-elected knight laid one hand on the Gospels, the other on the Cross of Allegiance, which contained a particle of the cross, and swore to abide by the statutes of the Order. Thereupon the sovereign of the Order placed the neckchain of the Order around his neck. On festive occasions, the Knights of the Fleece wore the neckchains of their Order over the ceremonial robes, which were decorated in bright red, white or black according to the occasion.

To attend to the Order's affairs, four officers were appointed to assist the sovereign: a chancellor (chancelier), a treasurer (trésorier), a secretary and historian of the Order (greffier) and a king-at-arms (roi d'armes), to whom the other heralds were subordinate. The seat of the Order was the ducal Palace Chapel in Dijon, until the city was lost to France in 1477. Chapters of the Order could be held at any place whatsoever. The title of Head and Sovereign of the Order of the Golden Fleece (Ordre de la Toison d'Or) passed from Karl V to Philip II, and after the extinction of the Spanish line of the House of Habsburg to Emperor Karl VI, who renounced the throne of Spain in 1713, although he received the southern Netherlands as an addition to the Austrian Hereditary Lands. After Spain passed to the Bourbons, there existed two Orders of the Golden Fleece, the Habsburg Order being awarded by the head of the House of Austria, the other by the head of the Spanish Bourbons.

Emperor Karl V enlarged the number of knights to 51. Eventually, it was even increased to 70. The last chapter of the Order according to the original statutes was held under King Philip II in 1559, in Ghent, in order to propose new elections and subject the conduct of the sovereign and some of the other knights to profound criticism. Philip II was warned not to undertake any important action without previously consulting his brothers. After he had ordered the execution of the Counts Egmont and Horn in 1568, against the rule that knights of the Order could only be sentenced by their brothers (confrères), he stopped calling chapters of the Order and procured a brief from the Pope which empowered the sovereign of the Order thereafter to fill vacant seats by nomination. The Order was thus divested of the one feature which had distinguished it from all other knightly orders. The treasure of the Order of the Golden Fleece was preserved in Brussels for centuries, until the Treasurer, under pressure from the French revolutionary army, evacuated it to Vienna. In 1797, the liturgical vestments were deposited in the Vienna Treasury, and later added to the Imperial art collections.   H. T.

Ref.: K. de Lettenhove, La Toison d'Or, Brussels 1907; L. Hommel, L'Histoire du noble Ordre de la Toison d'Or, Brussels 1947; V. Tourneur, Les origines de l'Ordre de la Toison d'Or et la symbolique des insignes de celui-ci, in: Académie Royale de Belgique, Bulletin de la Classe des Lettres, 5th Series 42, 1956/57, p. 300 ff.; exhibition catalogue, Het Gulden Vlies. Vijf Eeuwen Kunst en Geschiedenis, Bruges 1962; C. de Terlinden, Der Orden vom Goldenen Vließ, Vienna/Munich 1970.

207 VESTMENTS OF A KNIGHT OF THE ORDER OF THE GOLDEN FLEECE

Vienna, 1712 or 1755
Velvet, silk, gold, silver and silk embroidery (Monturdepot, Inv. No. TO 5)
The vestments consist of three parts:

a) Mantle

The wide mantle with train is worn draped from the right shoulder. Of crimson velvet, it is richly embroidered in gold thread with representations of the emblems of the order: fire steels and flints, emitting tongues of flame and sparks, together with the Golden Fleece. The gold embroidery is partially edged with blue, green and black silk embroidery. The mantle is edged with white silk, embroidered with the repeated motto of Charles the Bold: JE L'AY EMPRINS (I have dared). White silk lining. On the inside a sewn label inscribed: *His Majesty.*

b) Undergarment

Red velvet lined with white silk.

c) Chaperon

The same velvet as the mantle, with gold embroidery. The velvet band (cornette) measuring 165 cms, which is fastened to the cap, falls on the left.
                                                                           R. B.

Ref.: Auer 1951, p. 3 ff.

208 NECKCHAIN OF THE ORDER OF THE GOLDEN FLEECE

Vienna, 1836
Joseph Schmidt's Witwe, manufacturers of gold and fancy articles for the Imperial-Royal Court
Gold, partially enamelled; 136 cms long (Inv. No. XIa 55)

The neckchain consists of two repeated elements placed side by side: the flint, black enamelled with white dots, and two fire steels. The Golden Fleece hangs from the middle. This neckchain was worn by the Emperor as Seignor of the Order of the Fleece, together with the neckchains of the Order of the House of Austria (Cat. Nos. 72, 74, 76) as Grand Master of the latter order.
                                                                           R. B.

209 CHILD'S VESTMENTS OF THE ORDER OF THE GOLDEN FLEECE

Vienna, 1755
Velvet, silk, gold, silver and silk embroidery (Monturdepot, Inv. No. TO 45)

Until 1755, minors were exceptionally admitted as members of the Order but not invested until they had reached majority. However, in 1755 Emperor Franz Stephan I of Lorraine ordered two sets of child's vestments for the investiture of two of his sons, the ten-year-old Archduke Karl Joseph and the eight-year-old Archduke Peter Leopold, which were exact replicas of the knights' vestments. The chaperons have not been preserved. These vestments were used again in 1830 for the two thirteen-year-old Archdukes Albrecht and Stephan. The vestments on display are labelled *Archduke Stephan* (1817—1867).   R. B.

Ref.: Auer 1951, p. 5.

210 ROBES OF A KNIGHT OF THE ORDER OF THE GOLDEN FLEECE
As Cat. No. 207 (Monturdepot, Inv. No. TO 18)

According to the sewn-in piece of paper, these robes were last worn by *'Prince Adolph Schwarzenberg'* (1832—1914).   R. B.

211 TABARD FOR THE STATT-HOLDER-FIRST KING-AT-ARMS, CALLED TOISON D'OR (GOLDEN FLEECE)
Brussels, between 1580—1598 or 1621—1700
Velet, gold and silver lamé, silk, gold and silver embroidery; 84 cms long, 126 cms wide (Monturdepot III/TO 1).

Front and back: the arms of King Philip II of Spain after the acquisition of Portugal in 1580. Arms divided horizontally: above divided, right, quartered into Castile and Leon, left, divided into Aragon and Sicily. Charged with the arms of Portugal; below in a concave-sided triangle the pomegranate of Granada. Below, quartered: 1. Austria, 2. New Burgundy, 3. Old Burgundy, 4. Brabant. Charged with a vertically divided inescutcheon, left Flanders, right Tyrol. On the shoulder-pieces, the same arms rotated laterally through 90 degrees. Appliqué work, partially embroidered. On the most solemn state occasions, the Toison d'Or wore the Potence (Cat. No. 213) with the long vestments; on less official occasions he wore the Enamel, a small escutcheon with the arms of the sovereign, together with the tabard.   R. B.

212 HERALD'S STAFF OF THE TOISON D'OR
Brussels, 1781
Wood, velvet, silver lamé, silver, mostly gilded; 80 cms long (Inv. No. XIV 98)

The emblems of the order in silver lamé are appliquéd on the red velvet and partially embroidered. Made in 1781 for the state entry of Emperor Joseph II into the Netherlands.   R. B.

213 THE POTENCE (CHAIN OF ARMS) OF THE HERALD OF THE ORDER OF THE GOLDEN FLEECE
Netherlandish, probably 1517
Gold, enamel en ronde bosse, champlevé enamel; dimensions: outer circumference 143 cms, inner circumference 98.8 cms; total width including

Like those on the potence, these plaques derive from various periods: the oldest escutcheon was almost certainly made at the same time as the potence itself (1517, or shortly thereafter), while the most recent one dates from 1700. The basis for dating is provided by the year in which the bearer of the escutcheon became a Knight of the Order.   H. T.

outer chain: 10.3 cms (without outer chain: 7.8 cms). On loan from the Order of the Golden Fleece (Dep. Prot. 4)

The chain of arms consists of a neck-chain of the Order and a closed collar of 26 double-walled plates. Each of these plates has a convex frame into which two armorial plaques are inserted. The plates are joined by radial hinges. The lower ends of the hinge-pins are attached to the back of the enamelled flints. Thus the spark-emitting flints form the rigid parts of the neck-chain. The individual links of the neckchain are loosely attached to each other by rings, making the pairs of links formed of intertwining fire steels flexible.

Each of the armorial plaques bears the arms of a Knight of the Order. Two fields are reserved for the arms of the sovereign. This gives a sum of 51 Knights of the Order, the number ordained by Charles V. The armorial plaques are interchangeable so that all the living members of the Order could be represented on the Potence; however, this rule was not necessarily observed.   H. T.

Ref.: E. v. Hartmann-Franzenshuld, Die Potence des Toison d'Or und ein Wappenbuch des Ordens vom Goldenen Vlies, in: Jahrbuch der k. k. heraldischen Gesellschaft 'Adler', Jg. X, 1883, p. 1 ff. (including attribution of the arms).

214 SIX ESCUTCHEONS FOR THE POTENCE

Gold with champlevé enamel; each 3.6 x 2.9 cms. On loan from the Order of the Golden Fleece (Dep. Prot. 5)

215 a) THE CROSS OF ALLEGIANCE OF THE ORDER OF THE GOLDEN FLEECE

French, c. 1400 (?); the stand, consisting of a foot and a clamping fixture for the cross, Netherlandish, between 1453 and 1467.

Gold, pearls, sapphires, rubies; 36 cms high. On loan from the Order of the Golden Fleece (Dep. Prot. 1)

Ever since the foundation of the Order, all newly appointed Knights and Officers of the Order have taken their oath of allegiance in this cross.

The cross itself is hollow and made of smooth gold foil with round profiled edges. The arms of the cross terminate in rhomboids, their profiled edges continuing into those of the arms, thus leaving the rhomboids open on one side. At the intersection of the arms, a cross-shaped piece has been cut out of the upper layer of the gold foil and a cross-shaped lid fitted over the cavity thus created, whitch at one time held a particle of the True Cross. The whole length of both arms is fitted with contiguous lozenge-shaped settings containing a total of 21 sapphires. The intersection and the centres of the extremities of the cross are decorated with rubies. The exterior angles of the rhomboids and the intersection of the arms are decorated with pearls gouped in threes. The lower end of the cross is joined to the solid conical stem of the stand, which has been recessed to accomodate the lowest pearl on the cross. The stand continues down into an octagonal oblong foot. Embossed on the concave sides of the narrow rim of the socle is a continuous pattern composed of the symbols of the fire steel and the spark-emitting flint. The flat parts of individual sections on the foot bear the engraved arms and emblems of Philip the Good. They indicate a probable dating for the foot of the cross of between 1453 and 1467. The cross sits firmly in the neck of the stand, held fast by a screw, the head of which is in the shape of a fire steel. The two parts are thus separable. This is surprising, since there had always been the one case for both the cross and the foot; on the other hand this was not uncommon in the Middle Ages.

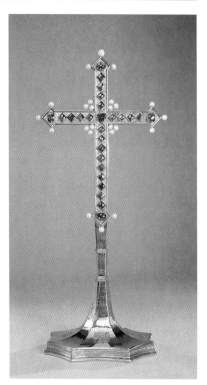

As Francis Salet has shown, the leather case that has also been preserved bears the arms of Jean de France, Duke of Berry, and must have been made before 1400, assuming that this cross is identical to the standing cross described as a *croix à lozanges* in the detailed inventory of 1401/02. However, there is no mention of a particle of the Cross, in contrast to other crosses listed in the inventory, where such particles are expressly mentioned. In Burgundian sources the crosss can be positively identified in the inventory of Philip the Good's estate, with the particle of the cross mentioned for the first time. As Salet has pointed out, Philip the Good placed this reliquary cross from his private possessions at the disposal of the Order of the Golden Fleece for the swearing of allegiance at chapters of the Order. It does not appear as a permanent possession of the Order until 1483.

Evidently the lozenge cross of the Duke of Berry was altered to accomodate the particle of the Cross, the foot on the other hand being replaced, whereby the ancient, noble form of the cross determined the shape of the new foot. Judging by the leather case which was retained after the alterations, the base of the original foot must have been higher and the transition from the cross to the foot have previously projected out further, since the disc-like bulge in the case would not otherwise have been necessary.

Ref.: F. Salet, La 'Croix du Serment' de l'ordre de la Toison d'Or, in: Journal des savants, 1974, p. 73 ff.; J. Ph. Lecat, Le siècle de la Toison d'Or, Paris 1986, p. 13.

b) Case for the Cross of Allegiance

French, c. 1400

Leather, leather carving and blind-stamping; 39 cms high. On loan from the Order of the Golden Fleece (Dep. Prot. 2)

On the front the arms of Jean, Duke of Berry († 1416).   H. T.

THE LITURGICAL VESTMENTS OF THE ORDER
OF THE GOLDEN FLEECE

This set of over-garments for three priests and two antependia serving as altar paraments may be regarded as being covered by the traditional concept of liturgical vestments and parament treasure used in the Christian mass, even if in this case they are incomparably more precious. The chasuble is the liturgical over-garment worn by the bishop or priest officiating at Holy Mass. The deacon wears the dalmatic, the subdeacon the tunicle. In all other church services, pluvials (choir copes) are worn by the officiating clergy. According to the information provided by late-Gothic treasury inventories, a complete set of liturgical vestments, at one time also called a capella (chapelle), has to include two antependia ('curtains'). They are differentiated as frontal *(frontier)* and retrofrontal (*dossier,* back-cloth instead of a retable). This set of vestments was named after its one-time owners, the Order of the Golden Fleece, due to the fact that, after 1477, it was always listed in inventories as being in their possession. Since, however, no emblems of the order are embroidered anywhere on it, it was generally agreed that this capella was probably commissioned by Duke Philip the Good of Burgundy for his own personal use and was only donated to the order at a later date. This fact accounts for the second designation of these "most costly vestments in the world" as the *Burgundian parament treasure.*

In the 15th century, the Burgundian court radiated an unprecedented splendour. All the manifestations of courtly life served the end of princely representation. To provide the most sumptuous furnishings possible for the ducal court — on high days, the ecclesiastical became one with the secular — monumental tapestry sequences and costly fabrics were commissioned. The flourishing of trade experienced by numerous textile manufacturers in the Netherlands was due not least to the encouragement it received from the Burgundian court. As an easily moveable artistic asset, textiles could be folded up and taken on journeys. Duke Philip the Good of Burgundy was constantly travelling, moving from one residence to another throughout his realm.

The Burgundian parament treasure can be regarded as the finest work achieved in the art of European embroidery. Such success can only be achieved if extraordinarily fortunate circumstances concur, if creative powers combine in a fruitful historical situation, and if a patron inclined to maecenatism is prepared to take care of the high costs. Through their culture and art commissions, the Burgundian dukes acquired a lasting reputation.

The past and present cultural values that had been created in the north flowed together into the Burgundian provinces as if into a reservoir. With the political, economic and then also cultural shift of importance from the Burgundian mother country to the gradually acquired northerly possessions in the Netherlands, it seemed as if even the Franco-Flemish court artists who had played such an important role in French — and therefore also Burgundian — art throughout several of its courtly phases of style ever since the last quarter of the 14th century, were gradually being replaced by Netherlandish artists. The latter advocated a conception of art which was increasingly oriented towards worldly reality. As a result of this change of direction towards the New Realism, early Netherlandish panel painting had, by 1430, already achieved artistic preeminence among the various branches of the arts, which had previously all been of equal standing. The major occupation of the Flemish painters at this time appears to have been that of making suitable designs and cartoons for tapestries. Art for art's sake did not essentially exist in the Middle Ages. Since branches such as carpet weaving and pictorial embroidery had already reached an artistic peak in their evolution, the history of this field of art takes the same course as other, more general developments. Of the liturgical vestments, the dalmatic, the tunicle and the three choir copes (with the exception of their non-functional hoods) have each been made as one piece on a strong linen ground. Their heavily patterned gold borders have also

been embroidered instead of being sewn on. However, all the figures of the antependia have been embroidered individually, and separately from their pictorial
fields, such as the banderoles or the furnishings. All these separately finished
pieces were then appliquéd, i.e. sewn on, to the common linen ground. In the case
of the chasuble the same thing happened with the scenic representations. They
too were divided into individual elements and embroidered separately. Handfuls
of pearls are dispersed over all the liturgical garments, being combined in rosettes
and the beading which outlines the form.

One of the reasons for the high esteem enjoyed by the Burgundian paraments is
to be found in the perfect fusion of two embroidery techniques: that of needle
painting and that of the newly developed lazur embroidery *(or nué)*, which
perhaps emerged as a complete success for the first time ever here. Even the technique of needle painting, which had been developed a century earlier, achieves
the height of perfection in these Burgundian-Netherlandish paraments. Using
densely embroidered silk threads and finely graded transitions of colour tones,
the impression of painting is suggested and, in the shimmer of light, even surpassed. Needle painting occurs in the carnation, that is, in the flesh tones of the
skin; above all in faces and hands, but also in hair and in the fur trimmings of
clothes.

Everything else within the pictorial field is executed in costly lazur embroidery.
The whole embroidered surface is covered by gold threads laid very closely
together horizontally on the backing and held in place by polychrome silk
threads; two gold threads each are held in place by silk stitches sewn vertically.
The contours and modelling of the individual representation results from the unequal distribution of these silk stitches: at wider intervals, the self-illuminating
gold shimmers as the highpoint of the figural relief, until its luminosity dimin-
ishes with the increasing closeness of the coloured silk threads and is replaced by
physical modelling. Although little of the shining gold comes through in those
places darkened by shadow, the intensity of colour of the silk is at its greatest
there. The colourful silk is flashed with gold as if by translucent coloured glazes,
shining through the silk's own sheen and gleaming almost unhindered in the
reflected light of the gold highlights.

The combination of the two embroidery techniques and the impression of a wonderful, glimmering sheen over the whole, which accorded with the medieval
aspiration towards colour magic and other-worldly light-mysticism, endowed the
liturgical vestments with a unique artistic trait. The production of the parament
treasure may have been protracted by a gradual extension of the commission and
the programme.

In order to avoid any all-too-crass connections to reality and to lend the paraments the sacral dignity they deserved, all the existing possibilities of textile
craftsmanship were employed to build up a new language of light, unique in its
harmony of content and form. In particular, the effects inherent in gold were used
in a variety of ways. In the Middle Ages gold always signifies sacral light, and is
a symbol of holiness. As an artistic means of design, on the other hand, the light
of gold contributes to the unification of the whole. The presence of the gleam of
the gold transforms the pictorial representation into an unearthly place of the
manifestation of the holy. Gold is employed to give expression to the super-
natural, the miraculous. It communicates an idea of the true divine light. From
another point of view, the golden sheen unifies the pictorial effect of the
paraments.

It may be said that the pictorial light of this piece of embroidery, which thrives
on the tension between renunciation of the world and acceptance of the world,
is pervaded more intensively than any other piece of textile craftsmanship by two
languages of light: that centred on the representation, and that determined by the
material. In the parament treasure the light maintains a state of suspension between the self-illumination possessed by the gleaming gold and shimmering silk,

and the illuminating light which is represented in the picture itself as light entering from without, and is the source of the shadowing relief which models all the forms within the picture. With the exception of translucent gold *en baisse taille* enamel, it is only in the textile medium that gold-coloured highlights used for smooth transitions to gleaming pure gold are to be found prior to the middle of the 15th century.

Silk reflects incidental light: for this reason the parts which are wholly embroidered in needle painting — incarnation in the form of the flesh tints of the faces and bodies — light up silkily themselves. Everything which is shaded or darkened also shimmers, because it is likewise embroidered in self-illuminating silk. What occurs — both in details as in the whole — is thus a mutual permeation of the inherent self-illuminating light of the gold and silk and the inner illuminating light of the picture. The latter is light which has the effect of giving shape to bodies and creating space through shading. Those places where colour and gold merge with each other enable a unified relief of light and shade to emerge. From the relationship between the two languages of light there arises a concrete world of irreal world-detachment. This phenomenon of light can only be rendered incompletely by the term 'mystic light'.

A comparison with the achievements of Netherlandish panel painting from the same period enables us to outline the artistic significance of the Burgundian-Netherlandish parament treasure. As has now been discovered, the brothers van Eyck were the inventors not so much of oil painting as of a type of painting with self-illuminating colours which glow in the light. Owing to many-layered colour glazes, the light of their colours develops a sheen of its own and a power of illumination similar to that of precious stones, which they also love to represent in their pictures.

Jan van Eyck observes the light situation in natural illumination and reproduces it in the spatiality of his pictures exactly as it is, wholly in the sense of a naturalisation of the sacral domain, even if they are a depiction of the divine.

With the means provided by textiles, as they were used in the liturgical vestments, another goal was envisaged, and attained — a complementary goal. With sacral gold light it became possible to successfully render the miraculous, the beyond, visible (formerly it was called 'close to reality') and nevertheless to leave it in the detached sphere appropriate to it. Sacral art obeys its own rules, yet on the other hand the natural logic of vision is partially suspended. This resacralisation of art harmonises ideally with the intended purpose of the paraments.   H. T.

THE LITURGICAL VESTMENTS OF THE ORDER OF THE GOLDEN FLEECE

Burgundian, between 1425 and 1440
Linen, plain weave; on the garments the framing structure embroidered in polychrome silk and gold and silver metal threads in *or nué* technique; pearls, pastes (glass)

216 ANTEPENDIUM (Frontal)

Marriage of St. Catherine, prophets and apostles; 330 x 119 cms (Inv. No. Pl 17)

Flanked by John the Baptist and St. Catherine of Alexandria, the Virgin Mary is seated on a throne with the infant Jesus, in the middle of a Gothic church interior with a double-storeyed division of the walls. The surrounding arrangement of pillars, which is surmounted by triple-arched vaulting, leaves the view free and mediates between the inside and outside. The Vir-

gin Mary holds writing implements, namely an ink-pot with dipped quill and a quill case, and a manuscript roll which is spread across the child's lap. Reaching forward, the Holy Child places a ring of betrothal on St. Catherine's finger.

To the side of the central picture are a total of 12 'author portraits' arranged in two rows of three pictorial fields each. In these portraits there is a dis-

proportion between the figures and the space surrounding them. They are seated cramped in the midst of their furniture, despite the fact that, to judge from the vaulting and the rows of windows, their scholar's cells seem to be spacious enough. The scrolls weaving through the pictorial space can no longer be read, although the designation of the figures on the frame proves the upper row to be prophets and the figures below, who are provided with additional attributes, apostles.

Under the influence of the *devotio moderna,* a religious trend which sought to foster an emotional approach to the message of salvation, there were numerous subjective inventions in religious art around 1400. These new devotional pictures were supposed to lead to a more profound insight into the deeper connotations of the doctrine of salvation.

This can also be seen in the pictorial motif of the Virgin Mary enthroned and with the infant Jesus writing. This is here combined with a favourite theme of courtly painting, that of the mystic marriage of St. Catherine, to form a coherent pictorial whole. Even in the earliest known version, dating from 1386, the infant Jesus is shown turning, in the act of writing, to someone opposite. There it is a donor, whose plea is being written down by the Holy Child. In the embroidered centre picture of the antependium, the motif of the act of writing has been left out, although scroll and writing implements remain. It looks as if the infant Jesus has finished his inscription, put the quill back in the ink-pot, and is turning towards St. Catherine in order to perform the mystic marriage. The inscription on the scroll can no longer be read, which has left room for a series of interpretations. Most appropriate for the content of the picture would be the words of the saviour *"I am the way, the truth and the life",* which occur in a related version in a panel painting. The representation is directly related to Holy Mass, as may be concluded from the picture of the dossal above it and especially from the function of these two altar paraments. Just as the scroll makes the Word manifest, so the Saviour appears through Mary. The beginning and end of the salvation, childhood and suffering of the triune God are arranged together in two pictures. The reference to the role of the Virgin Mary as the co-saviour occurs in a disguised form, as does the announcement of the redemptive expiatory death of Christ. Foreseeing his self-sacrifice, the Holy Child announces his mission. In the inscription, on the other hand, the promise of salvation for all believers is concealed. The choice of a church choir as the scene of the mystical gathering beyond the bounds of time signifies that it takes place in the realm of heaven.

H. T.

217 ALTAR ANTEPENDIUM (Retrofrontal)

Notgottes-Trinity, prophets and apostles; 330 cms long, 119 cms wide (Inv. No. Pl 18)

The subject as depicted here is closely connected with the Eucharist. In this representation of the Trinity, God on his throne supports his Son, the Man of Sorrows, whose body is covered in wounds, while the Dove of the Holy Spirit hovers over Jesus' left shoulder. Here again, the church-like interior symbolises God's dwelling, the Kingdom of Heaven. This devotional image derives its meaning from Christ's sacrifice for the redemption of mankind. According to Christian doctrine, the priest at holy mass renews in unbloody sacrifice at the altar Christ's death on the cross as the sacrifice of the Son to the Father, who accords the world a share in the fruit of this act of atonement.

Thus this *Notgottes*-Trinity does not depict a historical event; Christ's expiatory death is here realised as a divine act of redemption. While this new mode of representing the Trinity derives from the spirit of the Passion, the blurring of the time-orientated limits of the event reinforces the impression of the timelessness of the image, thus intensifying its devotional character. The onlooker is as it were drawn into the events of the picture by God the Father displaying the body of his Son. Although the Man of Sorrows cannot stand unaided, God the Father does not really bear the whole weight of Christ's body. A spark of animation is transmitted in the open eyes of the dead Christ, who presents his wounds to the onlooker. His body is depicted in the act of sinking to the ground, but the impression of helplessness has been avoided, since the idea of a completely lifeless corpse, passively subject to the force of gravity, would have contradicted the devotional aspect of the image. The artist who drew the cartoons for the embroidery was concerned to evoke the strongest possible emotional bond between the image and the onlooker. The *Notgottes*-Trinity with the body of Christ presented contains a threefold appeal. It is first of all an image of the ineffable love of God: here, it is the compassion rather than the sorrow of the father that is depicted. For the first time, God the Father is represented as a loving and merciful father, devoted to mankind. Late medieval belief related everything to the Redemption. Thus God the Father presents the Redeemer as salvation for all mankind. The *Notgottes*-Trinity is furthermore an image of the self-sacrificing compassion of the Redeemer for mankind. Christ, the second person of the Trinity, identifies himself as one who has suffered on Earth. Finally, the image evokes the compassion of mankind for the God who suffers for their sake.

The Master of Flémalle — the name used for the anonymous artist of the cartoons for these embroideries, who has often been identified as Robert Campin (1375—1444), the Master from Tournai, — represents the transition to a period when a tangibly realistic representation of holy persons was striven for, so that they almost seem to be contemporaries transported into the religious events of the image. The artist probably drew the cartoons for the embroidered central panel himself.

In the spirit of the *devotio moderna,* both theologians and artists were concerned to translate into the present the doctrinal and devotional contents which refer to the incarnation of Christ as a historical event by representing them in contemporary terms. The more 'realistic' the image of the incarnation of Christ was, the more convincingly the religious truth seemed to be conveyed. This type of visualisation of the act of salvation, which demands empathy from the onlooker even with the inner life of divine figures, touched off

a revolutionary process in Christian art. At first it resulted in humanisation; eventually, however, it led to the secularisation of art and a weakening of religious faith. The realistic embodiment of religious subjects inevitably implied demystification of the religious mystery. Representation in three-dimensional space necessarily implies the question of the exact time and place of the individual stations of the divine plan of redemption. In answer to this profane question art could only counter with an illusionistic speculative narrative. The pioneer generation of new realism in the Netherlands, to which the Master of Flémalle belonged, was well aware of its precarious situation. Their artistic instincts impelled them to reproduce the world around them as their eyes saw it, and the artistic conquest of the visible world engaged their powers to the full. In spite of this, the challenge of simultaneously fulfilling the demands of religious painting prompted the consideration of possible solutions to this dilemma. Inspired by sculpted altar shrines, some painters attempted a depiction of alternating planes of reality. Whereas the Master of Flémalle in his earliest treatment of this subject (Leningrad) had depicted the Holy Trinity under a baldachin, the draped hangings of which allude to the

revelation of the divine mysteries, in the last version he portrays a sculptural group standing in a wall niche painted in stone-coloured grisaille (Frankfurt/M.). The Trinity appears transposed to a level of reality where the cultic image has been created by man.

The Trinity on the embroidered altar-retrofrontal is related in its sculptural composition to the later work; in iconographical terms, however, it goes back to another version by the Master of Flémalle, the original of which has been lost. In that version, two standing angels hold the implements of the Passion on either side of the Trinity, and two angels crouching in the foreground present the shroud of the body of Christ, held up for contemplation by God the Father. In the embroidered version, the shroud draped round the lower part of Christ's body recalls the lost painting. Here, the shroud additionally performs the function of a loincloth. All later versions are charac-

terised by the veristic depiction of the stigmata on both sides of the feet, on the instep and on the dusty sole.

The 24 individual figures of the seated apostles and prophets on the two antependia display certain idiosyncrasies of style which have been interpreted as characteristics of an earlier, somewhat stolid transitional style of the 1420's. That these figures are typically French is indubitable. Older elements, such as some of the facial types, their expression clouded with melancholy, or the peculiarly flat, almost boneless hands, are set against newer elements corresponding to contemporary concerns. This can be seen in the impressive, cubic presence of the weighty bodies.

If these seated figures were to stand up, they would burst the confines of their frames. The interior of the 'cells' where they sit is not visualised as empty space — on the contrary, the feeling of interiority is conveyed by the furnishings and the wealth of scholarly paraphernalia. It is striking that very few of the figures are depicted in the act of reading or writing. Possessed by inner visions, most of them seem to be either listening to the voice within them or gesticulating in debate.

Some, for example the prophet David in the upper right-hand row of the frontal, give vent to their inner agitation with a turn of their bodies expressive of pathos.

This contrapposto twisting of the body to an angle almost diametrically opposite to the direction in which the figure is sitting, and the tension resulting from this, does not occur in Early Netherlandish painting. It must have derived from a knowledge of Italian sculpture. In Burgundy itself, Claus Sluter, the most important sculptor of his time north of the Alps, had created sculptures imbued with an inner monumentality for the tombs of the Dukes of Burgundy at Champmol near Dijon. Sculptors and important panel painters were working at Champmol right up to the third quarter of the 15th century. However, the Burgundian-French cubic style has only been preserved in its transposed form; what remains can be seen in the lateral panels of the antependium. The art of e.g. Konrad Witz seems to have been inspired by such models and their impressive massivity.

Specifically French-Burgundian features are evident in the harmony of colours and the treatment of light.   H. T.

218 PLUVIAL
(so-called Cope of Christ)
Hood: the Almighty (or God the Father); orphreys: prophets and apostles; in 3 rows: Archangel Michael and cherubim, martyrs, saintly princes and clergy; 330 cms wide, 164 cms long (Inv. No. Pl 19)

Taken together, the three embroidered copes reproduce the triumphal display of the magnificence of God, interwoven with an 'Adoration of the Trinity' resolved into individual figures of the saints. In this way a meaningful whole is created, and in many points it corresponds to the scheme adopted in the Ghent Altarpiece, the chief masterpiece of early Netherlandish painting at that time. There, too, the starting point was a conceptual whole, derived from sources in the New Testament and various theological writings and divided up into several pictorial units. One main theme of the Ghent Altarpiece, however, does not occur in the copes, namely, that of the Adoration of the Lamb. Also, in the altarpiece the choirs of angels and the congregation of saints gather in groups, while in the pluvials, the surface of the cope is provided with a system of honeycombed pictorial fields organised as a basic radial framework interlocking in three concentric rows. Instead of spatial integration, a system of individual figures in fields of uniform shape is created. Bordered by apostles and prophets in the orphreys, those chosen to behold God are gathered together inside their architectonic housing, under the leadership of the hierarchy of angels. Depicted separately on the three pluvial hoods appear the Almighty and, on either side of him, the Virgin Mary and John the Baptist, both also enthroned. By the term 'Almighty', as St. Augustine, with all the authority of a Church Father, expresses it: *"neither the Father nor the Son nor the Holy Ghost is explicitly designated, but rather the Blessed and sole powerful One, the King of Kings and Lord of all Lords."*

In the Ghent Altarpiece, all these designations are to be found in inscription form in the representation of the

enthroned God in papal vestments. There, the semantic import of the Trinity overlaps in meaning with that of God the Father. It is sufficient to know that, in its content, the representation of God in the 'pluvial of Christ' signifies the Holy Trinity: most likely God the Father in his own right, but certainly not Christ as Judge of the World.

When he died in 1426, Hubert van Eyck had already begun to paint the Ghent Altarpiece and had nearly finished the four panels which are significant for comparison: representations of God the Father, the Virgin Mary and John the Baptist, and the oblong Adoration of the Lamb beneath. His brother, Jan van Eyck, cofounder of the New Realism, resumed the work upon his return from a journey to the Iberian peninusula on behalf of the Burgundian Duke in 1428/29, and completed the altar in 1432.

Striving for a canonical image of the Almighty, Hubert van Eyck, like others before him, must have used as his model a time-honoured Byzantine icon. The formal similarity to the type of Christ may be explained by the use of an icon which showed a Deesis in a half-figure arrangement of the group of the intercessors as represented in the Last Judgement. According to the Byzantine tradition, a Deesis consists of Christ and the two intercessors, the Virgin Mary and John the Baptist, who plead for mercy on behalf of mankind. It is possible that the Master of Flé-

malle was also familiar with the same icon and reproduced it even more faithfully in form, as may be concluded from a panel painting of his (Philadelphia). In our opinion a comparison of styles reveals that it was the Master of Flémalle who freely adapted the exemplary Eyckian compositions of the Ghent Altarpiece as a creation of his own, resolving them into separate pictorial fields and adapting them as cartoons for the embroiderers.

The compositional principles developed by the Master of Flémalle basically refer to the pictorial surface as a projective plane and not so much to the constructive coordinates of the representation of three-dimensional space. For him, it is not so much a matter of rendering everything in true perspective in its spatial position; what matters to him is to achieve a pictorial pattern which is as densely knit as possible and which fills the whole surface. In order to achieve such an arrangement of planes, he even accepts the distortions of those forms which are to be enlarged or extended.

The spatial scene in which this physical manifestation of the divine takes place is a baldachin whose sides are folded back over a wall, thus becoming part of the plane. They provide a view of the semicircular furniture of the throne with its drape of glory. The top of the baldachin, above the figure of the Almighty, finds a parallel in the space-creating curve of its base. If the baldachin is intended in a figurative sense as the tabernacle of the heavens, it can be inferred that the globe at the feet of the Divinity is an attribute: the universe is his footstool.

What most catches the eye in this composition is the still unresolved state of tension between physical space and surface relations, as can be seen at the level of the throne, the curve of which is folded-down and projected out-of-perspective. In a whole range of Flémallesque pictorial formulas — as also in the solutions of Hubert van Eyck, and in contrast to those of Jan van Eyck — the visual distortion in the transition from the frontal aspect to the top-view emerges as a still unresolved state of suspense, even through the latter definitely treates space. The cause of this lies in the conflict betweeen the front view and the plan view. However, in the parament treasure, the visual distortion is offset to a great extent by the roundness formally predetermined by the shape of the pluvial hood.   H. T.

the pillars behind the seated figure of the Virgin creates an impression of space, the semicircle being repeated in the wall behind them. The frontal projection is indicated merely by the rounding of the base and the roof, and remains two-dimensional. The introduction of the curtains wound around the shafts of the pillars represents an astounding innovation. They herald the unveiling of the divine mysteries. In all likelihood, the artistic inspiration for this derives from monumental compositions of late antiquity. These were accessible to artists who travelled to the Holy Land or Constantinople, where (from c. 1250) these motifs had been revived in the Byzantine art of the era of the Paleologi.

Although the individual details of the throne's architecture give the impres-

219 COPE OF THE VIRGIN MARY (Pluvial)

Hood: Virgin Mary; orphreys: Apostles and Prophets; in three rows: Archangel Gabriel with angels, holy virgins, women and widows; 330 cms wide, 164 cms long (Inv. No. Pl 21)

The designs of the Master of Flémalle transform the throne of the Virgin Mary into the architectonic form of a rotunda. It stands in the middle of a three-dimensional dais extending back into a semicircle. In the representation of God the Father, short pillars were used as the posts of his Throne; here, finely-proportioned pillars with Romanesque capitals support the round, richly-profiled roof covering the heavenly throne. The arrangement of

sion of plasticity, the artist does not seem to have been concerned to dimensionalise the motif of the seated figure itself. The figure remains two-dimensional; the forms of the body are concealed under the drapery of the garments and the folds are developed as surface projections in flowing transitions along the projective plane of the picture.

In striking contrast to its forerunner in the Ghent altar, where the Virgin is depicted reading, she is here seen in a more conventionally religious role as the Mother of God, as intercessor and in adoration of the Almighty. However, neither her face nor the gesture of her hands express deeper emotions. The Master of Flémalle was attempting to achieve a certain neutralisation of the religious moment. His figures remain unmoved, mutely inexpressive.   H. T.

220 PLUVIAL
(Cope of John the Baptist)

Hood: John the Baptist; orphreys: prophets and apostles; in 3 rows: Archangel Raphael and angels, patriarchs, prophets, saintly monks and hermits; 330 cms wide, 164 cms high (Inv. No. Pl 20)

John the Baptist is enthroned beneath a baldachin. The remarkable thing here is the fact that the figure honoured in this majestic way is at the same time a hermit, here living in the depth of the forest instead of the desert. His indistinct hermitage is almost completely hidden by the bench: the beginning of it is discernible to the left of the figure, although at first sight it seems as if the saint is crouching on rocky ground. John the Baptist is depicted as a reader looking up from his book to witness Christ as the Lamb of God — the reference is to the representation of the Trinity. In the conception of this picture, a touch of antiquity comes through in motifs such as that of the baldachin stretched between trees, the tent awning blown by a gust of wind

into a forked bough. In this, the Master once again seems to have based his design on Greek models.

The wilderness of the landscape corresponds to the international Gothic style. The spectator's eye also has to wander for a rather long time across the surface features before the front and back of the pictorial space can be distinguished.

The landscape scenery in the background flows with smooth transitions into the spatial setting at the front. The individual blocks of rock seem to be so near that their spatiality appears tangible. Within the picture, the suggestion of the spatiality of this rocky terrain, the depth of which has been built up and extended, is heightened considerably by the rounded border of the pictorial field resulting from the form of the pluvial hood.

The ascetic figure of the hermit living in the wilderness, overcoming his uncouthness with his intellect, and displaying such unmistakable features as the perfect modelling of his powerful feet, derive from pictorial formulations associated with Hubert van Eyck. Among others, characteristics such as the hard and brittle congestion of the

folds of the drapery (quite different to the 'angular' style of Jan van Eyck or Konrad Witz) are typical of the formal repertoire of Hubert van Eyck or of the Master of Flémalle.

Broad gold braiding creates a system of individual honeycombs with rosettes in the six corners. Inside each honeycomb, the red velvet braiding and two differently patterned narrow gold borders lead into the arcade and its tracery; behind that begins the illusionistic pictorial space.

As a spatial extension of the traditional motif of the *homme arcade,* chapel-like compartments were developed, in order to provide a background for the individual figures standing within. The first pictorial evidence of this can be found in Netherlandish book illumination from the beginning of the 15th century, although in their earliest form such chapel structures go back to Franco-Flemish tapestries from the end of the 14th century. There, too, are to be found integrated facade effects, with uniform development of the spatial elements, although not with such rigorous geometrical-abstract order and without any decorative-ornamental surface connections in the structural arrangement. Such figure-niches do not open out into pictorial depth, not even in the case of the spatialised niches of the apostles and prophet on the orphreys, i.e. the broad border along the front hem of the cope. The wall-openings of the chapel structures are faced with gold patterns lacking a view of the outside, so that the barrel-vaulted walls with their flat figure-niches, which appear massive anyway, seem to be hung with a gold-coloured textile wall-hanging.

There is evidence of both kinds of figure-niche in the oeuvre of the principal masters of early Netherlandish painting: of the latter, on the outside of the altar as stone-coloured (grisaille) barrel-vaulted sculpture-niches, of the former as painted orphreys on the liturgical garments of the clergy represented in the picture.

Within the scope of the present work, it is impossible to go into more detail about the multitude of angels and saints. There is not enough space either to list individually the figures represented, or to say much about the style in which they have been painted. What can be pointed out is that everything displays great originality and quality, not a single figure occurs twice or has been directly adopted from an altar panel. Only the Master of Flémalle and his pupil and equal Rogier van der Weyden come into consideration as the possible designer. With subtle needlework, the embroiders have congenially transformed even the finest details and nuances of colour into the medium of embroidery. For instance, with the help of the magnifying glass it is possible to ascertain three or four nuances of colour in the silk thread used for the blue or brown of the iris in the minute eyeball. In pointillistic manner a plum-blue colour in the cope becomes resolved into blues, reds, browns and even ochre silk; on the other hand, this mosaic composed of individual stiches is only optically recombined into a plum-blue in the eye of the spectator. In the same way, physical or spatial shadows often arise as changes of colour; new colours are also added, not only deepened.

The embroiderers were adept at incorporating the colours they derived from a close observation of nature into their own artistic medium. It may be assumed that the supreme artistic achievement of the embroiderers lies in the translation of natural, illuminative light into the more complex language of light that is characteristic of lazur embroidery on a gold ground.

An indication that the embroidery workshops became integrated into French-Burgundian artistic life is provided by their belief in the primacy of colour, and their choice and use of the palette of colours. In French art the blue or red tones of the figures of the angels — compare the cherubim on the 'Cope of Christ' — have a long tradition. Such representations of angels might also be present as cloudy, fleeting points of golden light on a colourful ground or stippled decoration on a smooth gold ground. Since the language of Franco-Flemish art merged with the early Netherlandish New Realism style of painting, it is difficult to localise the embroidery workshops. Burgundy was most receptive towards the Italian influence. Much may be said in favour of the argument that at least the beginnings of this important embroidery undertaking are to be found in Burgundy, probably in Dijon. The pioneer generation of early Netherlandish panel painters also worked for the ducal Palace Chapel in Dijon and the Carthusian monastery of Champmol.   H. T.

221 CHASUBLE (CASULA)

Front: the Baptism of Christ; in two rows: angels; back: the Transfiguration of Christ; in three rows: angels; 149.5 cms long, 135.5 cms wide (Inv. No. Pl 14)

On the banderole above God the Father in the representation of the Baptism: HIC EST FILIVS MEVS DI-LECTVS IN QVO MI(HI) B(E)N(E) CO(MPLACVI) (This is my beloved Son in whom I am well pleased). On the banderoles in the representation of the Transfiguration: beside God the Father: HIC EST FILIVS MEVS DILECTVS IN QUO MIHI BENE CO(M)PLAC(VI) (see above); beside Christ: NEMINI DIXERITIS VI-SIONE(M) DONEC FILIVS HOM-INIS A (mortuis resurgat) (Tell the vision to no man, until the Son of Man [be risen again from the dead]; beside Peter: D(OMI)NE BONV(M) EST NOS HIC ESSE SI VIS FACIAM(VS) HIC (Master, it is good for us to be here; if thou wilt, let us make here three tabernacles).

In contrast to the clear structure of the two antependia, the panels of which form a system of similar interiors, the considerably more complex structure of the chasuble aims at achieving a harmonious balance between various different demands which are extremely difficult to reconcile. These arise from the conflict between the chasuble's function as a liturgical vestment and its role as the vehicle of a pictorial scheme

and its message. Three entirely different types of formal organisation are present on the chasuble, and these at times even mutually overlap. This implies an alternation in the illusionistic effect of what is represented, leading to multiple refractions of the pictorial references to reality. However, it also particularly emphasises the textile character of the vestment. This in turn accentuates the liturgically determined form of the chasuble, with its broad orphreys forming a stylised chasuble cross on both sides. Both chasuble crosses are superimposed on the geometrical honeycomb structure, which opens up into a corresponding system of chapel-like compartments enclosing figures of angels. The borders of the orphreys, which are in actual fact entirely embroidered, seem as if they have been woven from brocade, and the individual figures subsequently embroidered onto them. This imaginative game with different planes of reality is taken even further. The scenes represented on the front and back of the chasuble (the Baptism and Transfiguration of Christ) consist of separated, individual figures. For the flanking pairs of figures there remains only a strip of rocky ground as a residual form of the dissolved spatial coherence. In the representation of the Baptism, this spills over the edge of the orphrey to enclose the waters of the River Jordan. The figures are localised on a common ground, yet there is no pictorial space above them. The outlines of the figures seem as if they have been superimposed onto the honeycomb pattern.

It should be emphasised that all the overlapping exists only ostensibly, i.e. as a means of illusion. In reality, all the appliqués were exactly planned beforehand, like those of the earlier antependia, and none of them actually overlap at all.

The structural elements of the liturgical form of the chasuble-cross and the honeycombing ornamentation, like the prototypes of the pluvials, were used consciously, with additional formal means being employed to heighten the illusion, so as to prevent the development of a unified pictorial space. Any tendencies within the pictures themselves towards spatial narrative are also surpressed; these separated, individual figures, placed in a two-dimensional setting, seem as if they have been sewn onto a finished pictorial chasuble, as indeed has often been asserted in the past. The question remains as to why this extraordinary formal solution with the three superimposed structures was adopted. The theme of the Transfiguration of Christ demonstrates incisively the degree to which the technique of *or nué* embroidery, with its own highly developed language of light, is equal to the task of representing the Transfiguration of Christ as a phenomenon of celestial light and thus endowing it with immediacy for the onlooker.

Transfiguration means transformation into a state of glory. At the Transfiguration of Christ, the theophany, i.e. the manifestation of his divine nature, emerges far more clearly than at his Baptism. The voice of God testifies to Jesus as his Son, using the same words on both occasions. In the representation of the Baptism, the theophany is used to represent the Trinity; in the Transfiguration, the Dove of the Holy Spirit is absent, since it is not expressly mentioned in the Gospels.

At the Transfiguration on the mountain, God's revelation transfigures Jesus into celestial light: *And his face did shine as the sun, and his raiment was white as the light.* In Byzantine art, from the 14th century onwards, the disciples' fear of the power of the divine, transfiguring light is heightened dramatically. This is also the case here,

with the hands of the apostles John and James raised as if to protect themselves.

Represented on the long arm of the orphrey are: God the Father in the cloud; hovering in the middle, Christ as Redeemer, as in the formulation of Jan van Eyck; below: St. Peter, who has remained behind, his arms open in adoration. All these figures, however, appear in a completely incoherent spatial system. The figure of Peter goes over the edge of the orphrey, forming a compositional link to his companions in the lateral panels. Depicted on the diagonal arms of the orphrey, as related in the Gospels, is the appearance of Moses (bearing the Tables of the Law) and Elijah.

As mentioned above, the pictorial representations of the Burgundian paraments seem as if they were projected in front of a golden light. Here, a pictorial system has been developed which exploits two different aspects of the nature of light: on the one hand, there are the effects created by the reflexions from the gold and the silks. On the other hand, as opposed to light reflected by matter, the artists have also introduced the light which is immanent to the scenes depicted. The convergence of these phenomena in this *or nué* embroidery creates a unique, indeterminable, almost iridescent state of light. In this golden lustre, the transcendental assumes concrete shape, while earthly bodies and space dissolve into pure light. Yet this not only captures the transcendental element, the simultaneous renunciation and acceptance of the world, with everything depicted floating in a vision of light. In this 'mystic' light, the gold ground also irradiates the intrinsic lustre of the silk. Thus both the mediation of celestial light and the ideal transfiguration of concretely represented forms is achieved. In this respect, the light emanating from the *or nué* embroidery represents the ideal medium for the christological theme of transfiguration.

Of all the figures on the paraments, the transfigured Christ is the only one where the flesh tints were also worked in *or nué* embroidery. Christ's face, in particular, glows red-gold, corresponding to the description in the Scriptures. The figure of Christ seems to radiate more light than the others, an effect achieved by the light tones used for his robes. However, this luminosity is limited to the outline of the figure, since the phenomenon of the 'mystic' light remains bound to the textile nature of the gold, silver and silk, from whose surface characteristics it emanates. Thus the limits of what can be achieved by the light issuing from the *or nué* embroidery are defined: the light remains bound to the surface. It can counteract tendencies towards spatiality; conversely, however, the light itself cannot be transported into the space of the picture, i.e. it cannot illuminate the contents of the picture itself.

The rays of light which issue from the figure of Christ as individual beams are not visualised as a source of light but translated into the traditional form of radiating lines. Despite the almost cylindrical volume of his body, which seems to float without material form, the transfigured Christ is visualised as a luminous but not radiant source of light. Probably aware of the limits of the in-

trinsic possibilities of the medium, the artists wisely avoided attempting a representation of sacred radiance, in which the figure of Christ himself would have functioned as the source of spatial light. In fact, by omitting all spatial references and adopting the ingenious system of the three overlapping decorational structures, the artists of the chasuble emphasised the original, textile character of this liturgical vestment.

The vestments for Holy Mass, i.e. the chasuble and the two dalmatics, would seem to have been the last of the paraments to be executed. Compositions such as the Baptism and Transfiguration of Christ display the stylistic influence of Hubert van Eyck and the Master of Flémalle himself. The somewhat rough-hewn figure of John the Baptist is reminiscent of the former, while the virtuoso composition of the two-dimensional structures is more characteristic of the latter. The delicate figures of the angels were possibly drawn by Rogier van der Weyden, although his teacher, the Master of Flémalle, himself imitated the style of his former pupil in his own late works. The proposed dating of c. 1430—40 would seem most likely, in that the figure of Christ in the Transfiguration is the only really concrete evidence for the influence of Jan van Eyck's newly-introduced 'angular style', with its massive statuary forms. There is a hypothesis supporting a later dating of the liturgical vestments, based on the supposed influence of Hugo van der Goes; however, there is no sign of the latter's dramatic, psychologising mis-en-scène, exaggerated diagonal interlinking of the dramatic relations or his unmistakeable use of light, developed from the spirit of the pictorial narrative, and thus this theory remains ultimately unconvincing.   H. T.

222 DALMATIC

Orphreys: angels; in 3 rows: male saints; 128 cms long, 161.5 cms wide (Inv. No. Pl 16)

223 TUNICLE (tunicella)

Orphreys: angels; in 3 rows: female saints; 128.5 cms long, 160 cms wide (Inv. No. Pl 15)

Virtually no distinction is made between the DALMATIC and the TUNICLE, both being liturgical overgarments open under the sleeves and at the sides since Gothic times. Here the tunicle has sleeves of the same length as the dalmatic, albeit slightly narrower. The dalmatic was worn by the deacon, the tunicle by the subdeacon. As regards the ornamentation, it would seem that the apparels of the sleeves, which are slit underneath, probably once had a border; similarly, the long orphreys — typical of both garments — which decorate the front and back might have had a lateral border either just below the neck or across the breast.

The borders and orphreys are sewn with pearls and bear depictions of angels. On the orphreys there is a continuous storey-like structure of vertical panels with exterior and interior views of the enclosing architectonic motifs. The individual hexagonal panels of the familiar framing honeycomb structure are more elongated than in the other vestments.   H. T.

Ref.: J. v. Schlosser, Der Burgundische Paramentenschatz des Ordens vom Goldenen Vließe, Vienna 1912; M. Dvorák, Das Rätsel der Kunst der Brüder van Eyck (Jahrbuch 1904). Mit einem Anhang über die Anfänge der holländischen Malerei, Munich 1925, p. 205 ff.; M. Schütte und S. Müller-Christensen, Das Stickereiwerk, Tübingen 1963, p. 42 f.; H. v. Einem, Bemerkungen zur Sinneinheit des Genter Altares, in: Miscellanea Jozef Duverger vol. I, Ghent 1968, p. 24 ff.; M. F. Freeman, The St. Martin Embroideries, New York 1968, p. 110 ff.; O. Pächt, Gestaltungsprinzipien der westlichen Malerei (1933), in: Methodisches zur kunsthistorischen Praxis. Ausgewählte Schriften, Munich 1977, p. 17 ff.

224 THE MORSES FOR THE PLUVIALS OF THE LITURGICAL VESTMENTS

Netherlandish, around 1500
Silver-gilt, the arms enamelled; the Vienna additions from the beginning of the 19th century are painted; 19 cms high. On loan from the Order of the Golden Fleece (Dep. Prot. 31)

In the middle of all three identical morses for the vesper copes are the arms of Archduke Philip, who took the whole of the liturgical vestments with him on his journey to Spain in 1501. The neckchain of the Order surrounds the escutcheon. Two lions rampant hold the shield and the chain. The archducal coronets above the arms seem to be the addition mentioned in the records of the accounts. The fact that they are painted, yet simulate the characteristics of enamelling, indicates that they have been restored.

Around 1500, the Order of the Golden Fleece had two seignors. After Charles the Bold had died in battle, and before his grandson had come of age, Emperor Maximilian became head of the Order, acting as *pére et chef* (father and master). In 1482, Archduke Philip the Handsome, after the death of his mother, Duchess Mary of Burgundy, who was the sovereign of the Netherlands, was nominated Knight of the Order *fils chef et souverain de l'ordre de la Toison d'or* (junior master and seignor of the Order of the Golden Fleece). Even when he was a boy, Philip the Handsome took his place as sovereign of the Order at its chapters,

223

which Emperor Maximilian then deliberately did not attend.

After the early death of Philip the Handsome (1506), who had been recognised as King of Spain since 1504, Maximilian made use of his own rights and as the guardian of his grandson Karl once again took over the position of head of the Order until Karl came of age in 1517.   H. T.

The Ecclesiastical Treasury

Stefan Krenn

The Ecclesiastical Treasury contains the liturgical implements, relics and paraments which were used and collected at the Imperial court.

Its development can be traced back to the 14th century. The first mention of religious or ecclesiastical treasures in the Vienna Burg occurs in 1337, when Duke Albert II brought back a number of precious reliquaries with him from a pilgrimage to Aachen. They were kept in the vaults of the chapel in the Burg, which were collectively known as the sacrarium or (in German) *Sagrer,* and are repeatedly mentioned in documents of the time. The vaults were immediately adjacent to the Hofburg chapel and could be entered by a door which can still be seen today to the left of the altar. In the lower room of the vaults were kept the treasures and reliquaries, while the room above contained the archducal archive, which included the documents authenticating the relics. As may be gathered from the sources, the "holy reliques" were preserved together with the secular treasure.

A great number of documents bear witness to the constant endeavours to avoid dividing up the dynastic treasure, which was particularly threatened at times of family disputes over inheritances.

Yet it was not until 1407 that arbitration between the Dukes Leopold and Ernst successfully guaranteed the unity of the collection. Duke Friedrich IV subsequently made great efforts to conserve the treasure, as can be seen from a letter of 1439: *"item all sacred relics mounted and unmounted, letters, silverware, treasure and objects shall be inspected, recorded and the vault and chamber of the sagrer closed and sealed again, so that it remaineth together undiminished."*

Before the late 16th century there is no exact information about the Ecclesiastical Treasury. However, early 17th century sources already mention it, together with the Secular Treasury, as an independent collection in the so-called *"Kunsthaus",* a building which was located in the vicinity of the Summer Riding School. In 1677 the Ecclesiastical Treasury was described as being " . . . *24 paces long and 12 paces wide, 5 windows, two opening on to the Burg and 3 on to the Kohlmarkt."* In 1738, Emperor Karl VI commissioned a new vault, with 13 windows, to be constructed for the ecclesiastical treasure, as the old vaults were too small and in need of renovation. Finally, in 1747, Empress Maria Theresia arranged for a radical reorganisation of the Imperial art collections, in the process of which a new inventory was drawn up. Even after this reorganisation, the division into Secular and Ecclesiastical treasuries remained, and of all the inventories of the collections the last to be submitted was the magnificent inventory of the Ecclesiastical Treasury, dated 1758, which has been preserved. Since all the inventories prior to this date have disappeared, it constitutes the oldest surviving inventory of this collection. According to the entries, the collection at that time comprised some 500 objects, exhibited in nine large cases, and 78 paintings, including the 'Adoration of the Trinity' by Albrecht Dürer.

Surprising as it may seem today, the treasure chambers were open to the general public in the 17th and 18th centuries, when they constituted one of the most famous attractions in Vienna. A travel journal dating from 1741 informs the reader that: *"The gratuity which one must give upon visiting the Treasury is set at five and twenty gulden, and in the picture gallery one pays twelve gulden. However, six or seven persons can join together in a group and in this way facilitate one another's expenses."*

The possibility of visiting the Ecclesiastical Treasury ended abruptly, on 27. 6. 1782, when Emperor Joseph II gave orders for the collection to be completely separated from the Secular Treasury and transferred to the administration of the priest at the Hofburg. The treasure then remained in the custody of the court priest until the monarchy came to an end in 1918. During this period the objects were housed in the sacristy of the Hofburg chapel and could only be visited with difficulty. As a result, the public was hardly aware of the existence of the Ecclesiastical Treasury at all. Only after 1918 was it once again combined with the Secular Treasury for administrative purposes and in 1954 exhibited in the vaults of the Secular Treasury. The exceptionally rich and costly interior furnishing of the rooms — the exhibition cases and wooden panelling — partly derive from the middle of the 18th century, the epoch of Empress Maria Theresia. The last reorganisation took place in 1987.

Apart from the traditional reliquary treasures, the Ecclesiastical Treasury at present also incorporates the liturgical implements and paraments from the chapel in the Hofburg, as well as the furnishings of the various chapels at the Imperial residences of Schönbrunn, Belvedere, Laxenburg, Hetzendorf and Baden. At one time, Vienna possessed yet another Imperial ecclesiastical treasury, situated in the Capuchin Monastery. The monastery was founded by Empress Anna (1585—1618), the wife of Emperor Matthias, in 1618, the year of her death. With the foundation of the monastery, the Empress also had a tomb built for herself and her husband, little suspecting that it would later develop into the family vault of the Habsburgs. As a further legacy, the Empress Anna donated her important collection of precious relics and liturgical implements to the monastery. In order to comply with the Capuchins' vows of poverty, however, the donation was made with the stipulation that, while the treasure itself should indeed be kept in the monastery, it should otherwise remain in Imperial possession. In compliance with the Empress' last will and testament, her treasure was deposited in the church in 1626, in a vault above the sacristy of the monastery church. According to the 1626 inventory of the donation, it comprised more than 400 objects. In the following centuries, the "treasure at the Imperial tomb", as it was known, came to enjoy great importance after the tomb became adopted as the place of burial for the Imperial family. For many members of the Imperial court — foremost among them Empress Maria Theresia — the ecclesiastical treasures were a source of constant edification and they supplemented them with donations of their own. The Treasury of the Capuchin monastery existed until 1921. In order to exhibit and preserve this collection under museum conditions, it was incorporated into the Ecclesiastical Treasury in the Hofburg. The objects which derive from the Capuchin monastery are designated by the addition of "Kap." to the inventory number.

Although the number of objects in the Ecclesiastical Treasury was subject to great fluctuation as a result of various historical events, it is today a unique collection comprising 600 objects and a rich selection of paraments. Its significance is manifold. In accordance with the status of the Imperial court, most of the objects are works of art which can be considered masterpieces of their time. Geographically, they come from all over Europe, and in some cases even from America and Asia; historically, they range from the 12th to the 20th century. Comparable objects have often disappeared at their place of origin; alternatively, those which have survived are no longer of the same quality as the ones preserved here. From a historical point of view, the Ecclesiastical Treasury is a conspicuous monument to that religiosity of the House of Habsburg which in its time was renowned as the *Pietas Austriaca*. Finally, since the connection between Church and Empire constituted part of the ruler's apotheosis, and had a variety of historical consequences, the collection also documents an important chapter in the history of Austrian culture and thought.

1 REPRODUCTION OF THE COLUMN OF THE VIRGIN MARY, AM HOF, VIENNA

Philipp Küsel (Augsburg 1642—1700 Augsburg)
Augsburg, c. 1670—1680
Silver-gilt on iron foundation, enamel painting, precious stones, semi-precious stones, pearls, pastes (glass); maker's mark PK, Augsburg hallmark; 129 cms high (Inv. No. 882)

The column dedicated to the Virgin Mary which stands on the square in Vienna called 'Am Hof', was erected in consequence of a vow made by Emperor Ferdinand III in 1645, as Swedish troops were threatening Vienna during the Thirty Years' War. After the Swedes had been successfully repelled, an act which was ascribed to the intercession of the Madonna, building started immediately on the column. The Emperor wished the designs to be based on the famous column that Elector Maximilian I of Bavaria had had built in Munich in 1638, also in thanksgiving for the city having been saved from the Swedes. Thus there are today two very similar columns, one in Vienna's 'Am Hof' and the other in the Marienplatz in Munich. In Vienna, a column executed in marble by Johann Jakob Pock was consecrated in 1647. Seventeen years later, Emperor Leopold decided to replace this marble column (today in Wernstein am Inn) with a copy in bronze. The bronze column, which is still standing today and which was originally gilded, was executed by Balthasar Herold during the years

1664—1667. The monument consists of a surrounding balustrade, a square socle, on which four cherubs clad in armour are vanquishing dragons and the serpents of unbelief and evil, and the column itself with the figure of Mary. Compared to the original column in Munich, only the figure of Mary is different. The Munich column has the Madonna with Child as its crowning element, whereas in Vienna, Mary stands without Child on an apocalyptic dragon pierced by an arrow, which she has vanquished with the power of her prayer. In this way the iconographic image of the Virgin Mother of God, undefiled by original sin (Maria Immaculata, a dogma of the Catholic Church), is expanded into an image of Victrix over Satan and the enemies of the Church. The Marian theme and the emphasis on the militant element are characteristic of the Counter-Reformation and of the conflicts that resulted in the Thirty Years' War. The rest of the programmatic scheme is devoted to Mary and Christ, the saints of the Counter-Reformation, the plague saints and the patron saints of Austria. When the bronze column was erected, Emperor Leopold I commissioned a miniature copy from the Augsburg goldsmith Philipp Küsel as a cabinet piece for the Treasury.

The silver work is closely set with enamel, enamelled ornaments and a combination of semi-precious stones including garnets, turquoises and green chrysolites. Of the 3,753 gemstones still remaining today, there are

324 emeralds, 68 rubies and 452 amethysts. The basic architectonic form of the column thus acquires a new significance through its transformation into a decorative object. The rich, colourful ornamentation is typical of the prevailing artistic principle in the last third of the 17th century. The fact that this important commission was entrusted to an Augsburg artist throws light on the work of Viennese goldsmiths in the second half of the 17th century. It seems that in comparison with the outstanding achievements of Augsburg goldsmiths, Viennese artists were unable to produce work that would have satisfied the demands of the Court. In view of this, a number of works which have until now been attributed to Viennese goldsmiths should perhaps be reexamined (cf. e.g. Cat. No. 135).

Inventory of 1731 — fol. 215
Inventory of 1758 — fol. 111

PARAMENTS

The Ecclesiastical Treasury possesses a significant collection of sets of liturgical vestments for pontifical mass, pontifical vespers and processions, together with a number of single pieces, dating from the 17th to the 20th century. The main part of the collection consists of vestments from the 18th century, deriving from the rich donations made by Emperor Karl VI and his wife, Elisabeth Christine, as well as their daughter, Maria Theresia. Frequently, precious fabrics from France and Italy were used for the paraments; often, however, Imperial garments and other exquisite fabrics were used for liturgical vestments. Thus the so-called 'Paperl' (parrot) vestment (Inv. No. A 4) commissioned by Elisabeth Christine, was made from a wall-hanging, probably of Spanish provenance, the heads of the parrots being "decently" covered with embroidery. For the donor, too, the paraments could be associated with important events and memories. For example the 'Mantelkleid' vestment (Inv. No. A 17) was made from the gold-embroidered robe which Franz Stephan of Lorraine had worn at his marriage to Maria Theresia in 1736. The Red Chasuble (Inv. No. A 64) was made from material originally used for the wedding dress of the Archduchess Maria Rainer (1852—1902); she had the grey material dyed red for the chasuble. Around 1890, a black chasuble (Inv. No. A 245) was made from the satin of a dress belonging to the Empress Elisabeth. In 1916, Empress Zita ordered a chasuble (Inv. No. A 255) to be made from the ruby red velvet that had decorated the walls of the Church of St. Matthew at the coronation of Emperor Karl in Budapest. There are two main reasons for the size and magnificence of this collection: firstly, the representative function of religious services at court — the magnificence of the vestments and ritual were an expression of the ruler's dignity — and secondly, in addition to the chapel at the Hofburg, each of the chapels at the various Imperial summer residences such as Schönbrunn, Hetzendorf, Laxenburg etc., needed its own sets of vestments.

R. B.

2 LIGHT-BLUE VESTMENTS

Vienna, 1st quarter of the 18th century
Fabric: French, c. 1710/1720
(Inv. No. A 19)

a) Cope
136 cms high, 288 cms wide
Ground material and hood: warp satin in blue silk, brocaded with smooth and frisé gold. Asymmetrical, ascending pattern, composed of fanciful intertwining flowers and decorative forms, filled with small, plant-like elements. Pattern repeat: H 43 cms, W 17.5 cms. The trimming on the orphrey bands is identical with the inserts on the dalmatic. Gold silver-gilt fastening, blue-gold passamenterie tassels.

b) Dalmatic
105 cms high, 114 wide
Ground material as in the cope. Inserts and apparels on the sleeves: ground weave of warp satin in blue silk. Pattern ground: white silk rep (gros de Tours). Pattern brocaded in gold and silver and floated in white. Pointed oval, composed of rosettes, inside these pinecones in gold on a latticework ground and set within a delicate garland of leaves, surrounded by silver ears of wheat and fruits. Above it are broad festoons of leaves and poppy-heads, and below is a semicircular pendant garland of leaves. Pattern repeat: H 62.5 cms, W 39 cms. Narrow gold braiding, five blue-gold tassels.

c) Chasuble
103.5 cms, 71.5 cms wide
Of the same material as the ground of
the pluvial. Gold braiding.   R. B.

tion with Salzburg may not be entirely
unfounded, since St. Peter's Cathedral
in Salzburg also possesses two croziers
made of narwhal tusk.

Inventory of 1752 — No. 24 (447)

Ref.: Schönberger 1935/1936, p. 235 f., illus. 246.

3 PASTORALE/CROZIER
Mounting and crook: Vienna, 19th
century (?)
Staff: tusk of a narwhal (older than
mounting)
Brass, gilded and silvered, pastes
(glass); 185 cms long (Inv. No. Kap. 26)

The staff of this pastorale consists of
three separate pieces from the tusk of a
narwhal. Until the 19th century, these
tusks were believed to be the horns of
the mythical unicorn and thus highly
prized. Symbolic interpretation compared the unicorn to Christ and its
horn to the Tree of the Cross. Thus the
tusk represented an eminently suitable
— if somewhat rare — material for
episcopal croziers. Possibly in the 19th
century, a simple screw mounting was
made for this (much older) narwhal
tusk, together with a crook of gilded
brass decorated with an overlaid pattern of gilt acanthus leaves and coloured glass pastes. The staff has been
associated with St. Rupert († c. 720),
the first Bishop of Salzburg, although
this tradition is not documented until
the 19th century. However, the connec-

4 CRUCIFIX
Leonhard Kern (Forchtenberg 1588—
1662 Schwäbisch Hall)
Schwäbisch Hall, c. 1625/1630
Ebonised wood and walnut(?) 4th and
5th fingers of both hands missing.
Height of the corpus up to the crown of
the head 53.6 cms, armspan 53.3 cms
(Inv. No. E 109)

Christ is depicted in strict frontality;
only the head is inclined slightly to the
right. In this way, the artist achieves a
distinctly monumental effect in his
depiction of the powerfully built body.
Only the creased loincloth, pulled behind the right thigh and fluttering
towards the right, sets a counter-accent
to the composition's strict axiality. The
expression of the evenly-formed head
and face of Christ is exceptionally
penetrating. The anatomy is minutely
depicted, even down to the veins, the
tension of the skin between the nipples
caused by the outstretched arms, and

the fine strands of wavy hair and curly beard. Yet the effect is not one of a punctilious accretion of detail, since everything is subordinated to the over-all concept of the heavily idealised composition, thus avoiding the in-different smoothness of Classicism. Remarkable (and in Kern's oeuvre also the exception) are the large dimensions of the corpus.

The monumental appearance of the corpus goes far beyond Kern's early compositions, such as the crucified Christ (Cat. No. 127) or the Lamenta-tion groups (Cat. Nos. 129 and 144), and yet it does not display that degree of compositional concision and ab-straction which seems to be charac-teristic of his later work. This Christ is related to Kern's earlier work by the painstaking differentiation of details, which means that the probable date of its execution is somewhere around 1625/1630.

This crucifix is presumably the same one which is named in the 1776 invent-ory of the Xavery Chapel in the Vienna Hofburg. Transferred to the Hofburg chapel prior to 1813, it was then moved to the palace chapel of Schönbrunn sometime between 1820 and 1829. Transferred to the Treasury in 1986.

M. L.-J.

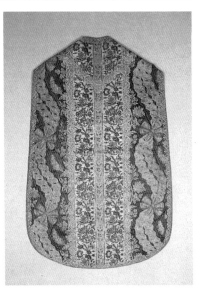

terns and butterflies on a silver ground; in the middle is a narrow gold band with stylised flowers arranged one above the other. Pattern repeat: H 14 cms, W 14.5 cms.   R. B.

Ref.: Carol Bier, Woven from the soul, spun from the heart, Washington 1987, e.g. p. 173

5 RED CHASUBLE

Vienna, 3rd quarter of the 18th century Persian silk fabric: 2nd half of the 17th century; 107 cms long, 72 cms wide (Inv. No. A 108)

This chasuble is made from two differ-ent fabrics. The side panels are of red satin brocaded in smooth and frisé gold thread and light green silk. As-cending, undulating garlands are tied together with bows. Pattern repeat: H 35 cms, W not ascertainable. The orphrey band is of the finest Persian silver lamé brocaded in gold and poly-chrome silk with naturalistic floral pat-

6 VIOLET COPE

Vienna, 1724
Fabric: French, c. 1710/1715; 104 cms long, 295.5 cms wide (Inv. No. A 28)

Violet silk damask, brocaded in smooth and frisé gold, smooth and frisé silver and polychrome silk. Asymmetrical, ascending pattern. Large leaf shapes, overlaid with bizarre flowers and connected to each other by S-shaped decorative bands and sprays piercing the leaves. Pattern repeat: H 58 cms, W 27 cms. Gold braiding, gold fringes, golden passementerie tassels. The silver fastening with the Vienna hallmark for 1724, engraved double-eagle and C VI proves the pluvial to be a donation of Emperor Karl VI. Individual piece.   R. B.

7 DALMATIC FROM THE 'FLECKERLORNAT' (PATCHWORK VESTMENTS)
Vienna, c. 1720—1730
98 cms long, 111 cms wide (Inv. No. A 20)

Appliqué work on white satin with various polychrome silk fabrics; hence the name of the vestments. The satin has been replaced, with the ornamental motifs being cut out and transferred. Symmetrical ascending pattern: in the centre two vases with flowers, one above the other, surrounded by curved gold bands and fanciful flowers. Gold and silver embroidery. Gold braiding, three gold passementerie tassels. R. B.

8 CORAL CHASUBLE
Italian, 1st half of the 18th century
106 cms long, 73 cms wide
(Inv. No. A 51)

Rich gold embroidery work on a silver lamé ground with coral beads and paillettes: ascending, symmetrical pattern over the whole width. Broad, sweeping, leaflike decoration extends from a vase and from a fan of leaves upon valanced drapery. From these branch out cornucopiae with ears of wheat or flowers. The rows of coral beads follow most of the contours and outer edges. The central orphrey is enclosed by a row of coralbeads and gold embroidery. This chasuble is an individual piece with a matching stole and maniple.   R. B.

9 VIOLET CHASUBLE
Vienna, 1st half of the 18th century
Fabric: French, c. 1710—1720; 111 cms long, 77 cms wide (Inv. No. A 140)

Violet silk damask, brocaded with smooth and frisé silver thread and polychrome silk. Ascending, asymmetrical undulating foliate motifs composed of cornucopiae, flowers, blossoms and leaves. Belongs to the group of 'bizarre' silk fabrics. Pattern repeat: H 63 cms, W not ascertainable. Gold braiding.   R. B.

in flushing warp. Overlaid with three vertical ospreys with gimp cords in shades of green. In between are flowers formed of polychrome gimp cords and silver foils. This is overlaid with embroidered silver bands with bows, silver cords, paillettes, silver braiding and three silver passamenterie tassels. Embroidered on silver foil in the middle of the lower border is *M. T. 1780,* indicating that the vestment was donated by Maria Theresia.   R. B.

11 COPE FROM THE BLACK 'DAMENORNAT' (LADY VESTMENTS)

Vienna, marked *M. T. 1776*
136 cms long, 238 cms wide (Inv. No. A 16)

Onto the black silk damask are couched gimp cords in shades of grey combined with metal foils. The bands thus formed are connected by single flowers and sheaves of wheat ears. The black silk damask has been replaced, the embroidery cut out and transferred to the new fabric. The hood and orphrey band are of silver lamé, decorated with leaves and ears of wheat executed in gimps and silver tinsel. This kind of gimp cording was also produced by Maria Theresia and her ladies-in-waiting. On the middle of the lower edge, embroidered on silver foil: *M. T. 1776,* which indicates that the vestments were donated by Maria Theresia. Silver-gilt fastenings, gold braiding, gold passamenterie tassels.
          R. B.

10 DALMATIC FROM THE 'KUGELORNAT' (GLOBE VESTMENTS)

Vienna, marked *M. T. 1780*
Fabric: French, mid-18th century; 102 cms long, 120 cms wide (Inv. No. A 45)

Ground material: gold lamé, brocaded in smooth gold, gold and silver tinsel, frisé silver and polychrome silk. The pattern is composed of parallel ascending golden undulating tendrils with groups of three round fruits with small flowers, from which the vestments take their name. Between the undulating tendrils are small islands with little silver trees, and polychrome and silver flowers. Pattern repeat: H 44.5 cms, W 26.5 cms. Inserts and apparels: white gros de Tours (rep) with small pattern

12 GREEN CHASUBLE

Vienna, 1st half of the 18th century
Fabric: French, c. 1710/1720; 110 cms long, 76 cms wide (Inv. No. A 162)

Green silk damask, brocaded in smooth and frisé gold, frisé silver and polychrome silk. The pattern displays double, ascending, asymmetrical, undulating gold bands; in between these silver decoration contoured in red. Sprays of flowers and leaves open out

from the bands. Pattern repeat: H 46.5 cms, W not ascertainable. Gold braiding.   R. B.

13 THE SO-CALLED POUCH OF KING STEPHAN OF HUNGARY

Russia, 2nd half of the 11th or 12th century

Gold and silk embroidery on silk, silver gilt, pearls, garnets, smoky quartz, pastes (glass); 15.5 cms high, 13.5 cms wide (Inv. No. Kap. 186)

This red silk pouch is first mentioned in the inventory of the Capuchin Treasury in 1752, and described there as the purse (Latin: *crumena*) of King Stephan of Hungary († 1038). There is, however, no historical foundation for this tradition. It is rather a unique item of inestimable value from the early period of Russian art and one of the earliest surviving pieces of Russian embroidery, perhaps even the earliest. The exact function of the pouch is uncertain, but it was probably intended to hold relics. Hardly any comparable textiles have survived; however, dating and localisation can be narrowed down somewhat in the light of the characteristics of the inscriptions. The front of the pouch is entirely covered in costly gold embroidery enclosing medallions with figures embroidered in silk. The effect is similar to that of splendid mosaics or pieces of goldsmiths' art. The high standard of the needlework — there are almost 700 stitches to one square centimetre — indicates that it originated from an important centre of embroidery, possibly from one of the great Russian convents. In the centre on the front, Christ is seated on his Throne, surrounded by the four archangels, a seraph, a cherub, St. Basil and St. Nicholas. The names of the persons represented are given in Cyrillic script. The back bears further Cyrillic inscriptions. The cruciform frame contains an extended version of Psalm 33,22 ("Let thy mercy, O Lord, be upon us, now and for ever"), and on the lower edge Psalm 67,1 ("God be merciful unto us, and cause his face to shine upon us"). Both texts figure prominently in the liturgy of Greek-Orthodox ritual. The pouch is fastened by means of a pin which is passed through the narrow hinge-like fittings attached to the edges. The inventory of

1752 records that the large smoky quartz was attached to the pouch. Its mount has been fitted in between the hinges, one of which appears to have been damaged in the process. This and the garnet cross are obviously later additions, as is the braid above the fastening (perhaps from the 17th century?). This piece was until recently called a marsupium, a term which was, however, not used for the pouch until the 20th century.

Inventory of 1752 — No. 59 (482)

Ref.: P. Király, Der sogenannte Beutel König Stephans von Ungarn, in: Studia Slavonica Hungarica XVII (1971), pp. 219—248.

14 IVORY RELIQUARY CASKET

Sicily (Siculo-Arabic), 12th century
Ivory on a wooden foundation, brass, silver; 13.5 cms high, 20.5 cms wide, 9.5 cms deep (Inv. No. Kap. 55)

This wooden casket overlaid with ivory panels was made in a 12th century Sicilian workshop, and thus originated from a region in which the local Chris-

tian culture had already come into contact with Islamic culture. The unique lanceolate mounts are rooted in the formal tradition of Islamic art. Pieces of this kind, which were being exported to countries all over Europe even in the Middle Ages, were originally designed for use as jewellery boxes, but in treasuries have primarily survived as reliquary caskets. The silver band at the top, which identifies the relics preserved inside, was only added to the casket in 1752.

Inventory of 1626 — No. F/19 (192)
Inventory of 1752 — No. 118 (542)

Ref.: P. B. Cott, Siculo-Arabic Ivories, Princeton 1939, p. 39, no. 54.

15 THE SO-CALLED MONILE (RELIQUARY PENDANT) OF CHARLEMAGNE

Prague (?), mid-14th century
Gold foil on a wooden foundation, rock crystal, semi-precious stones, onyx cameo; 14.5 cms high, 9.3 cms wide (Inv. No. D 128)

The narrow sides of the diamond-shaped reliquary pendant (monile) bear the inscription: MONILE MAGNI KAROLI IMPERATORIS VERACITER DE LIGNO S(AN)C(TE) CRVCIS CONTINENS (Monile of Charlemagne, containing a particle of wood from the True Cross).
The relic of the cross named in the inscription is preserved under the pointed oval plate of rock crystal and covered with a strip of parchment bearing the inscription DE LIGNO D(OMI)NI (from the wood — i.e. cross — of the Lord). The rest of the surface is decorated with semi-precious stones placed radially around the central plate (four have been replaced at a later date and underlaid with coloured foil), and a round onyx cameo at the lower end depicting a dancing maenad (Roman, 2nd half of 1st century, A. D.). A large pearl originally hung from the lower

point of the pendant. Although the way the gold foil and the stones have been set to display their intrinsic nature to full effect is reminiscent of works from the 9th century, the piece is actually from the 14th century, having been intentionally executed in a retrospective style. This was probably due to the increased veneration of the newly-canonised Emperor, which was intensively promoted by his successor, Karl IV. At the court of Emperor Karl IV numerous works of art were created which betray a distinct historicising tendency and share stylistic characteristics with the monile (the Book of Gospels in the library of the Cathedral Chapter at Prague and the crown of the reliquary of Charlemagne in the cathedral at Aix-la-Chapelle). On the back is an inscription on paper, today only partly legible but reconstructed from entries in earlier inventories, which explains the provenance of the jewel: *This particle of the Holy Cross was carried by Karl V on all his journeys and in all his battles and was presented to Emperor Ferdinand in Prague in 1651 by the Elector of Brandenburg.*

Inventory of 1758 — Case I, No. 16

Ref.: Catalogue, Kaiser Karl IV 1316—1378, Nuremberg 1978, p. 93, no. 95; Fritz 1982, p. 187, no. 34; E. Zwierlein-Diehl III 1991, no. 2539.

16 ROCK CRYSTAL RELIQUARY
Germany (?), 2nd quarter of the 14th century
Silver mounting, black paint; 16 cms high, 6.2 cms diameter (Inv. No. Kap. 187)

The upright rock crystal receptacle consists of a twelve-sided, facetted cylinder held by a silver mounting with a serrated edge, and rests on four slender animal legs with paws, one of which has been replaced (in the 18th century?). A gilded medallion with a silver carving of the Annunciation has been inserted into the top of the lid. It may originally have been a translucent enamel, which later lost its enamel coating. The artistic style of the representation is that of the second quarter of the 14th century, although it is not possible to localise it precisely. In this vessel used to be preserved a cap (not exhibited) which was mistakenly associated with King Stephan I of Hungary († 1038). The costly weave of this fabric — red silk embroidered with gold — was first worked at the beginning of the 13th century in Lower Italy. Its nearest parallel is to be found in the gloves of the coronation robes of the Holy Roman Empire (Secular Treasury, Cat. No. 148).

Inventory of 1626 — No. C/78 (154)
Inventory of 1752 — No. 60 (483)

Ref.: K. Lind, Aus dem Schatze des Capuciner-Klosters in Wien, in: Mittheilungen der k.k. Central-Commission IX (1883), p. 111 f. (Illustrated).

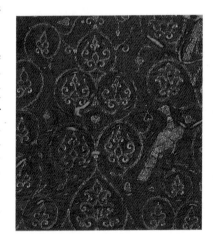

17 RELIQUARY OF ST. HEDWIG

Germany or Bohemia, end of the 14th century
Silver-gilt, glass; 7.8 cms high, 8.5 cms long (Inv. No. Kap. 105)

This horizontal glass cylinder borne on thin legs with animal paws displays a relic of St. Hedwig, Duchess of Silesia (1174—1243). Both ends of the cylinder are enclosed in plain silver-gilt mounts. On one of the ends is carved a crouching Atlas figure who carries on his shoulders a banderole with the inscription S(AN)C(T)E HEDWIGIS in Gothic minuscules. The style of the figure and the formal language of the gold work belong to the end of the 14th century, although this type of reliquary had been popular since the 12th century. Similar reliquaries can be found in the tradition of both German and Bohemian goldsmith's art.

Inventory of 1626 — No. V/6 (366)
Inventory of 1752 — No. 15 (438)

18 MONSTRANCE OF THE SACRED BLOOD

Transylvania, 3rd quarter of the 15th century, with older additions
Silver-gilt, rock crystal, precious stones, semi-precious stones, corals, pearls, pastes (glass), parchment miniatures; 69 cms high; foot: 23 cms diameter (Inv. No. Kap. 56)

As the inscription SANGUIS DOM-

INI informs us, the reliquary capsule in the centre of this monstrance is supposed to contain the blood of Christ. The Empress Anna, wife of Emperor Matthias, received the reliquary as a gift from Cardinal Prince Alexander Orsini on 25. 4. 1615, and it later entered the treasury in the Capuchin Monastery as part of the Empress's estate. The receptacle consists of a round foot, a flat shaft with a large disc-shaped nodus, a quatrefoil cross with a capsule containing the Holy Blood, and a crowning element flanked by pinnacles. In the front of the knop, beneath a plate of rock crystal, ten different relics are preserved. The front of the pediment displays a miniature of Christ, on the reverse of which is a relief of an enthroned bishop "S. IACOBVS".

Until the end of the 19th century, a rock crystal cylinder (today lost) concealed the capsule with the blood of Christ in the rectangular space of the quatrefoil cross. Some of the valuable stones with which the cross was set were also lost, or exchanged for less

valuable ones, such as a diamond cross described in the inventory of 1626. Until recently, the reliquary has been regarded as a piece of Venetian workmanship, probably because some of the motifs derive from Byzantine art. In classifying this object, it should be borne in mind that elements from older pieces have obviously been incorporated into it as well; for instance, the pediment and the nodus. An important indication of the provenance of the monstrance is provided by the impression of the seal on the reverse of the nodus, which has so far received little attention. It is the seal of the Peace of Saxony from 1291 and bears the inscription: SIGILLUM IUDICUM PACIS SAXONIE GENERALIS (Seal of the Tribunal for the Peace of all Saxony). On the basis of the motifs of the composition and the technical execution, this piece can be classified as a piece of Gothic goldsmiths' work from Transylvania. The presence of the seal can perhaps be explained by a connection between Saxony and the ethnic Saxon community in Transylvania. A distant memory of its origins in southeastern Europe could be the reason for the tradition, first recorded in the 19th century, that the monstrance once belonged to the Church of St. Sophia (Hagia Sophia) in Constantinople.

Inventory of 1626 — No. M (243)
Inventory of 1752 — No. 184 (617)

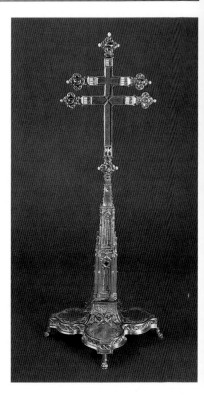

19 RELIQUARY CROSS OF KING LUDWIG THE GREAT OF HUNGARY

Hungary (successors of Pietro di Simone da Siena?), 1370/1382
Gold, silver-gilt, champlevé enamel, precious stones, pearls, rock crystal; 67.2 cms high; cross: 33.7 cms high
(Inv. No. D 251/252)

This patriarchal cross contains several particles of the True Cross fitted together and preserved under plates of rock crystal. The particles are enclosed between five arms of the Alliance of Hungary and Anjou on the sides and above, and the arms of the Kingdom of Poland below. Two further Hungarian arms decorate the intersections of the two cross-beams on the back. The emblems refer to King Ludwig the Great of Hungary (1326—1382) from the House of Anjou, who was also King of Poland from 1370. The cross must therefore have been made between 1370 and 1382, a dating also supported by the style of the goldsmith's work. The presence of the French arms of Anjou is explained by complicated dynastic connections. Having conquered Naples, Charles of Anjou, the brother of King Louis XI of France, had the rightful heir, Conradin, executed and founded a new ruling dynasty there himself. A connection and temporary union arose between Hungary and Naples through the marriage of Maria, the only child of King Stephan V of Hungary, to King Charles II of Naples, Charles of Anjou's son. Ludwig, Maria's great-grandchild, became Ludwig the Great of Hungary and his brother Andrew († 1345) King of Naples. According to earlier sources, the particles of the Cross contained here could have originated from a patriarchal cross bequeathed by King Stephan V to his daughter Maria, who had it returned to Hungary from Naples. Following the ancient form of the *crux gemmata* (cf. the cross of the Imperial insignia), the quatrefoil ends of the cross-beams are set with precious stones. The back of the upper quatrefoil bears the inscription VERA PARTICULI SANCTA CRUCIS (True Particle of the Holy Cross), and on the lateral quatrefoils enamels of the four symbols of the evangelists. The bull of St. Luke and the Imperial double-headed eagle are later additions, possibly from the 17th century. The foot of the cross imitates the form of a two-storey steeple, standing on a quatrefoil socle borne on four lion's paws. The four original quatrefoil enamels are now missing. This type of double-armed cross on a steeple-like foot was widespread in European goldsmiths' art of the 14th century. In addition to this, the patriarchal cross is a special symbol of the Kingdom of Hungary, adopted as the sign of victory by the Christian rulers of Byzantium. Thus the Hungarian Imperial orb is also surmounted by a cross of this type. King Ludwig's father had summoned the goldsmith Pietro di Simone da Siena from Naples, and his presence as court goldsmith in Hungary is documented in 1331 and 1340. This reliquary cross was probably executed at the workshop of one of his successors, which would explain the correspondence between these enamels and Italian enamel work. In recent times the cross suffered a strange fate: around 1865—1875, it was entrusted to the restorer and antique dealer Salomon Weininger for restoration. Substituting a forgery, he separated the foot and the cross and sold them on the art market. The forgery, which went undiscovered, was handed over to Hungary under the terms of the Treaty of Partition between Austria and Hungary in 1921 as the 'original', and is today in the National Museum of Hungary in Budapest. In 1957, an extraordinary stroke of good fortune enabled the Kunsthistorische Museum to acquire

the foot from a museum in London and the cross from a private collection in Copenhagen, so that the original cross is now back in Vienna again.

Inventory of 1758 — Case I, No. 4

Ref.: J. F. Hayward, Salomon Weininger, Master Faker, in: The Connoisseur, vol. 187, Nov. 1974, pp. 170—179; J. Kolba, Zur ungarischen Goldschmiedekunst der Parlerzeit, in: Catalogue, Die Parler und der schöne Stil 1350—1400, vol. IV, Cologne, 1980, p. 149.

20 RELIQUARY CROSS
Prague (?), c. 1380/1400
Silver-gilt; 45 cms high; foot: 21 cms wide, 13 cms deep (Inv. No. Kap. 223)

This silver-gilt double cross once enclosed a particle of the cross of Christ, visible through the tracery on the arms of the cross. Neither the relic nor the plate at the back have survived. Also missing today are the four symbols of the Evangelists on the ends of the cross at the front, and the angels with instruments of the Passion at the back. They were probably executed in relief (enamelled?), since the marks of burin incisions are still visible. The style of the figures indicates the last quarter of the 14th century. In the 16th century, the decoration on the ends of the cross was removed and the body added, which then covered both the tracery and the evangelical symbol at the bottom. At that time the cross was probably also regilded. The elongated foot, with its double-trefoils, the stand in the form of a tower complete with pinnacles, as well as the mounting are all to be found on pieces of Prague goldsmiths' work dating from the last quarter of the 14th century, which are attributed to one of the Parler studios. On the basis of its close similarity with these works, it may be presumed that the cross originated in Prague.

Inventory of 1626 — No. C/84 (160)
Inventory of 1752 — No. 140 (573)

21 CHALICE FROM THE ESTATE OF EMPEROR MAXIMILIAN OF MEXICO

Siena, circle of Tondino di Guerrino (?), 2nd quarter of the 14th century
Silver-gilt, copper-gilt, champlevé enamel; 20.3 cms high (Inv. No. B 3)

The accentuated profiles of this gilt chalice of silver and copper effectively set off the contrasting volumes of its individual sections. The copper foot consists of a six-foil intersected by a hexagon. This motif is repeated on the bowl, which rises from the stem like a flower from its calyx. Six champlevé enamel tondi on the nodus depict Christ crucified and five saints respectively. Foot, nodus and shaft ring are additionally ornamented with floral motifs. This type of communion chalice was common in central Italy in the 14th century, and the form was retained until well into the 15th century. Both the artistic conception of the chalice and the enamels relate this piece to others from the workshop of the Siennese goldsmith, Tondino di

Guerrino (active 1308—1338). The chalice, the oldest in the Ecclesiastical Treasury, came from the estate of Emperor Maximilian I of Mexico (1837—1867) and until 1901 was kept in the chapel at Castle Miramar near Trieste.

Ref.: P. Leone de Castris, Tondino di Guerrino e Andrea Riguardi. Orafi e smaltisti a Siena (1308—1338), in: Prospettiva no. 21 (1980), pp. 24—44 (the Viennese chalice is not mentioned).

22 CHALICE WITH THE DEVICE OF EMPEROR FRIEDRICH III

Southern Germany (Nuremberg ?), 1438
Silver, parcel-gilt; 19 cms high; foot: 12 cms diameter (Inv. No. B 1)

The inscription A.E.I.O.U. and the date 1438 on the upper side of the base indicate that the chalice was donated by Emperor Friedrich III, who used these vowels as an multivalent device (e.g. "Austria Est Imperare Orbi Universo" — It is for Austria to rule the whole world). It was understood as meaning that the House of Austria was legitimately entitled to the Kingdom of Germany and the Roman Empire. This

piece and the sundial in the Kunstkammer (Inv. No. 166), which is also dated 1438, provide the earliest testimony to the dynasty's clear consciousness of its own significance and mission in the world. The octagonal shaft-rings bear the inscription: + GOT BUES + ZU DIER AMEN (God atones for thee. Amen). The composition of the chalice juxtaposes smooth zones with zones of ornamental decoration. The bulbous, ajouré nodus has been worked in two layers. Its outer layer consists of a plaited central ring, bordered on each side by a sequence of six identical ornamental leaves. Since the leaves were only adapted for this purpose afterwards, and the inner mounting of the nodus does not belong to the original either, this unusual form of nodus is probably the result of modern restoration (17th century? — cf. the plaited band of Cat. No. 157). The original nodus perhaps had tracery decoration or lozenge-shaped rotoli. On account of the wide distribution of this type of chalice, the artistic origin of this piece cannot be determined for certain. Similar proportions are to be found in other pieces too, above all in chalices from Nuremberg, a centre which seems to have supplied the Emperor with other implements as well (chrismatory

in the Neukloster Monastery, Wiener Neustadt). The chalice was formerly kept in the Chapel of St. George, founded by Emperor Friedrich III in the Burg in Wiener Neustadt, and was not transferred to the Vienna Treasury until 1831.

Ref.: Schramm/Fillitz 1978, p. 78, no. 88; Fritz 1982, p. 269, no. 582.

23 LATE GOTHIC CHALICE
Hungary, c. 1500
Silver-gilt, semi-precious stones, pastes (glass); 23.3 cms high (Inv. No. B 10)

Although the basic motifs of this sumptuous chalice are in fact similar to those of the chalice Cat. No. 21, its conception is completely different, being characteristic of the last phase of the late Gothic era. Each of the individual sections seems to flow into the next, the barely conspicuous outlines overlaid with rich leafwork extending halfway up the bowl. The chalice thus evokes the impression of a natural, organic structure, an impression reinforced by the ascendant curve of the six-lobed socle and the six flower-shaped rotoli of the nodus. This type of chalice was widespread in Hungarian goldsmithery; related examples have been preserved in Slovakian churches, in Transylvania and in the Treasury of

San Marco in Venice. The chalice was not transferred from the chapel in the Hofburg to the Ecclesiastical Treasury until 1854.

Ref.: Fritz 1982, p. 303, no. 843.

24 RELIEF OF ST. CHRISTOPHER
Upper Rhine (?), 3rd quarter of the 15th century
Gilded copper cast, pastes (glass), mother-of-pearl; 18.2 cms high, 14.7 cms wide; frame: 22.5 cms high, 19.2 cms wide (Inv. No. D 170)

This relief depicts the legend of St. Christopher, which has become a folk tradition in German-speaking countries. Unsuited for fasting and praying, the giant Christopher serves God with his strength. On the advice of a hermit he starts carrying pilgrims across a fast-flowing river beside the hermitage. One evening, Christ avails himself of his services and, adopting the shape of a child, lets himself be carried across. To Christopher, who almost collapses under the weight, Christ reveals himself as the Lord and Creator of the world, and baptises him, turning the giant's staff green as proof of his word. The Gothic artist does not present a uniform view of this episode, but enlarges the two figures according to their importance. Behind them extends a bird's eye view of a landscape, which is depicted with great narrative delight. Besides towns, villages and castles one can even see, at the left-hand edge of the picture, the hermitage and the hermit with his lantern, keeping watch for the giant. Various figures, such as a man on horseback, an oarsman, and a miller with laden asses, remind one that St. Christopher is the patron saint of sailors, travellers and porters (today, also of motorists). The goldsmith may have taken his model for the copper cast directly from contemporary graphic work.

Inventory 1758 — Case IV, No. 18

25 TEMPIETTO CONTAINING VARIOUS RELICS OF CHRIST
Mantua, end of the 16th century
Rock crystal receptacle probably added at a later date, Hardwood foundation overlaid with ebony, gold enamel, silver, diamonds, garnets, pearls, rock crystal; 49 cms high (Inv. No. D 23)

This hexagonal ebony ostensory has always been highly venerated as a reliquary containing relics of Christ's Passion. The rock crystal receptacle is supposed to contain drops of Christ's blood, and the piece of linen visible in the socle is also said to have been soaked with his blood. Six further alleged relics of Christ's Passion can be seen in the roof section: hairs from Christ's beard, the crown of thorns, the lance, the martyr's column, the scourge and the reed. The Passion is symbolised again on the floor of the ostensory: an enamelled silver plate representing a meadow is covered with miniature gold and silver replicas of the implements of the Passion. Until recently, the ostensory was held to be the work of a Southern German artist. However, the wooden structure, the gold enamel ornamentation and the settings of the gemstones are all related to works commissioned by the court of the Dukes of Gonzaga at Mantua and were thus probably made there. The cathedral of S. Pietro in Mantua possesses a comparable octagonal ostensory, albeit less richly ornamented.

Inventory of 1758 — Case I, No. 3

26 OSTENSORY WITH A THORN FROM CHRIST'S CROWN
Mantua, 1592
Oak foundation overlaid with ebony, gold, partially enamelled, partially painted, silver-gilt, diamonds, rubies, emeralds, pearls, rock crystal; 50.4 cms high (Inv. No. D 21)

The cylinder of this tower reliquary is a masterpiece of crystal cutting, consisting of flawless, perfectly cut rock crystal. The receptacle encloses a thorn from Christ's crown of thorns and relics of SS. Fabian and Sebastian. Through an oval rock crystal window in the foot can also be seen relics of St. Maximilian. In this type of receptacle, the cylinders are usually flanked by wooden columns, yet here there are two sets of slim rods in place of the columns, with gold enamel ornaments and large pearls between them. In addition, the ebony facings are furnished with costly gold mounts, pearls and precious stones. However, the highlight of the goldsmiths' work is the figure at the top, a symbolic representation of Faith militant: an enamelled golden statuette of a woman, clad in the armour of a Roman soldier, supporting a large cross with her right hand and holding a chalice in the left. The figure and the cross are set with large diamonds and rubies. The work derives its fascination from the superb technical execution, and this is probably why the reliquary, which bears the date of 1592 on the foot, was once regarded as being of Southern German origin. However, as in the case of Cat. No. 25, this reliquary is connected with pieces that originated at the court of the Gonzagas in Mantua (Collezione d'Arco, Mantua, as well as in various churches there). It should be remembered that Augsburg goldsmiths also worked at the ducal court in Mantua and that the city's cathedral treasury possesses a magnificent piece of gold-

However, it should also be noted that the Dukes of Mantua employed a number of goldsmiths from Augsburg whose names are also documented. This explains the difficulties in distinguishing works by Augsburg artists from those of their Mantuan contemporaries. The drops of Christ's blood were reputedly in the possession of the Savelli family in Rome and supposed to have been presented to Emperor Karl VI in 1721, together with the sudarium of Christ (cf. Cat. No. 121). The ostensory and the other relics probably came to Vienna through the close dynastic links of the Imperial House with the Dukes of Mantua. Eleonora, the daughter of Emperor Ferdinand I, married Duke Guglielmo of Mantua; her granddaughter, Anna of Tyrol, was married to Emperor Matthias, while another of her granddaughters, Eleonora Gonzaga, became the second wife of Emperor Ferdinand II, and her distant cousin, Eleonora, married Emperor Ferdinand III. Archival sources in Mantua report that the Duke com-

had been crowned with the crown of thorns, as well as relics of SS. Sigismund and Lambert. Relics of St. Peter are visible in the receptacle of the foot. A gold and enamelled statuette of this saint, holding a gold key set with diamonds, also forms the crowning element of the ostensory. The reliquary was made as a copy of its companion piece, possibly because a pendant to the first ostensory was needed to complete a costly gift. The work does not, however, attain the quality of the original. The receptacle for the relics is made of glass and not rock crystal. The appliqués, in particular, are technically inferior and of much simpler execution. The wooden corpus has also been simplified and reduced. Probably made in Mantua around 1600, the copy, unlike its companion piece, is not dated.

Inventory of 1758 — Case II, No. 3

smiths' work whose style (characterised as Southern German) closely resembles that of the figure at the top of this reliquary.

Inventory of 1758 — Case II, No. 3

27 OSTENSORY WITH A FRAGMENT OF THE REED OF CHRIST

Mantua, c. 1600
Hardwood foundation overlaid with ebony, silver-gilt, partially enamelled, diamonds, emeralds, rubies, pearls, glass, glass beads, rock crystal; 54.8 cms high (Inv. No. D 22)

This companion piece to Cat. No. 26 is supposed to contain a fragment of the reed given to Christ as a sceptre after he

28 HOUSE ALTAR WITH THE REVELATION TO THE SHEPHERDS

Munich, c. 1600
Design: Hans Krumper (Weilheim, c. 1570—1634 Munich)
Silver-gilt, hardwood foundation overlaid with ebony, gold enamel, topazes, almandine, pearls, rock crystal; 37.5 cms high, 21 cms wide (Inv. No. D 174)

An angel descends to the shepherds depicted in the lower half of the relief and announces the birth of Christ. In the upper part, the heavens open and a choir of angels with instruments sing GLORIA IN EXCELSIS DEO (Praise be to God in the highest), which can also be read on the banderole. In the pediment above it, God the Father appears holding the globe and bestowing his benediction. The sketches for the design of this silver-gilt relief were made by the Munich court artist Hans Krumper. They are preserved in the Kunsthalle in Bremen (Revelation to the Shepherds, Inv. No. 58) and in the collection of copper engravings in the Museum der Bildenden Künste in Leipzig (God the Father, Inv. No. 4703). The ebony frame of the relief is set with gold enamel, topazes, almandine and pearls. Architectural motifs similar to that of the pediment of the frame (e.g. South Gate of the Munich Residenz) were current in the circle of Hans Krumper, who also worked as a sculptor and architect. Munich court artists produced several of these exquisite pieces of goldsmiths' work; a gold relief from 1598 of the Madonna in Majesty, after Christoph Schwarz, is in the possession of the Treasury of the Munich Residenz.

Inventory of 1758 — Case I, No. 40

Ref.: Catalogue, Die Bildhauerfamilie Zürn 1585/ 1724, Braunau am Inn 1979, p. 271 f., no. 135; D. Diemer, Hans Krumper, in: Catalogue: Wittelsbach und Bayern II/I, Munich 1980, p. 292; Weber 1975, no. 472.

29 RELIQUARY OF DUKE WILHELM V OF BAVARIA

Munich, c. 1600
Hardwood foundation overlaid with ebony, gold enamel, rubies, emeralds,

pearls, cameos, jasper, glass; 59 cms high, 28 cms wide (Inv. No. D 68)

The gold enamelled arms of Bavaria and the letters W.H.I.B. (Wilhelm, Herzog in Bayern: Wilhelm, Duke in Bavaria) on the pediment mark this reliquary as a donation of Duke Wilhelm V of Bavaria (1548—1626, ruled 1579—1597). The composition corresponds to the form of contemporary altar retables. Over a predella rises a centrepiece flanked by pillars and surmounted by a broken pediment with a crowning element. The relics of various saints are arranged behind a glass plate; other relics are preserved in drawers in the frame. The large reliquary shrine of rock crystal in the Chamber of Relics of the Residenz in Munich, which has similar gold ornamentation and mounted cameos, is probably from the same workshop. Other related pieces in Munich indicate that the workshop which produced this reliquary was closely associated with the court there.

Inventory of 1758 — Case N, No. 4

30 OSTENSORY WITH A THORN FROM THE CROWN OF CHRIST AND A PARTICLE FROM THE CROSS

Augsburg (?), end of the 16th century
Silver, enamelled gold, rock crystal; 32 cms high (Inv. No. D 67)

This silver lyre-shaped ostensory displays the relics of Christ behind plates of rock crystal. Two angels hold an enamelled gold crown of thorns, above which rises an obelisk made of rock crystal, enclosing a thorn from Christ's crown. The oblong receptacle underneath conceals a particle of the cross and other relics. This ingenious reliquary is decorated with late Renaissance chased ornamentation on the sides, on the knop and on the eight-foiled foot. The top is formed by a gold and white enamelled crucifix, flanked by figures of the Virgin Mary and John the Baptist, who stand slightly lower down on pedestals. The richly orna-

mented knop displays a remarkable design, opening into niches on both the front and back, with an enamelled figure of an angel on either side. The goldsmiths' work was presumably executed in Augsburg, although hardly any comparable pieces from this centre have survived.

Inventory of 1758 — Case I, No. 128

31 FRAME-SHAPED RELIQUARY WITH MOTHER-OF-PEARL RELIEF

Germany, c. 1500, and Augsburg, c. 1600
Enamel on reverse: after a painting by Christoph Schwarz (Munich 1548—1592 Munich)
Ebony, silver, parcel-gilt, translucent enamel, mother-of-pearl; 19.5 cms high; mother-of-pearl relief: 6 cms diameter (Inv. No. D 209)

This small ostensory consists of two parts, each of which originates from a different epoch. The late Gothic ajouré mother-of-pearl relief, dating from

around 1500, was incorporated into an upright ebony frame about a century later. It is possible that the relief was already in Imperial possession and was then adapted for use as a devotional image. A colonnaded hall represents the stable at Bethlehem, over which a star shines. In front of this architectural motif sit the Virgin Mary and Child, to whom the Three Wise Men are offering their gifts. The delicate proportions of the figures and the stiff folds of their drapery correspond to the ideal of late Gothic art. The blue enamel ground provides an effective representation of the sky, which can be seen between the columns. The relief was probably based on a graphic design from the Upper Rhine area. The obverse displays a translucent enamel representing the Flight into Egypt. Its composition echoes a painting by the Munich court painter Christoph Schwarz, which had been copied by Johannes Sadeler I as an engraving.

Inventory of 1758 — Case II, No. 18

Ref.: G. E. Pazaurek, Perlmutter, Berlin 1937, p. 21.

32 HOUSE ALTAR WITH A MINIATURE OF THE VIRGIN MARY

Augsburg, c. 1590/1600
After an engraving by Federico Barocci (Urbino 1535—1612 Urbino)
Walnut veneer and ebony facing on oak foundation, silver, parcel-gilt, oil on copper; 57 cms high, 26.5 cms wide (Inv. No. D 15)

The Virgin Mary, appearing on clouds and illuminated by an aureole, holds her Child tenderly with clasped hands. The composition of this small oil painting goes back to a widely known copper engraving from 1570 by Federico Barocci, thus raising interesting questions of artistic originality. Barocci's engraving was imitated by Agostino Carracci in 1582; around 1588, Hans von Aachen, in his altar painting for the Church of Maria im Kapitol in Cologne, made an exact copy of the Madonna figure. Around 1590 a further copy followed, done by Johannes Sadeler I — possibly on the mediation of Hans von Aachen. The picture in this small house altar could have been prompted by this last engraving. The facial type — delicate, inclined, pointed, with a high forehead — also goes back to Barocci's Madonna figures. On the other hand, the cool, enamel-like shades of colour, and the heavily drawn figure, point to its origin in the circle of the Munich court painter Peter Candid. All the wooden parts of the surrounding upright frame have silver mounts; at the top are two silver flower vases and a figure of St. Michael. Comparable statuettes were also made in the circle of the goldsmith Matthias Walbaum (Cat. No. 58). The relics in the oblong receptacle in the foot and in the oval were already missing in 1758.

Inventory of 1758 — Case III, No. 21

Ref.: A. Emiliani, Federico Barocci, vol. I, Pesaro 1985, p. 76 f.

33 HOUSE ALTAR WITH MARY AS QUEEN OF HEAVEN
Italy (Florence ?), end of the 16th century, and Augsburg, c. 1600
Oak foundation overlaid with ebony, walnut veneer, silver, parcel-gilt, turquoises, watercolour on parchment, glass; 45.9 cms high, 22.3 cms wide (Inv. No. D 175)

The unsigned parchment miniature presents Mary as the Queen of Heaven. She holds the Infant Jesus on her arm, with two angels hovering above her and two others sitting at her feet. Similar Madonna figures are to be found in Siennese painting of the late 16th century, for example in the works of Francesco Vanni. The contours of the two-piece wooden frame are embellished with silver beads and overlapping silver mounts. Both the miniature and the wooden structure are related to pieces of Italian provenance. This piece was executed at the end of the 16th century in Italy and not, as was formerly thought, in Augsburg. It resembles Cat. Nos. 34, 104 and 108 (cf. head of lower angel). However, the cube-shaped pedestal is a later addition. Its

silver mounts, which bear the letters IHS in the centre at the front and MRA on the back, as the initials of Jesus and Mary respectively, are quite different from those on the frame. The pedestal was probably made in a workshop in either Augsburg or Munich: a similarly ornamented pedestal in the Treasury in Munich has an ivory figure of the Infant Jesus which originated from the circle of Christoph Angermair.

34 HOUSE ALTAR WITH THE ANNUNCIATION
Italy (Florence?), c. 1600
Ebonised hardwood foundation, ebony, silver, bronze, parcel-gilt, watercolour on parchment, glass; 48 cms high, 28 cms wide (Inv. No. D 17)

In the base and in the rectangular foot of this house altar are six receptacles in which the relics of various saints have been placed. Above this is a broad frame with a broken pediment, which contains a parchment miniature of the

Annunciation: the Virgin is startled at her prayers by the Archangel Gabriel approaching from the right on a cloud. He presents her with a lily, the symbol of chastity, and therefore that of Mary herself. Three angels witness the event from heaven. The miniature is framed by an ornamental silver band. Carved silver mounts cover the volutes which form the transition to the foot and the frame, and are also present as volutes on the outside of the frame. Both the wooden structure and the silver mounts are related to Italian work of the late 16th century. The altar comes from the same workshop as Cat. No. 108.

Inventory of 1758 — Case IV, No. 15

35 OSTENSORY
Mantua (?), c. 1600
Ebonised hardwood, silver-gilt, partially enamelled, rubies, pearls, glass; 50 cms high, 17.7 cms wide (Inv. No. D 107)

This tower-shaped reliquary of ebonised wood is flanked by arches under which stand vases of flowers. Relics of SS. Maximilian, Regina and Agnes are visible through the three glass windows of the main section. Further relics are contained in the superstructure and the crowning element. A part of the gilded and enamelled silver appliqués has been lost but not replaced, for reasons of conservation. According to the inventory of 1758, this ostensory and its companion piece were originally crowned with gilded roses, although these were already listed as missing even at that time. The appliqués came from the same workshop which produced the two ostensories Cat. Nos. 37 and 38, the ornamentation on all four pieces being virtually identical. These four ostensories are stylistically related to the reliquaries Cat. Nos. 25—27 and also to works preserved in various churches in Mantua. They were probably made in a workshop in the service of the ducal court at Mantua and sent to Vienna as gifts.

Inventory of 1758 — Case IX, No. 2

36 OSTENSORY
Mantua (?), c. 1600
Ebonised hardwood, silver-gilt, partially enamelled, rubies, pearls, glass; 50 cms high, 17.7 cms wide (Inv. No. D 114)

In the large compartments of this companion piece to Cat. No. 35 are displayed the relics of SS. Andrew, Stephen and Mary of Egypt; in the superstructure above them are the relics of St. Britius and in the crowning element those of St. Maximus.

Inventory of 1758 — Case IX, No. 2

37 OSTENSORY
Mantua (?), c. 1600
Hardwood foundation overlaid with ebony, silver-gilt, partially enamelled, diamonds, rubies, pearls, glass; 33.5 cms high (Inv. No. D 116)

The glass cylinder, flanked by two elaborately turned columns, contains a relic of St. Achatius, which is ornamented with pearls. The foot and crowning element contain relics of a fellow martyr of SS. Maurice and James the Less, displayed under several glass plates. This ostensory, like its companion piece and Cat. Nos. 35 and 36, was probably comissioned by the ducal court of the Gonzaga at Mantua.

Inventory of 1758 — Case III, No. 7

38 OSTENSORY
Mantua (?), c. 1600
Hardwood foundation overlaid with ebony, silver-gilt, partially enamelled, diamonds, rubies, pearls, glass; 33.5 cms high (Inv. No. D 115)

In the glass cylinder of this companion piece to Cat. No. 37 are the relics of St. Longinus; in the superstructure above it, those of St. James the Great. The inscriptions identifying the relics concealed beneath the cylinder have been lost, although the inventory of 1758 states that they are the relics of St. Sunidonius.

Inventory of 1758 — Case III, No. 7

39 RELIQUARY OF ST. STANISLAS
David Altenstetter (?)
(Colmar, c. 1540/1550—1617 Augsburg)
Augsburg, 1597
Gold enamelled, smoky quartz, ruby; 28 cms high (Inv. No. D 112)

This reliquary of gold was presented in 1597 to Archduchess Maria (1551—1608), the mother of Emperor Ferdinand II, by the Cardinal and Bishop of Cracow, Prince Georg Christoph Radziwill († 1600 in Vienna) and the Cathedral Chapter. Maria's daughter, Anna, was married to King Sigismund Wasa III of Poland. The reliquary contains a particle from the armbone of St. Stanislas, Bishop of Cracow († 1097). On the front, above the nodus, are the arms of Sweden, since the ruling dynasty in Poland at that time was a branch of the Swedish royal family. Inscribed on the foot is the dedication: GEOR.CARDLIS. RADZIWIL.EPVS.CRACOVIEN.ET. EJVS:DEM:ECCLAE.CAPLUM. MARIAE.ARCHIDUCISSAE. AUSTRIAE.DE.BRACHIO.S. STANISLAI.EPI.ET.MARTYRIS. D.D.MDXCVII. The relic is displayed between two plates of smoky quartz, to which two tiny figures, one of St. Paul and the other an allegory of faith (Fides), are affixed at the sides. The whole structure is crowned by a crucifix enamelled in gold and white. The partly translucent, partly opaque enamel on the stand of the ostensory unfolds into a display of extraordinarily rich and luminous colours. Both the pattern of scattered flowers inter-

spersed with animals and the virtuoso execution resemble works by the Augsburg goldsmith David Altenstetter, one of the great masters of this technique.

Inventory of 1758 — Case I, No. 82

Ref.: Seling 1980, vol. I, p. 50, vol. II, illus. 11

40 HOUSE ALTAR WITH CRYSTAL CARVINGS

Munich, end of the 16th century
After a design by Christoph Schwarz
(Munich 1548—1592 Munich)
Hardwood foundation overlaid with ebony, rock crystal, gold foil, silver, almandine, pastes (glass), wax beads; 25.5 cms high, 16.5 cms wide (Inv. No. Kap. 181)

The two crystal carvings of this ebony altar are dedicated to the Virgin Mary. Depicted on the smaller rock crystal plate, which has been inserted into the foot, is the Annunciation; on the larger one, Mary is being venerated by the angels as the Queen of Heaven. The composition is based on a painting from 1584, depicting the Madonna in Majesty, by the Munich court painter Christoph Schwarz, which was once on a side altar in the Jesuit Church of St. Salvator in Augsburg and is today in the church of St. Anna im Lehel, in Munich. The crystal cutter, who has succeeded admirably in translating the designs into his own medium, can almost certainly be assigned to the circle of artists at the Munich court. From the back of the crystal plate he has carved various deep layers in order to bring out the plasticity of the figures. At one time, the ebony frame displayed a costly set of jewels, but (as a result of the

1810 wartime levy on gold and silver?) this was later replaced by stones of inferior quality. In the inventory of 1626 the frame is described as having: *"mouldings of ebony, on which are 12 roses of enamelled gold, and in the middle of each a ruby, together with six others each with a medium-sized diamond in the middle, and five smaller rubies, one of them missing, and up above three small pyramids of smelted gold with small pearls."*

Inventory of 1626 — No. A/3 (3)
Inventory of 1752 — No. 83 (507)

41 PILGRIM'S STAFF
Italy, c. 1600
Bamboo cane, silver filigree, amethyst, 136 cms long (Inv. No. D 207)

A landscape and fourteen engraved scenes from the New Testament (from the Annunciation to the Coronation of the Virgin) are arranged one above the other on this bamboo staff. Each scene is engraved on a band extending nearly all the way around the staff and separated from the next by a purely ornamental band. Since the staff tapers towards the bottom, the pictures become gradually smaller. In contrast to the engravings on Cat. No. 42, which derive from the serial production of craftsmen, the execution of the pictures on this staff exhibits an impressive technical mastery. They were probably copied from Italian engravings at the end of the 16th century. The mounts match the high standard of the engraving work. The pommel is of ajouré silver filigree, set with large amethysts. Seven similar ornamental bands conceal the knots of the bamboo and decorate its tip.

Inventory of 1758 — Case IX, No. 7

Ref.: Weixlgärtner 1910/1911, p. 338, fig. 30.

42 STAFF OF DUKE WILHELM V OF BAVARIA
Sicily, end of the 16th century, and Munich (?), 1606
Engraved bamboo cane, silver-gilt; 137.5 cms long (Inv. No. D 208)

42, 41

This bamboo staff can be dismantled into five parts, which are connected by silver collars. Its shaft is decorated with 108 engraved pictorial medallions, arranged in 36 rows. The first 20 rows display scenes from the Old Testament and the Life and Passion of Christ, the next 12 rows present scenes from the lives of the Carmelite saints, followed finally by 4 rows with tondi of the 12 apostles. The inscriptions beneath the pictures are partly in Latin and partly in Italian, which in itself provides an important clue as to the origin of the staff. Staves like these were offered for sale in Italy at the larger centres of pilgrimage. The engraved designs are the work of a devotional artist and can thus be dated to the end of the 16th century. The above-mentioned Carmelite saints narrow down the possible place of origin. Most of the pictures are dedicated to St. Angelus of Leocata (near Agrigento), a saint venerated in Sicily. On the silver-gilt ajouré pommel are the Bavarian arms, the letters W.H.I.B. (Wilhelm Herzog in Bayern

— Wilhelm Duke of Bavaria) and the date 1606. Duke Wilhelm V of Bavaria (1548—1626, ruled 1579—1597) undertook a pilgrimage to the Casa Santa of Loreto in 1585 and could have acquired the staff on this occasion. How the staff came to be in Vienna is not known, but it is already listed as a "patriarchal staff" in the inventory of 1758.

Inventory of 1758 — Case IX, No. 6

Ref.: Weixlgärtner 1910/1911, p. 337 f.; Catalogue, Wallfahrt kennt keine Grenzen, Munich 1984, p. 123 f., no. 171.

Cross on the front and the Lamb of God on the back. The other pictures depict those saints whose relics are contained in the compartments behind them, each identified by a tiny plaque; these have, however, faded completely. Although pieces of this type have been attributed to southern German artists, crosses similar to this one (St. Michael in Munich, St. Barbara in Mantua) have been localised in Florence. Apart from stylistic similarities, the technical execution of the cross also points to Italy as its place of origin, since this technique was rarely used in Augsburg. The appliqués are partly made of gold enamel (name-plaques) and partly of gilded and painted brass (ends of the cross, frames of the medallions (partly replaced c. 1920/1930?).

Inventory of 1758 — Case III, No. 29

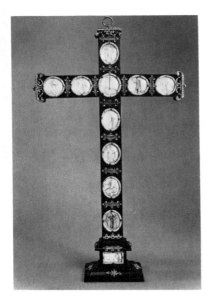

44 RELIQUARY OF ST. ELISABETH

Augsburg, beginning of the 17th century
Hardwood foundation overlaid with ebony, silver, partially gilded and enamelled, rubies, pearls, silk, gold braid, wax; 31 cms high, 30.4 cms wide, 19 cms deep (Inv. No. D 48)

Inside this small glazed reliquary sarcophagus, placed upon a cushion decorated with gold braid and rows of pearls, lies half of a tibia belonging to St. Elisabeth of Thuringia (1207—

43 RELIQUARY CROSS

Florence (?), end of the 16th century
Oak foundation overlaid with ebony, watercolour on parchment, rock crystal, gilded and painted brass, gold enamel; 32.9 cms high, 21.4 cms wide (Inv. No. E 3)

Carved into each side of this ebony-faced cross are ten medallion-shaped receptacles and a square compartment in the base. These are all covered by parchment miniatures and plates of rock crystal. Those at the intersection of the arms of the cross depict the Holy

1231). In 1588, Archduke Maximilian the Teutonic Master (1558—1618) ordered the saint's skull and two of her tibia to be removed from the Church of St. Elisabeth in Marburg and brought to Vienna, where the relic exhibited here was later separated from the rest. The skull and the other part of the tibia were bequeathed by the Archduke to the Convent of St. Clare, which had been founded by his sister, Elisabeth. After the closure of the convent, Emperor Joseph II presented the relics to the Convent of St. Elisabeth in Vienna (3rd District), where the saint's skull is still venerated today in the choir of the Convent church. A wax boss depicting St. Elisabeth sitting on a tree-trunk feeding the poor has been set into the roof above the relic. On the top is a crowning element with curved silver feet, supporting a small vase set with rubies. The reliquary was probably made in Augsburg in the early 17th century.

Inventory of 1758 — Case VII, No. 6

Ref.: T. Francke, Zur Geschichte der Elisabethreliquien im Mittelalter und in der frühen Neuzeit, in: Catalogue, Sankt Elisabeth. Fürstin, Dienerin, Heilige, Marburg 1981/82, p. 172.

figures as well as casting moulds for his sculptures. The two figures (Cat. No. 45 and 46) probably belonged to a larger series. Several wax busts of this type are listed in the inventory of 1758, and in 1626 the treasury of the Capuchin Monastery is also recorded as possessing a figure of St. Cecilia, the description of which tallies with the appearance of the two figures in the Ecclesiastical Treasury. This reliquary, like its counterpart, displays similar gold enamel ornamentation to the house altar Cat. No. 28.

Inventory of 1758 — Case IX, No. 21

Ref.: D. Diemer, Hans Krumper, in: Catalogue, Wittelsbach und Bayern II/I, Munich 1980, p. 293, illus. 169—171.

45 WAX FIGURE
OF ST. TIBURTIUS
Munich, beginning of the 17th century
Design: Hans Krumper (Weilheim, c. 1570—1643 Munich)
Wax, fabric, pearls, hardwood overlaid with ebony, gold enamel, bronze-gilt; 36 cms high, 22.5 cms wide (Inv. No. D 71)

This wax figure of St. Tiburtius holds a sword, the symbol of his martyrdom. To the left kneels a putto, in the act of presenting him with a laurel wreath, which is now missing. In 1780 the socle still contained the relics of St. Tiburtius, but these were later replaced with those of St. Crispin. The reliquary was executed after a design by Hans Krumper (Munich, Stadtmuseum Inv. No. 36/1895). Although Krumper was chiefly active as a bronze sculptor, sources attest that he produced a number of wax

46 WAX FIGURE OF ST. VALERIAN
Munich, beginning of the 17th century
Design: Hans Krumper (Weilheim, c. 1570—1634 Munich)
Wax, fabric, pearls, hardwood overlaid with ebony, gold enamel, bronze-gilt; 36 cms high, 22.5 cms wide (Inv. No. D 70)

This wax bust representing St. Valerian is the companion piece to Cat. No. 45. The pediment once contained the saint's relics, but after 1780 these were

replaced with those of St. Maurice. Although Krumper's design for this reliquary has been lost, the sketch for the companion piece indicates that the putto would originally have held a laurel wreath above the saint's head. The figures (as in the companion piece) are clothed in costly garments decorated with pearls.

Inventory of 1758 — Case IX, No. 20

Ref.: R. Büll, Das große Buch vom Wachs, vol. II, Frankfurt 1977, p. 943, illus. 698; Diemer, op. cit. Cat. No. 45.

47 THE CRUCIFIXION

Hans Bol (Mecheln 1534—1593 Amsterdam)
Amsterdam, 1591
Frame: Augsburg (?), c. 1600, silver mounts: Vienna, after 1780
Oak foundation overlaid with ebony, silver, gouache on parchment; signed, dated; 19.7 cms high, 7 cms wide (Inv. No. D 96)

The round parchment miniature was signed HBOL 1591 by Hans Bol, the most important Netherlandish miniaturist of the late 16th century. Placed along a diagonal are three crosses receding into the scene, which, in the foreground, is enclosed by tall scenery.

The middle ground of the painting opens out into a distant vista of Jerusalem. Mary Magdalen kneels at the foot of the cross, to the left stand Mary and John; to the right the soldiers dice for Christ's robe, and a mounted soldier holds out the sponge soaked in vinegar on the end of his lance. Hans Bol used this compositional formula for several crucifixion scenes painted during his last period. The upright ebony frame was probably made in Augsburg around 1600. The oval cavity in the foot originally held a receptacle for relics, but this was subsequently lost, together with the original ornamental mounts. In 1758, the frame was recorded as being decorated with gold enamel, six rubies and six pearls. After the death of Empress Maria Theresia, the ostensory was returned from her private chambers to the Treasury, *"stripped of all its ornaments."* The silver mounts that decorate it today were added at this time. Their rather arbitrary adaptation is especially apparent in the elements on the socle and the cavity for the reliquary.

Inventory of 1758 — Case I, No. 33

Ref.: H. G. Franz, Beiträge zum Werk des Hans Bol, in: Kunsthistorisches Jahrbuch Graz XIV (1979), pp. 199—208; H. G. Franz, Die Niederländische Kabinettminiatur. Zum Werk von Hans Bol und Frans Boels, in: Kunst und Antiqitäten 1985/3, pp. 12—23 (the Viennese examples are not discussed).

48 THE RESURRECTION OF CHRIST

Hans Bol (Mecheln 1534—1593 Amsterdam)

Amsterdam, probably 1591

Frame: Augsburg (?), c. 1600. Silver mounts: Vienna, after 1780

Oak foundation overlaid with ebony, silver, gouache on parchment, unsigned; 19.7 cms high, 7 cms wide (Inv. No. D 97)

This ostensory shared the same fate as its companion piece Cat. No. 47, and the unsigned miniature here was probably also executed in 1591. Christ rises from the grave in a cloud of glory, escorted by angels, at the sight of which the guards flee in panic. An angel on the upper left points towards the risen Christ, while to the right the rocky landscape opens out on to a view of the encounter between Christ and the disciples from Emmaus. The composition corresponds closely to the Resurrection from a small triptych (privately owned) bearing the signature H. BOL F. This identifies the miniature in the Treasury with certainty as one of Hans Bol's later works.

Inventory of 1758 — Case I, No. 33

Ref.: Franz, op. cit. Cat. No. 47.

49 RELIQUARY CASKET

Venice (?), 3rd quarter of the 16th century

Miniature: Joris Hoefnagel (Antwerp 1542—1600 Vienna), Prague (?), end of the 16th century

Wood, ebonised and gilded, sardonyx, lapis lazuli, watercolour on parchment; 26 cms high, 48 cms wide, 31 cms deep (Inv. No. D 185)

The outer surface of the casket is covered in a mosaic of rectangular and oval onyx plates enclosed by gilded wooden mouldings. Despite its ornamental overlay, the casket is constructed according to strict architectonic principles and resembles a sarcophagus or a shrine. The structure follows motifs from classical architecture, which was the obligatory model for the Renaissance. Pilasters standing on a pedestal element frame the corners and divide the long sides into three zones, the central section being double the width of the side sections. On this rests an architrave supporting the roof and triglyphs, both architectural elements deriving from the classical Greek temple. The inside of the lid is faced with plates of lapis lazuli and has the same structure as the outer sides. Set into the centre of the lid is a miniature of the Ascension by the Netherlandish miniaturist Joris Hoefnagel. The casket itself is probably Venetian. The same principle of overlaying architectural forms with decorative surface elements can also be found in the Renaissance architecture of Venice, for example in the buildings of the Lombardo family of master builders, such as the church Sta. Maria dei Miracoli, or those of Jacopo Sanso-

vino. The casket formerly (1780) contained the skull and bones of a companion of St. Ursula.

Inventory of 1758 — Case III (below), No. 4
Inventory of 1780 — Case X, No. 1

Ref.: H. J. Hermann, Zwei unbekannte Arbeiten des Georg Hoefnagel, in: Mitteilungen des Instituts für Österreichische Geschichtsforschung XX (1899), pp. 480—483; T. Vignau-Wilberg, Joris Hoefnagel in München: Jahrbuch 81 (1985).

50 ROSARY DECADE FROM THE ESTATE OF QUEEN ANNA

Germany (?), 1st quarter of the 16th century
Agate, ivory, silver-gilt; 55.5 cms long
(Inv. No. D 5)

The decade has been used as the open form of the rosary ever since the 15th century. It was usual to hang the beads one after another on the fingers and thumb of one hand, while reciting the five chaplets of the rosary. This agate decade was owned by Queen Anna of Bohemia and Hungary (1503—1547), the wife of Emperor Ferdinand I. In 1780, all ten of the elongated agate beads and the two nut-shaped, silver-gilt beads were still extant; today, two of the agate beads are missing. At the upper end a ring is attached, by which the rosary was held. The vanitas of the large ivory pendant serves as a reminder of the transience of the world: on one side are the busts of a queen and a monk beneath a baldachin, on the other that of Death.

Inventory of 1758 — Case III, No. 11

Ref.: H. Zimmerman, Urkunden, Acten und Regesten aus dem Archiv des k.k. Ministeriums des Inneren, in: Jahrbuch V (1887), Reg. No. 4525 (Nachlass der Königin Anna), p. CXLIV — no. 233.

on metal foils, a technique for which the name 'églomisé' has been adopted. These depict scenes from the Old and New Testaments and various saints. The rosary is further decorated with a ring and a pendant Greek cross. The style of the miniatures indicates that this piece was made around 1600. The Musée du Louvre in Paris and the Museo Civico in Turin possess similar rosaries.

Inventory of 1758 — Case III, No. 12

51 ROSARY DECADE

Milan (?), c. 1600
Rock crystal. silver-gilt, églomisé; 28.5 cms long (Inv. No. D 184)

One bead is missing from this rosary decade. Each of the remaining nine beads consists of two rock crystal calottes enclosing miniatures painted

53 PRAYER-BOOK OF EMPEROR FERDINAND II
Augsburg (?), 1590
Gold enamelled, parchment with gilt edges; 6 cms high, 4.8 cms wide; page size: 5.6 cms high, 4.4 cms wide (Inv. No. D 27)

The first six pages of this miniature prayer-book contain the devices of various members of the Habsburg and Wittelsbach families, mostly written in their own hands. These entries and certain references in the following prayer texts indicate that it was owned by Emperor Ferdinand II. The Emperor received it as a boy from his parents, Archduke Karl II of Inner Austria and Archduchess Maria, daughter of Duke

52 ST. ANNE WITH MARY AND THE CHILD JESUS
Bavaria (Weilheim carver ?), c. 1620 (before 1626)
Polychromed wood, brass-gilt; sculpture: 15 cms high; socle: 15 cms high (Inv. No. Kap. 159)

Surrounded by a gilded aureole, St. Anne is enthroned with the infant Jesus on her lap and her left hand placed around the shoulder of her daughter, who is depicted as a small girl. Mary holds a bowl of fruits and is offering the child a pear. The chalice and the fruit are to be understood as symbols of the Passion of Christ. The small wooden group is characterised by a continuous outline, an expression of inner spirituality and the generous rhythm of the draperies. A comparable conception of figure and a similar facial type appear in the first quarter of the 17th century, in the work of Bavarian sculptors from the carving centre of Weilheim, in particular that of the pupils of Hans Degler, such as Christoph Angermair or Philip Dirr. The gilt wooden socle once contained relics of St. Anne.

Inventory of 1626 — No. S/19 (344)

Albrecht V of Bavaria, when he began his studies at the Jesuit College in Ingolstadt. Although miniature prayer-books were popular in European court art around 1600, only isolated examples have survived. The costly gold cover is richly enamelled with a scrolling pattern enclosing an oval cartouche. This contains the initials MA for Maria on the front cover, and IHS surrounded by a cross and the three nails from the cross for Jesus on the back. As is typical for the style of the late 16th century, the scrollwork does not develop freely, but is incorporated into the superordinate motif enclosing the cartouche. Enamel work of this kind was chiefly executed at Augsburg and Nuremberg, but also at other centres such as Munich and Salzburg.

Inventory of 1758 — Case I, No. 85

Ref.: H. Fillitz, Ein Gebetbuch Kaiser Ferdinands II., in: Mitteilungen des Instituts für Österreichische Geschichtsforschung LX (1952), pp. 232—237; E. von Philippovich, Anhängebüchlein oder Schmuckstück, in: Weltkunst LVII (1986), p. 664 f.

54 RELIQUARY TREE

Rome, 1608/09, and Vienna, between 1626 and 1752
Gold; reliquary pendants; silver, parcel-gilt, jasper, rock crystal, pearls, enamel, glass; 57 cm high (Inv. No. Kap. 103a)

The reliquary tree was originally a Golden Rose commissioned by Pope Paul V (1605—1621) — a member of the Borghese family — in Rome in 1608/09. According to ancient tradition, the Pope presented the Golden Rose to personages or institutions distinguished for their exceptional piety (cf. Secular Treasury, Cat. No. 136). The Rose in the Ecclesiastical Treasury was presented to Empress Anna, wife of Emperor Matthias, for her exemplary virtuousness. In a communication from Prague dated 14. 7. 1616, the Emperor expresses his thanks for the Rose sent to his wife. Only the lower part of the relic survives today, and the actual rose has been lost. The piece passed from the Empress' estate to the treasury of the Capuchin Monastery and was there refashioned into a reliquary tree. The flowers were replaced by the roughly worked golden branches extant today, which are hung with precious relics, among them a molar reputedly belonging to St. Peter. The work of the original Roman goldsmith, on the other hand, is distinguished by the high quality of its execution. Three dragons — the dragon was the heraldic symbol of the House of the Borghese — bear a flower vase which displays the Borghese arms of Pope Paul V as well as the donative inscription: PAULUS V. PON. MAX. ANN. IIII (Paul V, Pontificus Maximus in the year 4 (of his office).

Inventory of 1626 — No. R/10 (322)
Inventory of 1752 — No. 87 (511)

Ref.: H. von Voltelini, Urkunden aus dem k. und k. Haus-, Hof- und Staats-Archiv in Wien, in: Jahrbuch XX (1899), p. XXIX — Reg. No. 17358.

55 SCOURGE OF EMPRESS ANNA

Austria (?), beginning of the 17th century
Silver-gilt, brass-gilt, silk; 70 cms long (Inv. No. Kap. 147)

Scourges were popular instruments of penance from the Middle Ages onwards. During the Counter-Reformation both clergy and laity chastised themselves with scourges, known as 'disciplines'. According to counter-reformationary doctrine, the suppression of the flesh liberated and purified the spirit. Thus the Capuchin monks in Vienna, for example, were obliged to 'discipline' themselves once a week. This scourge has a handle of braided silver wire with

a silk core and four cords of red silk tipped with brass-gilt beads. This combination of materials is not without a certain sensuous charm. The sumptuousness of this piece indicates the high rank of its owner, Empress Anna, the wife of Emperor Matthias, who in her estate left four of these scourges, which she had probably used for penitential exercises.

Inventory of 1626 — No. D/2 (172)
Inventory of 1752 — No. 106 (530)

56 SCOURGE OF EMPRESS ANNA

Austria (?), beginning of the 17th century
Silver-gilt, brass-gilt, silk; 73 cms long
(Inv. No. Kap. 148)

This scourge was at one time associated with Empress Eleonora, the second wife of Emperor Ferdinand II. In actual fact, like its companion piece, it derives from the estate of the Empress Anna, who donated her four scourges to the treasury of the Capuchin Monastery. This piece has three green silk cords, on the ends of which are brass-gilt beads.

Inventory of 1626 — No. D/1 (171)
Inventory of 1752 — No. 106 (530)

57 OSTENSORY

Matthias Walbaum (Kiel, c. 1554—1632 Augsburg).
Augsburg, c. 1600/1605
Oak foundation overlaid with ebony, ebonised hardwood, silver, parcel-gilt; Walbaum's maker's mark, Augsburg

hallmark; 49 cms high, 28.8 cms wide
(Inv. No. D 89)

This is the only surviving example of an ostensory by Walbaum and can be ranked as one of his finest and most magnificent works. It has the same structure as full-sized altars, being divided into predella, centrepiece, pediment, and crowning element. The wooden corpus is decorated with a profusion of silver scrollwork which virtually dissolves the contours, giving an impression of bewildering richness. A harmonious balance exists between the wooden corpus and the silver ornamentation, each enhancing the effect of the other. The relics of various saints are displayed in 17 small compartments. These are flanked by four figures on consoles representing (from top left to bottom right): Caritas (Charity), Temperantia (Temperance), Fides (Faith) and Spes (Hope). In the predella, the Madonna is being worshipped by angels, in the superstructure, the Pietà is surrounded by saints and angels, and the figure of a bishop-saint forms the crowning element. One of the most original features is that of the two angels balancing on the volutes. The silver mounts provide an insight into the techniques used in Walbaum's workshop. Similar ornaments and figures can also be found in other

works by Walbaum in the Ecclesiastical Treasury.

Inventory of 1780 — Case V, No. 8

Ref.: Löwe 1975, pp. 52—54; no. 32; Seling 1980, vol. III, p. 112, no. 1060 s; F. Windisch-Graetz, Möbel Europas. Renaissance und Manierismus, Munich 1983, p. 131 f.

58 WINGED HOUSE ALTAR FROM THE ESTATE OF EMPEROR MATTHIAS

Matthias Walbaum (Kiel, c. 1554—1632 Augsburg)
Augsburg, c. 1600 (between 1596 and 1608)
Oak foundation overlaid with ebony, silver, parcel-gilt, miniatures on copper; 40.7 cms high, 18.5 cms wide (Inv. No. D 179)

This type of house altar with a high stand constituted one of the most successful products of the workshop of Matthias Walbaum. The simple basic form of the wooden construction is concealed beneath the rich ornamentation of silver mounts, into which figures have been incorporated. On the outside of the wings is the Annunciation, while to the right and left of the shrine are depictions of St. George and St. Michael beneath round arches crowned with angels; on the nodus is a pietà and above that the three women at Christ's tomb; in the intermediate section is the risen Christ and, finally, St. Peter and St. Paul in the lateral pinnacles. With the wings opened, a miniature of the Adoration of the Shepherds is displayed on the centre panel, flanked on the wings by the Circumcision of Christ and the Presentation in the Temple. Apart from the two house altars in the Ecclesiastical Treasury, other pieces which display this widely acclaimed composition exist in the Museums of Decorative Art in Budapest and Berlin, in the Metropolitan Museum in New York and in the Abegg Foundation in Riggisberg/Berne. On the reverse of this piece there is a flower vase corresponding to the arms of the Archduke (and later Emperor) Matthias on the companion piece.

Inventory of 1758 — Case II, No. 13

Ref.: Löwe 1975, p. 39 f., no. 13; Seling 1980, vol. III, p. 112, no. 1060 m.

59 WINGED HOUSE ALTAR FROM THE ESTATE OF EMPEROR MATTHIAS

Matthias Walbaum (Kiel, c. 1554—1632 Augsburg)
Augsburg, c. 1600 (between 1596 and 1608)
Oak foundation overlaid with ebony, silver, parcel-gilt, miniatures on copper; 40.7 cms high, 18.5 cms wide (Inv. No. D 178)

This small house altar is identical to its companion piece Cat. No. 58, apart from minimal differences in the silver mounts. However, the central miniature, signed LW 1588 and depicting the Adoration of the Shepherds, has been almost entirely obliterated. Referring to the miniatures, the inventory of 1780 records that *"almost everything"* which was returned from the private cham-

bers of the Empress Maria Theresia after her death *"was faded"*. However, the paintings are probably older than the two altars. On the back are the arms of the Archduke (and later Emperor) Matthias, crowned with the archducal coronet and enclosed by the neckchain of the Order of the Golden Fleece. Since Matthias did not become a Knight of the Order until 1596 and was not crowned King of Hungary until 1608, the altar can be dated to this period with certainty. It is assumed to have been commissioned from Walbaum directly.

Inventory of 1758 — Case II, No. 13

Ref.: Löwe 1975, p. 38—40, no. 12; Seling 1980, vol. III, p. 112, no. 1060 1.

60 OSCULATORY FROM THE ESTATE OF EMPEROR MATTHIAS

Matthias Walbaum (Kiel, c. 1554—1632 Augsburg)
Augsburg, c. 1600 (between 1596 and 1608)
Oak foundation overlaid with ebony, silver, parcel-gilt; 36.4 cms high, 17 cms wide (Inv. No. D 173)

In all likelihood, this monstrance-like ebony house altar was originally intended as an osculatory (pax), designed to be passed around during the ceremony of High Mass for the kiss of peace. In the baroque scrollwork adjoining the frame are depicted scenes from the Life of the Virgin. They culminate in the silver relief of the embossed central section, where the Virgin Mary is venerated as the Queen of Heaven.

Around the relief are to be seen: left, the Angel of the Annunciation; right, Mary at a prie-dieu; on the nodus, the Adoration of the Shepherds; on the crowning element, the Adoration of the Magi. On the foot are reliefs of the four Evangelists. The figures of St. Veronica and Hope (Spes) constitute lateral crowning elements, while the figure at the very top is missing. Like Cat. No. 59, this small house altar also bears an emblem of the Archduke (and later Emperor) Matthias on the reverse. The archducal coronet and the neckchain of the Order of the Golden Fleece enclose a crane, the symbol of watchfulness, which the Archduke Matthias chose as his emblem.

Inventory of 1758 — Case III, No. 19

Ref.: Löwe 1975, p. 45, no. 19; Seling 1980, vol. III, p. 112, no. 1060 o.

61 OSCULATORY FROM THE ESTATE OF EMPEROR MATTHIAS

Matthias Walbaum (Kiel, c. 1554—1632 Augsburg)

Augsburg, c. 1600 (between 1596 and 1609)

Oak foundation overlaid with ebony, silver, parcel-gilt; 36.4 cms high, 17 cms wide (Inv. No. D 172)

Apart from minimal differences in the silver mounts, this osculatory is identical to its companion piece Cat. No. 60. The left-hand crowning element displays a personification of Faith (Fides) in place of the figure of St. Veronica, and the right a figure of Hope (Spes), which is repeated as the central figure above. The emblem on the back resembles that on Cat. Nos. 59 and 60; in the centrepiece, however, the name Matthias has been executed in ligature.

Inventory of 1758 — Case III, No. 19

Ref.: Löwe 1975, p. 44 f., no. 18; Seling 1980, vol. III, p. 112, no. 1060 n.

62 OSTENSORY

Circle of Matthias Walbaum

Augsburg, beginning of the 17th century

Hardwood foundation overlaid with ebony, partially ebonised, silver, parcel-gilt, glass; 46.8 cms high, 15.5 cms wide (Inv. No. D 90)

Integrated within this tower-shaped ostensory are three receptacles for relics: a glass cylinder, flanked by two pillars and angels with silver censers, containing unspecified relics (OSSA SANCTORUM); the socle, with relics of St. Apollinaire; and the superstructure, with relics of St. Sebastian. A statuette of St. Sebastian also forms the crowning element, while on the pillars are two silver statuettes of Roman soldiers (probably also martyrs). Neither the figures nor the ornamental decoration of this reliquary attain the quality of pieces made by Walbaum himself. The character of the interlocking scrollwork, which is carved from thick silver foil, corresponds more closely to the mounts of the house altar Cat. No. 68.

Inventory of 1758 — Case VIII, No. 3

Ref.: Löwe 1975, p. 100, no. 87 a.

63 OSTENSORY

Circle of Matthias Walbaum

Augsburg, beginning of the 17th century

Hardwood foundation overlaid with ebony, partially ebonised, silver, parcel-gilt, glass; 46.8 cms high, 15.5 cms wide (Inv. No. D 91)

This reliquary is a companion piece to Cat. No. 62. In this case, too, the glass cylinder contains the relics of anonymous saints, while the superstructure houses the relics of St. Mary Magdalen. The inscription identifying the relics preserved in the socle has been lost, but according to the inventory of 1758, they belonged to the saint and martyr Bishop Boniface. The same source mentions an abbess holding a staff as the crowning element which has been replaced with the figure of a Roman soldier. The missing figures above the columns were probably also soldiers, as in the case of its companion piece.

Inventory of 1758 — Case VIII, No. 4

Ref.: Löwe 1975, p. 100, no. 88 a.

64 WAX RELIEF: PIETÀ
Circle of Matthias Walbaum
Augsburg, c. 1600
Wax, ebony, silver, parcel-gilt, glass;
22.2 cms high, 11 cms wide (Inv. No. D 195)

This oval, embossed wax relief bears a depiction of the Pietà which is of outstanding quality. It is enclosed by a glass plate and an ornamental border decorated with pearls. The delicate upright ebony frame has plastic baroque scrollwork set with ingenious masks and angels' heads. Most of the appliqués are missing on the foot, as is the crowning element, which — according to the inventory of 1758 — consisted of a cross. The silver mounts are identical to those of the ostensories Cat. Nos. 71 and 72, and the latter were probably made in the same workshop as this upright frame and its companion piece.

Inventory of 1758 — Case VI, No. 18

65 WAX RELIEF OF CHRIST ON THE MOUNT OF OLIVES
Circle of Matthias Walbaum
Augsburg, c. 1600
Wax, ebony, silver, parcel-gilt, glass; 21 cms high, 10 cms wide (Inv. No. D 196)

This companion piece to Cat. No. 64 represents Christ praying to God on the Mount of Olives. Behind him are the sleeping apostles and the city of Jerusalem. The bright colouring imbues the relief with great vivacity. Of the enclosing inner frame, only the mounts have been preserved (cf. Cat. No. 64).

Inventory of 1758 — Case VI, No. 18

66 STANDING CROSS
Augsburg (?), end of the 16th century
Ebony, silver, gold; 80.8 cms high, 29.5 cms wide (Inv. No. E 49)

This tall, slender ebony cross is of unusual technical execution. Both the cross and its socle are completely covered with engraved gold and silver inlays. The figure of Christ is surrounded by the instruments of the Passion. On the ends of the cross are depicted: left, the cock which crowed three times at Peter's denial; at the top, the cup used at the Last Supper; and, right, the bowl in which Pilate washed his hands. On the beams, among other objects, are the scourge, the hammer, the lance with the sponge soaked in vinegar, Christ's garments, the dice used to gamble for them, and the skull of Adam. In the central field of the socle,

angels display the sudarium of St. Veronica. The exquisite depiction of the dead Christ can be observed in similar execution on sculpted crucifixes by contemporary Augsburg goldsmiths. In Augsburg, decorative engraved gold and silver inlays were primarily used for furniture. One of the most famous masters of this art was the carpenter Hans Georg Hertel, who made a large ornate table-top for the Prince Elector Maximilian I of Bavaria.

Inventory of 1758 — Case IX, No. 24

Ref.: Weixlgärtner 1910/1911, p. 331 f.

motifs are linked by the figure of the small boy holding a spoon on the left of the socle, who showed Augustine that to seek an explanation of the Holy Trinity is as vain as trying to empty the oceans with a spoon. Augustine is distinguished from the other figures by the emerald fastening of his pluvial. Behind him stand St. Peter, St. John the Baptist, St. Cyriacus with the Devil at his feet, and St. Jerome. The composition of this relief possibly derives from a figural group by Guglielmo della Porta. A replica of this relief in the Museum für Kunst und Gewerbe in Hamburg bears a Viennese (!) hallmark for 1806/07. The unusually high quality of the silver figures has suggested that these two works might have been executed by Matthias Walbaum. However, since Walbaum's work (cf. the ornamentation) displays considerable differences to this altar, the question of its authorship must remain open for the time being.

Inventory of 1758 — Case VIII, No. 5

Ref.: Löwe 1975, p. 102 f., nos. 94a, 95a.

68 WINGED HOUSE ALTAR
Successors of Matthias Walbaum (?)
Augsburg, 1st quarter of the 17th century
Ebonised hardwood, ebony, silver, re-

67 HOUSE ALTAR WITH A RELIEF OF ST. AUGUSTINE
Augsburg, Ist quarter of the 17th century
Oak foundation overlaid with ebony, walnut veneer, silver, parcel-gilt, 2 emeralds; 37.2 cms high, 20.2 cms wide (Inv. No. D 183)

Crowned by a Madonna and two flower vases, the structure of this house altar resembles that of a full-sized altar retable with a figure-niche. On a console in front of the niche stands a silver figure of St. Augustine, Bishop of Hippo and Doctor of the Church (354—430). Above the saint hovers the Dove of the Holy Ghost. These two

mains of gilding; 26 cms high, 14.4 cms wide (Inv. No. D 182)

Although the reliefs on the central panel, wings and predella of this house altar follow Matthias Walbaum's iconographical scheme for small winged altars, they nonetheless differ in style from his work as a whole. Depicted here are the Adoration of the Shepherds, the Presentation of Jesus at the Temple and, in the predella, the Flight into Egypt. The relief might originally have been intended for a small winged altar similar to Cat. Nos. 58 and 59, since the end of the arch of the triptych has been rather arbitrarily altered to a rectangle. There are also three further predella reliefs (the Annunciation, the Discovery of the twelve-year-old Jesus in the Temple, and the Adoration of the Magi). According to the inventory of 1758, these depict the *joyful secrets*. This scheme does not quite correspond to the Seven Joys of the Virgin Mary, which could be explained by the fact that it has been adapted from an earlier piece. The carved silver mounts are markedly different from Walbaum's miniature objects, which possess an exeptional plasticity of form, are finely and fully developed and never dissolve in merely superficial decorative forms. The silver figures were in fact made in Walbaum's workshop, and the angel with the torch and the book, for instance, is also to be found in Cat. Nos. 57—60. This small winged house altar must therefore derive from a workshop of his circle, or else from one of his successors. It is just possible that a piece by Walbaum has been reworked into a pastiche; however, since all of the ornamental mounts and the relief come from a different workshop, this is not very likely.

Inventory of 1758 — Case VIII, No. 6

Ref.: Löwe 1975, p. 97 f., no. 81a.

69 OSTENSORY IN THE SHAPE OF AN OBELISK
Circle of Matthias Walbaum
Augsburg, beginning of the 17th century

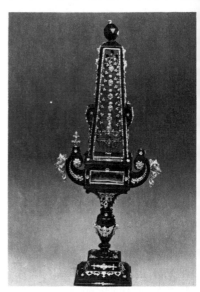

Ebonised hardwood, silver, jasper, pearls, glass; 29.8 cms high, 12.6 cms wide (Inv. No. D 105)

The obelisk contains a piece of white material richly set with pearls, supposedly part of the Virgin Mary's veil. The socle of the obelisk contains a relic of St. George. The ostensory was originally crowned by a silver statuette, which was replaced with the present facetted sphere of green jasper sometime before 1780. With a few exceptions, for example the flower vase on the right-hand volute, the rest of the silver mounts have been preserved. The finely executed appliqués are not characteristic of the work of Walbaum himself, but rather that of the workshop responsible for Cat. Nos. 64, 65, 71 and 72, where this ostensory and its companion piece must also have been made.

Inventory of 1758 — Case I, No. 68

70 OSTENSORY IN THE FORM OF AN OBELISK
Circle of Matthias Walbaum
Augsburg, beginning of the 17th century
Ebonised hardwood, silver, jasper, pearls, glass; 29.8 cms high, 12.6 cms wide (Inv. No. D 106)

The companion piece to Cat. No. 69, this ostensory is supposed to contain a fragment of the banner of St. George in the obelisk and a relic of St. Maurice in the base. Here, too, the piece was originally surmounted by a silver statuette, which was replaced by the present crowning element sometime before 1780.

Inventory of 1758 — Cabinet I, No. 68

71 OSTENSORY
Circle of Matthias Walbaum
Augsburg, beginning of the 17th century
Oak foundation overlaid with ebony, silver, pearls, glass; 22 cms high, 10 cms wide (Inv. No. D 50)

The piece of a white veil set with pearls which is visible in the oval receptacle is supposedly a fragment of the veil of the Virgin Mary. This was at one time indicated by the figure of the Virgin Mary of the Immaculate Conception (Maria Immaculata), which stood between the two flower vases and was lost sometime after 1856. The framing scrollwork is based on a spiralling motif and set with striking masks and heads. Part of the ornamentation is identical to that of Cat. Nos. 62 and 63.

Inventory of 1758 — Case I, No. 34

72 OSTENSORY WITH RELICS
Circle of Matthias Walbaum

Augsburg, beginning of the 17th century
Oak foundation overlaid with ebony, silver, pearls, glass; 22 cms high, 10 cms wide (Inv. No. D 49)

The companion piece to Cat. No. 71, this ostensory contains a remnant of black fabric. Here, too, the silver figure at the top, representing an anonymous saint in a nun's habit, is missing. Since this apparently represented either St. Scholastica or St. Theresa, this garment relic may also derive from one of these two saints.

Inventory of 1758 — Case I, No. 34

73 RELIQUARY CASKET
Augsburg, beginning of the 17th century
Beechwood overlaid with ebony, silver, parcel-gilt, mother-of-pearl; 19.5 cms high, 20.7 cms wide, 15 cms deep (Inv. No. Kap. 188)

This casket in the shape of a sarcophagus contains relics belonging to SS. Colonat and Totnan, whose silver figures form the crowning element of the piece. One of the figures has lost its martyr's palm. Together with St. Kilian, the two saints were missionaries in the area around Würzburg, where they were martyred in 689. The relics of their skulls are preserved in the mensa of the high altar in Würzburg Cathedral. The front of the casket is inlaid with plates of mother-of-pearl, ornamented like the framing sections with silver mounts. The severity of the contours is softened by silver scrollwork, which also forms the feet of the reliquary. Stylistically, the casket belongs to work produced in Augsburg around 1600, where parallels to the silver appliqués can be found in the circle of Matthias Walbaum.

Inventory of 1626 — No. A/22 (22)
Inventory of 1752 — No. 40 (463)

74 RELIQUARY CASKET
Augsburg, beginning of the 17th century
Beechwood overlaid with ebony, silver, parcel-gilt, mother-of-pearl; 19.5 cms

high, 20.7 cms wide, 15 cms deep (Inv. No. Kap. 189)

The companion piece to Cat. No. 73, this casket contains the relics of several saints. The surmounting silver figure of a boy with a skull and hour-glass, symbolising transience, serves as a reminder of the function of the casket.

Inventory of 1626 — No. A/22 (22)
Inventory of 1752 — No. 41 (464)

75 RELIQUARY CHEST
Augsburg (?), c. 1600
Silver, parcel-gilt; 17.5 cms high, 23.8 cms wide, 13 cms deep (Inv. No. Kap. 81)

Four small, gilt lions support this silver chest which contains relics of SS. Fabian and Sebastian. The entire surface of the chest is covered with plain yet extremely effective decoration. Narrow mouldings divide the surface into 18 sections, each of which encloses a separate engraving, eight depicting flower vases, the others displaying leaf-work, pendant clusters of fruit and

birds. Each motif is framed by a polished moulding which forms an effective contrast to the unpolished ground. The design of the keyhole is especially ingenious in that it also forms the gaping mouth of a mascaron. All the individual motifs are, however, subordinated to the clarity of the composition as a whole. The goldsmith's work still displays all the characteristics of the late Renaissance. The casket, together with its companion piece, belonged to the estate of Empress Anna, the wife of Emperor Matthias.

Inventory of 1626 — No. F/18 (191)
Inventory of 1752 — No. 116 (540)

76 RELIQUARY CHEST
Augsburg (?), c. 1600
Silver, parcel-gilt; 17.5 cms high, 23.8 cms wide, 13 cms deep (Inv. No. Kap. 82)

Identical to its companion piece, Cat. No. 75, this reliquary chest contains the relics of St. Adrian.

Inventory of 1626 — No. F/18 (191)
Inventory of 1752 — No. 115 (539)

77 CRUCIFIXION RELIEF
Matthias Walbaum (Kiel, c. 1554–1632 Augsburg) or Jeremias Flicker II († 1647 Augsburg)
Augsburg, c. 1615/1618
Silver on velvet, indistinct mark; 60 cms high, 40 cms wide (Inv. No. Kap. 40)

The dead Redeemer hangs from a cross decorated with ornamental trefoils; to either side stand Mary, with bowed head, wringing her hands, and John, his hand on his breast in sorrowful devotion. Two angels fly up to Christ bearing chalices to catch his blood, and in the upper corners, sun and moon conceal themselves behind clouds. The historical event of Christ's crucifixion on Golgotha seems here to have receded into the timeless sphere of a devotional image, to which the detailed motifs of the goldsmith's work form a fascinating contrast. The rendering of the hill — between the stones and

plants there is even a beetle (forming a pair to a lizard which is now missing) — is as remarkable as the engraving of the figures. The silver reliefs were originally applied on blue velvet and enclosed by an ebony frame set with silver mounts. The faded orange-red velvet extant today was fitted before 1752, while the gilt wooden frame dates from the 19th century. The relief, which was previously attributed to Albrecht von Horn or Andreas Hamburger, in fact goes back to a prototype by Guglielmo della Porta (the Escorial, bedchamber of Philip II), a composition widely used in pieces of goldsmiths' work produced in Augsburg. There are close similarities to the Viennese relief in the work of both Matthias Walbaum and Jeremias Flicker II, who was probably active in Walbaum's workshop for a time. Flicker and Walbaum were evidently more than just fellow goldsmiths; Walbaum died at the age of 78 in Flicker's house. Both men used the compositions of Guglielmo della Porta in their work on several occasions (Flicker's altar in the Maximilianmuseum at Augsburg; Walbaum's house altar in the Church of St. Ulrich and Afra in Augsburg).

Inventory of 1626 — No. Q/1 (276)
Inventory of 1752 — No. 208 (641)

78 ALTAR RELIEF OF THE VIRGIN MARY
Augsburg, c. 1600
Silver, parcel-gilt, four almandines; 33 cms high, 25 cms wide (Inv. No. Kap. 208)

Enthroned on clouds, the Madonna and Child are surrounded by four angels in adoration. Certain parts of this silver group, which is executed in high relief, are almost three dimensional. For a long time the piece was regarded as a perfect example of a devotional relief in its own right. However, the fragmentary character of the group alone is an indication that the original context of the piece was far more extensive, a supposition confirmed by the inventory of 1626. There, the figures can be identified as belonging to the central panel of a ebony altar which, except for this fragment, has been lost: "*. . . a little altar made of ebony (. . .) wholly decorated with silver, in the middle of which is the Virgin Mary with the Holy Child, in the clouds between 4 angels, all made of thick silver, the crown of the Virgin Mary gilded and set with five rubies. Roundabout are the 12 Apostles, also made of thick silver, where the pediment begins a small angel with the secrets of the Passion of Christ, somewhat higher the sacred blood, at the very top our Saviour and at the end of the pediment the name of*

Jesus in an aureole, all made of silver.''
The five rubies mentioned in the inventory are, in fact, (red) almandines. Four stones and an empty setting still exist. The figures are related to a wooden Augsburg statuette from around 1600, which matches this piece of goldsmiths' work not only in the type of figure but also in the richly detailed surface characterisation.

Inventory of 1626 — No. A/11 (11)
Inventory of 1752 — No. 202 (635)?

Ref.: T. Müller, Das kleine Andachtsbild in der Augsburger Plastik um 1600, in: Miscellanea pro arte. Festschrift Hermann Schnitzler, Düsseldorf 1965, p. 262.

Father and Christ crown the kneeling Mother of God, while the Dove of the Holy Ghost hovers aloft. The composition is based on a lost painting by the Flemish painter Maerten de Vos, which was copied in an engraving by Johannes Sadeler I around 1590. The Augsburg goldsmith Benedikt Engelschalk followed this model closely, merely adding a few angels' heads. The Museo Lazaro Galdiano in Madrid possesses a replica of this relief.

Inventory of 1626 — No. A/9 (9)
Inventory of 1752 — No. 206 (639)

Ref.: Seling 1980, vol. III, p. 146, no. 1266 a.

79 THE CORONATION OF THE VIRGIN

Benedikt Engelschalk (Augsburg, c. 1575—1623 Augsburg)
After a painting by Maerten de Vos (Antwerp 1531—1603 Antwerp)
Augsburg, c. 1613/1615
Silver, maker's mark BE, Augsburg hallmark; 24.7 cms high, 18.3 cms wide (Inv. No. Kap. 194)

This relief is the only surviving part of a small house altar of ebony and silver, of which it once formed the centrepiece. After her Ascension, the Virgin Mary is received into heaven by the Holy Trinity and the angels. God the

80 ADORATION OF THE SHEPHERDS

Augsburg, c. 1600
After a painting by Hans von Aachen (Cologne 1552—1615 Prague)
Silver; 20 cms high, 15.3 cms wide (Inv. No. Kap. 3)

Working in Augsburg around 1600, the unknown goldsmith who made this piece has here copied an altar picture, no longer extant, painted by Hans von Aachen between 1585 and 1587 for the Church of Il Gesù in Rome. The composition became widely known in 1588 through an engraving by Aegidius Sadeler. Two figures in the foreground draw the spectator's gaze towards the Madonna and Child, who are placed on a raised dais. The shepherds and angels are pictured hurrying along in great agitation, urgently gesticulating with their hands — a manner of representation which corresponded to the ecstatic sensitivity of the Counter-Reformation. The contemporary ebony frame of the relief originally bore silver mounts, indicating that it was used as a small private altar.

Inventory of 1626 — No. A/5 (5)
Inventory of 1752 — No. 220 (653)

81 MADONNA ON A CRESCENT MOON

Figure: Christoph Lencker (Ludwigsorget, c. 1556—1613 Augsburg)
Socle: Jeremias Wildt I († 1608 Augsburg)
Augsburg, c. 1608/1613
Silver, parcel-gilt, brass-gilt; maker's mark CL, maker's mark IW, Augsburg hallmark; 42.5 cms high; socle: 19 cms wide, 13 cms deep (Inv. No. Kap. 21)

Behind the glass plates in the front of the socle are displayed two fragments of the Virgin's veil. The Madonna is represented as the Queen of Heaven, standing in front of an aureole on a cloud above a crescent moon, a reference to the Revelation of St. John: "a woman clothed with the sun, and the moon under her feet." During the Baroque Age, this image was frequently associated with Maria Immaculata, the Mother of God, undefiled by original sin. The artistic conception of the statuette is based on the famous figure of the Virgin by Hubert Gerhard, completed in 1593 and placed on top of the Column of Mary in Munich in 1638 (cf. Cat. No. 1). The inherent artistic fascination of Gerhard's statue had a lasting influence on the goldsmith's art. The Viennese statuette was until recently attributed to the goldsmith Jeremias Wildt. However, Wildt's maker's mark is only to be found on the socle; Christoph Lencker's maker's mark on the back of the figure had been overlooked. This then explains the close relationship of the statuette to the famous Madonna of the Crescent Moon by Johannes Lencker in the Cathedral Treasury at Salzburg. The latter had spent a long period working in the workshop of his uncle, Christoph Lencker. The Viennese Madonna, imbued with an aura of dignified sensitivity by Christoph Lencker, was probably one of the models used for its companion piece in Salzburg.

Inventory of 1626 — No. S/6 (331)
Inventory of 1752 — No. 19 (442)

Ref.: Seling 1980, vol. III, p. 84, no. 891 b.

82 ST. JOSEPH

Melchior Mair († 1613 Augsburg)
Augsburg, c. 1613
Silver, parcel-gilt; maker's mark Melchior Mair (socle), Augsburg hallmark; 40.5 cms high; socle: 20 cms wide, 14.5 cms deep (Inv. No. Kap. 22)

The piece of fabric in the socle of the statuette is supposed to derive from the cloak in which St. Joseph wrapped the infant Jesus after he was born (inscription on the reverse of the socle). All the heightened emotion so typical of devotional pictures is here suppressed in

favour of the joy of narration, which characterises St. Joseph as a wandering carpenter. Posed in mid-stride, he bears a staff in his right hand and shoulders an axe with the left. From his lower right arm hangs a basket made of woven silver wire and containing 19 miniature tools used in the carpenter's trade; three further tools are hanging from his belt. Some of the more complicated tools (pincers, a saw) have been fashioned in endearing detail as fully functional tools. The companion piece to the figure of the Virgin Mary (Cat. No. 81), this statuette bears the maker's mark of the goldsmith Melchior Mair on the socle, although the figure itself is not signed. Since the socle and figure of the companion piece were made by different masters, it is possible that the same applies here; the figure may, therefore, have been made by Christoph Lencker. However that may be, the statuette is one of the most ingenious works of Augsburg goldsmithery.

Inventory of 1626 — No. S/7 (332)
Inventory of 1752 — No. 20 (443)

Refs: Catalogue Augsburger Barock, Augsburg 1968, p. 383, no. 565; Seling 1980, vol. I, p. 51, III, p. 123, no. 1131 c.

83 RELIQUARY OF ST. LEOPOLD
Augsburg (?), after 1592
Silver, gold enamel, glass; 30.3 cms high; foot: 10.6 cms long, 6.4 cms wide (Inv. No. Kap. 25)

The finger bone displayed in this ostensory originates from the margrave and saint Leopold III, (1095—1136), founder of the monastery at Klosterneuburg and patron saint of Lower Austria. The relic is enclosed in a spiral gold band bearing the inscription S. LEOP . MARCHI . AUST . (St. Leopold, Margrave of Austria) and crowned by an enamelled gold archducal coronet. According to one document, Archduke Ernst (1553—1595) ordered the relic to be taken from the grave of St. Leopold in 1592. This saint was venerated by the Archduke both as of one of the most important intercessors of his dynasty and as his precursor in the rule of Austria. The reliquary was probably commissioned by either Archduke Ernst or Archduke Maximilian and came into the possession of Empress Anna by way of inheritance. The donor is indicated by the arms of Old Burgundy on the socles of the flanking pinnacles and the two small escutcheons which hang below them, bearing the arms of Austria *(Bindenschild),* Old Burgundy and Tyrol as well as the Habsburg lion. The eliquary was executed after 1592 *"in he old manner,"* taking the form of a Gothic tower reliquary to express the venerable significance of the relic. In his historicizing recourse to the forms of Gothic architecture, its motifs were not employed according to their function, but merely juxtaposed as ornamental quotations. This is particularly evident in the pierced "tracery" of the tower roof. The formal repertoire of this reliquary, in particular the conception of the stand, has parallels in late 16th century goldsmiths' work from Augsburg (cf. Cat. No. 30).

Inventory of 1626 — No. M (245)
Inventory of 1752 — No. 77 (501)

his right the banner. In place of a breastplate, the chest of the statuette is covered by a plate of rock crystal, beneath which is preserved a relic of the saint. Presumably the figure once formed the crowning element of a pillar reliquary (no longer extant) mentioned in the inventory of 1758: *"Two silver pillars on silver-gilt pedestals, upon one of them St. Leopold, upon the other St. Theresa, in the middle of the two pillars an elongated glass in which are kept the relics of St. Leopold."*

Inventory of 1758 — Case IX, No. 4.

Ref.: Catalogue, Der heilige Leopold. Landesfürst und Staatssymbol, Klosterneuburg 1985, p. 388, no. 550.

84 STATUETTE OF ST. LEOPOLD

Augsburg, 1st quarter of the 17th century
Silver, parcel-gilt, rock crystal; 8.9 cms high (Inv. No. D 122)

This small statuette of St. Leopold also serves as a reliquary. The patron saint of Lower Austria is depicted in armour and cloak. In his left hand he holds his sword, pointing to the ground, and in

85 THE ADORATION OF THE MAGI

Augsburg, c. 1600
After a composition by Hans von Aachen (Cologne 1552—1615 Prague)
Silver; 16 cms high, 11.2 cms wide (Inv. No. Kap. 2)

The ebony frame of the relief was originally decorated with silver mounts, which have since been lost.

According to the inventory of 1752, this small house altar was used by Empress Anna, wife of Emperor Matthias, as a devotional image in her bedchamber. The Holy Family is installed beneath a baldachin draped between the massive stone walls of the stable in Bethlehem. The Magi are seen approaching from the right. Mary holds out the Child to the first king, who has sunk onto his knees, while Joseph courteously removes his hat in honour of their august visitors. Through the open double doors the kings' retinue and the Star of Bethlehem can be seen. The kings' search for the Redeemeer is here depicted as a simple, bourgeois family idyll. The anonymous Augsburg goldsmith has followed a composition by Hans von Aachen, court painter to Emperor Rudolf II, which was copied in an engraving by Aegidius Sadeler in 1590. The engraving belonged to an album entitled *Salus Generis Humanis* (The Salvation of the Human Race), which was dedicated to Archduke Ferdinand II of Tirol, the father of Empress Anna.

Inventory of 1626 — No. Q/4 (279)
Inventory of 1752 — No. 219 (652)

86 ROCK CRYSTAL STANDING CROSS
Workshop of the Saracchis
Milan, c. 1600
Silver mounts, gilded and enamelled; 54.5 cms high, 26.4 cms wide (Inv. No. E 43)

The cross is borne on a hemispherical foot and a baluster-shaped shaft which develops into two addorsed acanthus leaves. The same leaf form is also to be found at the ends of the cross, which achieve the traditional trefoil shape through the scrolled side-leaves. Not only the stand and the cross, but also the body of Christ is carved from rock crystal. In addition, the foot bears two crystal carvings: on the front, the Adoration of the Shepherds and, on the reverse, Christ carrying the Cross. The mounts are of gilded silver and partially enamelled. This piece comes from the workshop of the famous lapidary family of Saracchi, which was active in Milan for many generations. Several similar crosses from this workshop have also survived, of which the one in the Metropolitan Museum in New York matches not only the compositional motifs, but also the scenes on the foot of this cross.

Inventory of 1758 — Case I, No. 28

87 TWO ROCK CRYSTAL CANDLESTICKS
Workshop of the Saracchi
Milan, c. 1600
Silver mounts, gilded and enamelled; 20.8 cms high (Inv. No. 2393, 2396)

Although these two small rock crystal candlesticks do not form a set with the cross Cat. No. 86, they must at one time have belonged to a cross of this

type. Rock crystal crosses from the Saracchi workshop which form an ensemble with candlesticks of this type have been preserved (Munich, Residenz Treasury). The forms of the foot, shaft and socket also indicate the Saracchi workshop. These candlesticks originally belonged to the collections at Castle Ambras near Innsbruck.

Castle Ambras, Inventory of 1788 — p. 471, nos. 4, 5

88 ROCK CRYSTAL MEDALLION
Milan (?), end of the 16th century
Rock crystal, silver-gilt, partially enamelled, gouache on parchment; 7.5 cms high, 6.3 cms wide (Inv. No. D 32)

This oval rock crystal pendant is distinguished by two parchment miniatures of outstanding quality. Depicted on the front is the Crucifixion, on the reverse the miracle of the Brazen Serpent. Despite its lavish mounting, this was not a special piece, but rather a serial product from a crystal carving workshop. Such pendants were widespread and extremely popular as gifts (plague amulets?). It is highly probable that a series of similar medallions were produced in Milan. This city is indicated as the place of origin not only by the crystal carving but also by the gilded and enamelled silver mounts, which are similar to the settings for other pieces of Milan jewellery.

Inventory of 1758 — Case IX, No. 13

89 RELIQUARY VASE
Girolamo Coiro (?), (active c. 1600)
Mantua, c. 1610/1613
Oak foundation overlaid with ebony, glass, rock crystal, gold enamel, gilded brass; 18 cms high, 9.3 cms wide, 9.3 cms deep (Inv. No. Kap. 85)

According to the inscription plaque on the front of the socle, this vase once held the powdered blood of the holy martyr Maximina. The reliquary and its companion piece, Cat. No. 90, together with Cat. No. 91, were presumably presented to Empress Anna by Duke Ferdinand of Mantua as a gift in 1613 (cf. Cat. No. 91). The inventory of 1626 records the existence of a case, covered in red velvet and gold braid, which accomodated all three pieces. Characterised by identical composition, matching ebony socles and enamelled gold appliqués, they are all made of etched glass and have rock crystal lids fitted with gold enamelled mounts. Both reliquaries were restored, possibly around 1860/1870, when the gold appliqués from the sides and back of the socle were lost. Of the original gold ornamentation, only that on the front of the socles has survived. According to the inventory of 1626,

In this companion piece to Cat. No. 89 was once preserved the pulverised blood of the holy martyr St. Boniface. This receptacle, too, is an etched glass vase with a lid of rock crystal. As in the case of its companion piece, only the appliqués on the front derive from the original.

Inventory of 1626 — No. P/21 (270)
Inventory of 1752 — No. 179 (612)

91 FRAGMENT OF A RELIQUARY
Girolamo Coiro (?) (active c. 1600)
Mantua, c. 1610/1613
Hardwood overlaid with ebony, rock crystal, gold, gold enamel, pearls, diamonds; 46 cms high, 14 cms wide, 14 cms deep (Inv. No. Kap. 46)

One of the most regrettable losses recorded by the Treasury in the Second World War was that of the upper part of this reliquary. Duke Ferdinand of Mantua (1587—1626, ruled from 1613) gave this precious relic, which held drops of Christ's blood in the upper part and a particle of the Cross in the lower section, to his cousin, Empress Anna in 1613. The missing triangular superstructure, which was made of gold, was set with two large, 39 medium-sized and 102 small diamonds. The capsule with the blood of Christ bore a mother-of-pearl relief of the Madonna with Child on the front and a cross formed of twelve diamonds on the back. The surviving vase-shaped receptacle, which is made of rock crystal, still contains the particle of the cross mounted in gold. The mounts of the receptacle are also of gold, decorated with coloured enamel foliate motifs and set with pearls and diamonds. The receptacle must originally have been intended for profane purposes: the carved decoration at the top displays symmetrically arranged foliate motifs with clusters of pendant fruit, below which are hunting scenes. The reliquary was probably made in Mantua. It is known that Milanese gemcutters had settled in Mantua and that Girolamo Coiro executed commissions there for Duke Ferdinand. According to

there were stylised flowers of gold enamel on the other three sides. While the back was left plain, brass-gilt appliqués (some of them galvanoplastics) were attached to the sides, and the mountings for the vases were also replaced by ones made of gilded brass. It is possible that on this occasion the original vases of rock crystal (perhaps broken?) were replaced with others made of etched glass. This might explain the unusual combination of materials; however, Cat. Nos. 26 and 27 demonstrate that both this combination of materials and the technical precision of the etching were possible in the early 17th century.

Inventory of 1626 — No. P/21 (270)
Inventory of 1752 — No. 180 (613)

90 RELIQUARY VASE
Girolamo Coiro (?) (active c. 1600)
Mantua 1610/1613
Hardwood foundation overlaid with ebony, etched glass, rock crystal, gold enamel, brass-gilt; 18 cms high, 9.3 cms wide, 9.3 cms deep (Inv. No. Kap. 86)

documentary sources, he and Piotto Altobello delivered *diversi vasi et reliquari di cristallo* (various vases and reliquaries of crystal) to the Duke in 1612.

Inventory of 1626 — No. P/20 (269)
Inventory of 1752 — No. 178 (611)

92 STANDING CROSS OF HELIOTROPE

Florence, end of the 16th century
Heliotrope, lapis lazuli, bronze-gilt; 72 cms high (Inv. No. 8012)

This upright cross with trefoil ends has been carved almost entirely from a single piece of heliotrope and fitted with bronze-gilt mounts. It rises from a rectangular socle with volutes on both sides, and this in turn rests on a base with a projecting central section. The figure of Christ is made of gilded bronze and depicted at the moment of his death on the cross. His body, which displays exceptionally fine modelling, hangs straight down, with the head lowered. The bronze-gilt relief below shows the Mother of God in lamentation. The extreme sobriety of the decoration and the clarity of the forms set off the precious material of the cross most effectively. The lapidary work was probably carried out in the Grand Duke's workshops in Florence. This is indicated by the metal ornamentation which supplements the trefoils. Comparable forms are to be found in Cat. No. 108 and in a large reliquary in the Museo degli Argenti in the Palazzo Pitti in Florence. The piece formerly belonged to the collection of the Obizzi family in the Castle of Cataio, near Padua.

93 RELIQUARY HOUSE ALTAR

Workshop of the Miseroni in Milan
Milan, beginning of the 17th century
(before 1618)
Replacements (receptacle, the four
ajouré spheres, the plates on the
broken pediments, the two lower ornamental plates on the lateral volutes):
workshop of Ottavio Miseroni (Milan,
c. 1560—1624 Prague), Prague, 1618/
1622
Hardwood core overlaid with ebony,
jasper, jasper agate, gold enamel, diamonds, rubies, pearls, rock crystal,

44.2 cms high, 26 cms wide (Inv. No.
Kap. 221)

This magnificent house altar represents
a high point in the art of European
goldsmithery and gemcutting. Empress Anna, wife of Emperor Matthias,
received it as a gift from Duke Karl
Emmanuel I of Savoy (1562—1630,
ruled from 1580). The rock crystal
receptacle contains a thorn from
Christ's crown. The wooden structure
follows that of full-sized altar retables.
Jasper columns flank a niche of trans-

lucent green jasper containing an agate cross set with diamonds and pearls, to which a white jasper agate figure of Christ is attached with diamond nails. On either side of the cross stand enamelled gold figures of Mary and John. The ebony frame is decorated with gold ornamentation which is almost entirely enamelled and richly set with diamonds, rubies and pearls. The altar was made in the workshop of the Milanese gemcutting family of the Miseroni, who produced several works of outstanding artistic and technical quality around 1600 (reliquary casket in the Cathedral Treasury at Genoa and the small house altar No. 546 in the Museo Poldi-Pezzoli in Milan). The receptacle which holds the relic, however, was not part of the original. This, together with some of the ornamental plates was executed in Prague between 1618 and 1622. The Empress Anna was so pleased with the piece from Milan that she commissioned the gemcutter and goldsmith Ottavio Miseroni, who had settled in Prague, to complete it and execute a companion piece (Cat. No. 94). The Empress recorded the commission in her testament of 10. 11. 1618: *"to execute . . . namely a small altar of jasper decorated with diamonds and rubies, the same as that which the Duke of Savoy gave me and which has been entrusted to Miseron to copy."*

Inventory of 1626 — No. A/1 (1)
Inventory of 1752 — No. 182 (615)

94 HOUSE ALTAR WITH RELICS

Workshop of Ottavio Miseroni (Milan, c. 1560—1624 Prague)
Prague, 1618/1622
Oak foundation overlaid with ebony, jasper, gold enamel, diamonds, precious stones, pearls, glass, silk; 44.5 cms high, 26 cms wide (Inv. No. Kap. 222)

This small private altar was made as a companion piece to Cat. No. 93 in ex-

ecution of the will of Empress Anna. It was made between 1618 and 1622 in Prague, in the workshops of Ottavio Miseroni, who presented the piece to the Master of the Imperial Treasure in Vienna on 5. 9. 1622. However, the little altar was never completely finished and thus it was recorded that: *"Herr Miseroni nevertheless still has to send the niche and to finish the ecce homo picture."* The original intention was to insert a jasper niche with an ecce homo group, to match the companion piece. But Ottavio Miseroni was unable to fulfil the contract before his death in 1624, so that in 1655, as has been noted on a piece of paper on the reverse of the little altar, the relic of St. Timothy was "provisionally" placed in the central niche. As in the companion piece, the thorn from Christ's crown presented in the surmounting custodia, derives from the estate of Empress Anna. The ornamental mounts by the Prague workshop do not match the precision of those on the model from Milan and the two pieces also differ in the individual motifs.

Inventory of 1626 — No. A/2 (2)
Inventory of 1752 — No. 183 (616)

Inventory of 1626 — No. A/4 (4)
Inventory of 1752 — No. 169 (602)

Ref.: B. Bukowinska, Anmerkungen zur Persön-
lichkeit Ottavio Miseronis, in: Umeni XVIII/2
(1970), pp. 189—198.

95, 96

96 JASPER HOUSE ALTAR

Ottavio Miseroni (Milan, c. 1560—
1624 Prague)
Prague, c. 1620
Jasper, agate, lapis lazuli, diamonds,
rubies, pearls, gold enamel, silver-gilt;
signed; 33.5 cms high, 19 cms wide
(Inv. No. Kap. 220)

Like its companion piece Cat. No. 95,
this small private altar was commissioned from Ottavio Miseroni in
Prague, in execution of the will of the
Empress Anna. Depicted on the oval
mosaic relief is St. Anne, who holds the
infant Jesus on her right arm and embraces Mary with her left. Between the
socles of the pillars is preserved a piece
of the robe of St. Anne. As a crowning
element, a cross composed of 15 small
diamonds rises above a relief bust of
Christ.

Inventory of 1626 — No. A/4 (4)
Inventory of 1752 — No. 170 (603)

Ref.: Bukowinska, op. cit. Cat. No. 95.

95 HOUSE ALTAR OF JASPER

Ottavio Miseroni (Milan, c. 1560—
1624 Prague)
Prague, c. 1620
Jasper, agate, lapis lazuli, diamonds,
rubies, pearls, gold enamel, silver-gilt,
signed; 30 cms high, 19 cms wide (Inv.
No. Kap. 219)

The richly decorated jasper foot bears
two volutes of agate upon which rests
the altar itself. This takes the form of
an aedicule and is embellished with
further volutes. The precious lapidary
work encloses between the pillars an
oval relief composed of gemstones and
signed OTT. M. (Ottavio Miseroni). It
presents a half-length figure of Mary
who has bedded her Child on swaddling bands. This new mosaic relief
technique — called commesso — was
possibly developed by Miseroni himself. It represents both the continuation and the culmination of the art of
classical cameo carving. Enclosed between the socles of the columns underneath the relief is a piece of the robe of
the Blessed Virgin. On the superstructure, two vases with diamond flowers
flank a relief bust of the Virgin, which
was formerly crowned by a cross
formed of twelve small diamonds. In
addition, the whole altar is set with individual diamonds, rubies and pearls.

97 SIX CANDLESTICKS OF
JASPER AGATE

Workshop of Ottavio Miseroni (Milan,
c. 1560—1624 Prague)
Mounting: Master HC
Prague, 1618/1622
Jasper agate, silver-gilt; 53, 53, 57, 57,
63 and 63 cms high (Inv. Nos. 89—94)

These candlesticks were donated to the
Capuchin Monastery in Vienna by its
foundress, Empress Anna, for the altar
of the Imperial chapel. Like the small

Jasper-agate, silver-gilt; 27 and 27.2 cms high (Inv. No. 2065, 2066)

Apart from being shorter by three sections on the shafts, these two small candlesticks are replicas of the six large candlesticks from the workshops of Ottavio Miseroni, and exactly match the originals right down to the lapidary work. The silver-gilt mounts, consisting of ball-shaped feet, busts of angels, beading and candle sockets, were probably also made by the master HC. These two candlesticks are presumably the ones made of "Bohemian jasper", which are recorded as being in the Secular Treasury in 1750.

Inventory of 1750 — Case III, No. 97

99 CRUCIFIX
After Giambologna (Douai 1529—1608 Florence)
Florence, c. 1590
Ebonised wood, gilded bronze; height of corpus 49 cms, to the crown of the head 40.6 cms, armspan 36.6 cms (Inv. No. E 19)

This type of crucifix, known as a *Cristo Morto,* can be traced back to a model by Giambologna, two versions of which, documented since 1588, are preserved in the churches of Sta. Maria

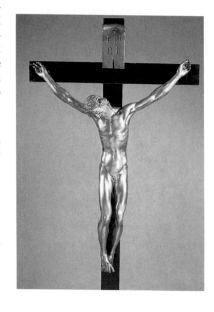

house altars Cat. Nos. 94—96, they were commissioned from the gemcutter Miseroni in Prague, who delivered them to the Imperial Treasurer in Vienna on 5. 9. 1622. Four busts of angels support the shallow foot, over which tower the four baluster-shaped parts of the shaft. The only ornamentation is the masterfully cut U-shaped depressions, known as 'pipes', a standard lapidary motif. The silver-gilt mounts of these unique pieces were executed by the master goldsmith HC, who worked chiefly for Ottavio Miseroni.

Inventory 1752 — No. 56 (479)

Ref.: R. Distelberger, Beobachtungen zu den Steinschneidewerkstätten der Miseroni in Mailand und Prag, in: Jahrbuch LXXIV (1978), p. 152.

98 TWO SMALL JASPER-AGATE CANDLESTICKS
Workshops of Ottavio Miseroni (Milan, c. 1560—1624 Prague)
Mounts: master HC
Prague, c. 1620

degli Angiolini and S. Marco in Florence respectively. The Christ in the Treasury differs from these examples in its complete nakedness and in the separately cast loincloth, which is probably of a later date and does not follow the usual scheme of Giambologna's crucifixes. The somewhat rounder contours of the body seem to prefigure the monumental Christ in the Church of St. Michael in Munich, cast by Giambologna for Duke Wilhelm V of Bavaria in 1594, which had great influence in Southern Germany. A similar figure, also without a loincloth, has been preserved in the Roman Catholic parish church of Wullenstetten in Bavaria. This corpus has been attributed to Adriaen de Vries on account of the lively, sensuous modelling of the anatomy and the generous handling of the hair. It differs, however, from the Christ of the Treasury in that the latter is characterised by a more sharply determined surface structure and is thus stylistically closer to the crucifixes by Giambologna in Florence.   M. L.-J.

Ref.: Catalogue: Giambologna 1978/79, p. 195, no. 107 a; Catalogue: Dürers Verwandlung 1981/1982, pp. 253—255, no. 161.

The shape of the magnificent octagonal wooden frame is concealed by ornamental brass volutes. Further brass decoration and silver appliqués cover the surface of the frame. In the centre is an engraved copper-plate with an oil on alabaster painting of the Adoration of the Shepherds. This small devotional picture, which comes close to folk art, moves the spectator precisely by virtue of its awkward but spiritualised style of representation. The picture once hung in the Small Privy Treasure Chamber of Emperor Karl VI.

Inventory of 1731 — fol. 262, No. 23

100 THE ADORATION OF THE SHEPHERDS

Central Italy (Florence ?), beginning of the 17th century

Oil on alabaster; frame: silvered hardwood, copper-gilt, brass-gilt; 36 cms diameter (Inv. No. D 151)

101 FEATHER PICTURE OF CHRIST

Juan Baptista Cuiris
Mexico, Michoacan (Pátzcuaro), 1550/1580

Colibri and parrot feathers on paper, wood; signed; 25.4 cms high, 18.2 cms wide; frame: 38 cms high, 24.3 cms wide (Inv. No. Kap. 321)

Among the most highly venerated artists of Mexican Indian culture were the feather artists or Amentaca, whose skill in creating precious cult objects, clothing and pictures out of feathers was unrivalled. The Spanish conquistadors also exploited this Tarascan tradition by having Christian motifs executed in the traditional techniques. An unusual exception to this policy of exploitation was represented by Vasco de Quiroga, the first bishop (1537—1556) of the province of Michoacan (west of Mexico City). Concerned to protect the Indians from general exploitation, he based his missionary ideas on Thomas More's "Utopia". Thus he founded settlements around his bishopric Pátzcuaro, also called Michoacan after the province, where the Indians could practice their traditional Tarascan craft within regulated working hours (a six-hour working day!) and with provision for their welfare. This picture and its companion piece were made in the workshops of Bishop Quiroga. Coloured drawings served as patterns for this extremely complicated techniques. A paper backing was prepared with an underlay consisting of cotton threads and lesser feathers. The parrot and colibri feathers were cut into tiny pieces, arranged on the backing and glued with a bone spatula, and then smoothed with a scraper. When looked at from a certain angle, the pictures reveal all their magic, the optical refraction of the light in the air-filled spaces of the feather shafts causing the pictures to gleam with iridescent luminosity. Virtually all the examples of early, 16th century colonial feather art have, however, been lost. Only some two dozen have survived in various museums; the seven pictures in museums in Vienna represent the largest collection in the world. The two pictures from the Treasury are exceptional even among these rarities. Not only is their luminosity undiminished thanks to their excellent state of preservation, but they are the only examples with an artist's signature (on the lower edge of the banderole). The Indian Juan Baptista Cuiris (the surname is still common today in Pátzcuaro) gives Michoacan as the provenance of his work. They are characterised both by luminous, compact expanses of colour and skilful effects of shading, which effectively convey the plasticity of the head.

Inventory of the Kunstkammer of Emperor Rudolf II 1607—11 (616)
Inventory of 1752 — No. 68 (491)

Ref.: F. Anders et al., Tesoros de Mexico — Arte Plumario y de Mosaico [Artes de Mexico XVII/137 (1971)], p. 42, 66, 111.

102 FEATHER PICTURE OF THE VIRGIN MARY

Juan Baptista Cuiris
Mexico, Michoacan (Pátzcuaro), 1550/1580
Colibri and parrot feathers on paper, wood; signed; 25.4 cms high, 18.2 wide; frame: 38 cms high, 24.3 cms wide (Inv. No. Kap. 322)

This picture bears the signature of the same artist as its companion piece, Cat. No. 101. The Virgin Mary is depicted in lamentation, tears flowing from her eyes. The Latin inscription is the question addressed by Mary to the twelve-year-old Jesus, after she had found him in the Temple: "Son, why hast thou thus dealt with us? behold, thy father and I have sought thee sorrowing." (Gospel according to St. Luke, 2/48). His answer: "How is it

that ye sought me? wist ye not that I must be about my Father's business?'' (Luke 2/49) is provided by the companion piece. Both pictures were at one time in the *Kunstkammer* of Emperor Rudolf II and were later transferred to the Capuchin Treasury.

Inventory of the Kunstkammer of Emperor Rudolf II 1607 — 11 (617)
Inventory of 1752 — No. 68 (491)

Ref.: Anders, op. cit. Cat. No. 101, p. 42, 64 ff., 94, 99, 111.

103 CRUCIFIX

Guglielmo della Porta (Porlezza, c. 1515—1577 Rome) (attrib.)
Rome, c. 1569
Ebonised wood; silver-gilt; height of corpus to crown of head 23.5 cms, arm span 23.6 cms (Inv. No. E 14)

The corpus was modelled and cast as a completely naked figure; the non-detachable loincloth of the same date was affixed afterwards. As the soft flowing contours of the obliquely twisted body indicate, Christ is represented as a dying man. Werner Gramberg (1981) has attributed the corpus to Guglielmo della Porta, and proposes Manno Sbarri as the goldsmith on account of the fine engraving. He has compared the corpus with the drawings of Christ in Guglielmo's

'Small Sketchbook' in Düsseldorf and with the two crucifixes — on the high altar and in the treasury respectively — of St. Peter's in Rome, although these are more monumental in effect. The torsion of the body is not as pronounced in the Roman pieces and the lower half of the body is twisted in the opposite direction. Gramberg believes the Christ in the Viennese Treasury to be the same as that mentioned in a letter of 23. 5. 1569 from Guglielmo della Porta to Emperor Maximilian. It is probably identical to the crucifix listed from 1770 onwards in the inventories of the Josephi Chapel in the Vienna Hofburg. The silver mounts on the socle date back to the early 18th century.   M. L.-J.

Ref.: Gramberg 1981, pp. 99—101.

104 THE REST ON THE FLIGHT INTO EGYPT

Florence (?), end of the 16th century
After a painting by Federico Barocci (Urbino 1532—1612 Urbino)
Oak foundation overlaid with walnut veneer and ebony, silver, parcel-gilt, brass-gilt, 31 cms high, 19 cms wide (Inv. No. D 176)

The chased silver relief of this small private altar is based on a painting by Federico Barocci in St. Stefano in Piobbico (reproduction in the Pinacoteca Vaticana), which was executed between 1570 and 1573 and was widely acclaimed at the time. The composition had achieved general renown through several engraved copies (one made by Cornelis Cort in 1575). Under the shade of a tree, the Holy Family rests beside a small stream. Mary scoops water with a bowl, while Joseph hands the child a cherry branch, its blood-red fruit symbolising his future Passion. The goldsmith brings out the plastic qualities of the figures in contrast to the landscape, and this makes the underlying triangular structure of the composition more obvious than in the original painting. The rigorous aedicule frame, surmounted by an angel's head, is oriented towards the classical models

of the Renaissance. In the similarity of its wooden construction and partially matching mounts, the frame is related to the small house altars Cat. Nos. 34 and 108. All these pieces probably derive from the same workshop. The appliqués have been cast from the moulds of the companion pieces. The masks on the socles of the pillars — in this form a frequent motif of works of Italian craftsmanship — also occur in Cat No. 108, there as console decoration. Both this work and its companion piece presumably derive from a workshop in Florence.

Inventory of 1758 — Case I, No. 80

Ref.: Tietze Conrat 1920/21, p. 145 f.; A. Emiliani, Federico Barocci, Pesaro 1985, p. 78 ff.

105 ST. ANNE WITH MARY, THE CHILD JESUS AND THE CHILD JOHN

Florence (?), end of the 16th century
After a painting from the school of Raphael (Urbino 1483—1520 Rome)
Oak and softwood foundation, walnut veneer, silver, parcel-gilt; 34 cms high, 20.5 cms wide (Inv. No. D 177)

This companion piece to Cat. No. 104 differs only in the ornamentation of the pillar socles on which, in this piece, the ajouré tendril motif of the central

section is continued. The silver relief is based on the well-known painting from the school of Raphael, 'La Madonna del Divino Amore' (Museo di Capodimonte, Naples). By the second half of the 16th century, the composition of this painting had — as an original by Raphael — become common cultural property through widespread engravings. Today the painting is ascribed to Giovanni Francesco Penni (c. 1488 — c. 1521 Naples), a pupil of Raphael's, and has been dated to c. 1520. St. Anne rests under a tree, the Child Jesus sits on his mother's knee and blesses St. John the Baptist, who kneels before him. The original lacks the spacious landscape which was added to the relief and the engravings.

Inventory of 1758 — Case I, No. 80

Ref.: Tietze Conrat 1920/21, p. 146, 176, no. 58; B. Molajoli, Notizie su Capodimonte, Naples 1964, p. 37, no. 146.

106 RELIQUARY CASKET

Daniel Michael I (Augsburg, c. 1570—1634 Augsburg)
Augsburg, 1610/1615
Silver, parcel-gilt, lead crystal, gold, rubies, pearls, silk, silver embroidery; maker's mark DM, Augsburg hall-

mark; 16.5 cms high, 22.7 cms long, 16.2 cms wide (Inv. No. Kap. 195)

A hand, surrounded by embroidered silk flowers, lies in this little sarcophagus-shaped casket. The relic is attached to a silk cushion by means of two gold bracelets set with rubies and pearls. It is supposed to be the right hand of St. Athanasius the Great (c. 296—373), with which he wrote his famous works directed against Arianism. The receptacle is of the same type as wooden-framed rock crystal caskets made in Venice in the 16th century. The Augsburg goldsmith Daniel Michael I has made an exact copy in silver of such a casket, for this reliquary. The unadorned textile decoration on the inside, which dates from the early 17th century, is of particular interest.

Inventory of 1626 — No. A/21 (21)
Inventory of 1752 — No. 80 (504)

108 RELIQUARY WITH THE ADORATION OF THE SHEPHERDS

Florence (?), c. 1600
Ebonised hardwood, silver, parcel-gilt, watercolour on parchment; 51 cms high, 35 cms wide (Inv. No. D 14)

Around the oval parchment miniature is a broad frame into which have been inserted twelve medallions with the relics of various saints. In the surviving corner spandrels, which are framed with strips of silver, are to be seen the four Evangelists. The birth of Christ is here depicted as having taken place in a splendid palace, indicated by the pillars in the background. According to apocryphal texts (e. g. the Vision of St. Bridget from the second half of the 14th century) the stable of Bethlehem was located in the ruined palace of King David. In the meditation of Pseudo Bonaventura (around 1300) it is reported that Mary, when her hour had arrived, leant against a pillar and there bore her son without any pain. The painter of this miniature was familiar with the work of Correggio, although he has adapted his model in a naive-folkloric narrative style. The wooden frame, with its magnificent broken pediment and crowning element, derives from the same workshops as Cat. No. 34. Its rich silver mounts are partly cast, partly chased

107 RELIQUARY CASKET

Daniel Michael I (Augsburg, c. 1570—1634 Augsburg)
Augsburg, 1610/1615
Silver, parcel-gilt, lead crystal, gold, rubies, pearls, silk, silver embroidery; maker's mark DM, Augsburg hallmark; 16.5 cms high, 22.7 cms wide, 16.2 cms deep (Inv. No. Kap. 196)

This companion piece to Cat. No. 106 contains the lower part of a child's leg bone. It is supposed to originate from one of the Innocents massacred on the orders of King Herod.

Inventory of 1626 — No. A/21 (21)
Inventory of 1752 — No. 79 (503)

and partly cut from silver plate. The masks on the lower corners are also to be found in Cat. No. 104.

A reliquary in the Museo degli Argenti in the Palazzo Pitti in Florence (Inv. No. 202/Cat. 327) exactly matches this small house altar in its appliqué work. Both pieces presumably derive from the same workshop in Florence.

Inventory of 1758 — Case VII, No. 13

109 TEMPIETTO WITH THE MAN OF SORROWS

Christoph Angermair (Weilheim, c. 1580—1633 Munich)
Munich, c. 1613/1620
Ivory, hardwood overlaid with ebony, silver-gilt, almandine; 71.5 cms high; statuette: 26.2 cms high (Inv. No. Kap. 297)

The square ebony baldachin with diagonally placed columns encloses an ivory figure of Christ as the Man of Sorrows. On the baldachin, volutes graduate into an octagonal domed superstructure with lateral oval openings. The crowning aureole of silver-gilt set with almandines — which supposedly contains a particle of the scourging column of Christ — was not added until 1922. The original relics were probably preserved in the socle of the tempietto, since two sides have drawers, today empty. The classification of the piece has until recently been hindered by the singular, almost "mannerist" figure of Christ, which was presumed to be of Spanish provenance. However, the slender proportions, narrow pectoral girdle, protruding belly and rounded hips are characteristic of a late Gothic Man of Sorrows from the end of the 15th century. Similar interpretations are to be found in the graphic art, painting and sculpture of this period. However, as the individual motifs indicate, it is not a late Gothic statuette but a work by an ivory carver of the early 17th century, who had closely followed a late Gothic model (perhaps a venerated miracle-working image or a graphic

model). Quite apart from the fascinating conception of the figure, the piece is notable for the technical brilliance of its carving. The stylistic idiosyncracies of the figure are also found in the works of the famous ivory carver from Munich, Christoph Angermair, to whom the statuette can be ascribed. The tempietto is first documented in 1752, in the treasury of the Capuchin Monastery.

Inventory of 1752 — No. 194 (627)

110 PIETÀ WITH ANGELS

Caspar Gras (?) (Mergentheim 1585—1674 Schwaz)
Innsbruck, c. 1630/1650
Bronze-gilt, wooden frame; 38 cms high, 31 cms wide (without frame) (Inv. No. D 218)

This relief vividly presents the corpse of Christ as a devotional image. The body is supported by two angels, surrounded by a whole host of smaller accompanying angels. There is lively

movement all around the heavy weight of the corpse. Elongated, expressive curves — in the hair and garments of the angels, as well as in the encircling clouds — produce the impression of great agitation. All heaven seems to be in commotion, mourning the dead saviour. The muscular, naked figure of Christ ultimately derives from Michelangelo's late Pietà group in the Duomo in Florence, graphic reproductions of which probably influenced Gras' design. This is probably why the artist pays more attention to the relief effects of the musculature than to the context of individual parts of the body. The piece was formerly supposed to have originated in Upper Italy. Yet it belongs to the tradition of Munich bronze work from the 1st quarter of the 17th century, even if the painterly conception of the relief does suggest a later date, most probably somewhere around the middle of the century. Comparable stylistic characteristics are also to be found in the work of the well-known artist in bronze Caspar Gras, pupil of Hubert Gerhard, sculptor to the Munich court, who worked in Innsbruck for the Tyrolean Archdukes (Innsbruck, Leopoldsbrunnen). The present relief may even be a previously unknown work by the master himself.

Inventory of 1758 — Painting No. 14 (fol. 113)

111 CRUCIFIXION GROUP

Jeremias Geisselbrunn (Augsburg, c. 1595—1660 Cologne)
Cologne, c. 1630/1640
Bronze, light brown patina, socle of wood; 101.5 cms high (crucifix), 38.6 cms high (Mary), 39.6 cms high (John) and 32 cms high (Mary Magdalen) (Inv. No. E 34)

With bowed head and closed eyes, Christ seems to have passed peacefully away. Mary Magdalen has sunk down at the foot of the cross; she clasps the cross and gazes up at Christ. Mary mourns on the left and John the Baptist on the right. This scupture belongs to the same tradition as that of the monumental two-figured bronze group in the Church of St. Michael in Munich (cf. Cat. No. 99). The latter's crucifix was executed for Duke Wilhelm V of Bavaria by the famous Florentine master, Giambologna, and completed by the Augsburg sculptor Hans Reichle with a kneeling figure of St. Mary Magdalen in 1593/94. The extraordinarily strong influence of this work in German art is indicated by the resultant series of copies and variations (e.g. the group by Georg Petel in the Niedermünster, Regensburg). Hans Reichle himself executed a monumental four-figured bronze group for the Church of St. Ulrich in Augsburg. The Viennese

group was evidently executed with knowledge of Reichle's work, but follows another model in the Christ figure, namely that of Giambologna (Florence, San Marco). However, its massive figures and large, flowing draperies, which preserve their independence from the movements of the body, differ distinctly from those of Reichle. Although the superb bronze work was until recently thought to be Southern German (circle of Hubert Gerhard?), it bears a close resemblance to the works of the Augsburg sculptor Jeremias Geisselbrunn, in particular to the monumental kneeling bronze figure of St. Helena in the Minster at Bonn and the Shrine of St. Engelbert in the cathedral treasury at Cologne. The group was probably executed in Cologne, where Jeremias had worked since around 1620.

Inventory of 1758 — Case I, No. 106 ?

Ref.: Catalogue, Giambologna 1978/79, p. 196, no. 107 b.

112 IVORY STANDING CROSS

Christoph Angermair (Weilheim, c. 1580—1633 Munich) and Munich workshops, c. 1620)
Hardwood foundation overlaid with ivory, ivory; 105 cms high, 31 cms wide (Inv. No. E 47)

With bowed head, the dead saviour hangs upon the cross, at the top of which is the inscription: "Jesus of Nazareth, King of the Jews", in Hebrew, Greek and Latin. The skull of Adam at the foot of the cross is a reminder that Christ was supposed to have been crucified at the very spot where Adam was buried, symbolising the fact that the original sin of the First Man was thus expiated through the crucifixion. Standing on a rectangular socle flanked by two volutes set with busts of angels, the cross is reminiscent of an imposing monument. With the exception of the proportions of the limbs and the strikingly elegant linework of the details, the figure of Christ seen here goes back to a prototype by Giambologna, in which Christ appears

to be fast asleep, the features on his face in repose. This piece, which for a long time remained anonymous, comes from the workshops of the Munich ivory carver Christoph Angermair; a related figure of Christ by him has also survived. Ivory ornamentation resembling that on the socle was used by Angermair in his famous coin cabinet (Bayerisches Nationalmuseum, Munich), for which he relied heavily on assistants — as was presumably also the case here.

Inventory of 1780 — Case V, No. 1 ?

113 HOUSE ALTAR WITH THE MONOGRAMME OF EMPEROR FERDINAND III

Augsburg, c. 1640/1650
Oak, ebony, rock crystal, agate, amber, ivory; 49.5 cms high, 29.5 cms wide (Inv. No. D 72)

This small house altar rests on ten small spheres of rock crystal. The eb-

ony receptacle is flanked by rock crystal columns and crowned by rock crystal, agate and amber appliqués. In the centre of the socle is a convex niche of rock crystal bearing the crowned initials in gold of Emperor Ferdinand III, indicating that this was his possession. This central projection continues above as a rock crystal cylinder, which encloses a Madonna with Child in amber, and ends in the crowning element with an ivory relief of the Crucifixion. The structuring of the wooden corpus with inlaid agate plates of various colours has direct parallels in the decoration of cabinets and small pieces of furniture from this period. The altar was probably made before the middle of the 17th century in an Augsburg atelier.

Inventory of 1758 — Case VIII, No. 2

114 STATUETTE OF THE BLESSED VIRGIN

Johann Seitz (active after 1636 — before 1680 Passau)
Passau, c. 1650/1670
Ivory, hardwood overlaid with ebony; 26.1 cms high (without socle) (Inv. No. 4535)

Around 1537/1540, Lucas Cranach the Elder painted a half-figure picture of the Blessed Virgin which soon acquired a reputation for miraculous powers. This picture arrived in Austria as a gift of Elector Johann Georg of Saxony to Archduke Leopold V, and was at first kept at Passau. In 1650 it was transferred to Innsbruck, where it was preserved in the parish church of St. Jacob's and became widely known as the *Mariahilf-Bild* (Image of the Blessed Virgin). The ivory figure in Vienna stands out from the numerous graphic and plastic copies made of the miraculous picture on account of its exceptional quality. In addition, it still has the original socle which was made for it. Although the ivory-carver's style is to a large extent determined by the Cranach picture, the work can nevertheless be ascribed to the Passau sculptor and ivory-carver Johann Seitz, who must certainly have been inspired in his work by the presence of the miraculous picture in Passau. The statuette itself, which was only transferred to Vienna in the 19th century, was at one time kept in the Große Galerie of the Residenz in Salzburg.

Inventory of the Große Galerie Salzburg 1776, No. 302

Ref.: Catalogue, Dürers Verwandlung in der Skulptur zwischen Renaissance und Barock, Frankfurt/M. 1982, p. 204 ff., No. 125.

version of the original. Michelangelo's sculpture of Christ embodies the classical ideal of the heroic nude. The statuette created a century later already expresses a different formal idea. It is not only the addition of a loincloth that transposes the classical nude into the Christian era; the whole conception of the figure has changed in order to correspond to the Baroque ideal: from the point of the foot through the protrusion of the right hip to the head inclined on one side, the figure has now become part of one large sweeping movement. It conforms to a type established by Georg Petel, the most famous ivory carver at the time of Rubens. Justus Glesker has been suggested as the author of this piece, as the soft, flowing details of form are closely related to his work. Glesker is mentioned in documentary sources as an outstanding ivory carver and could have executed this piece during his travels in Italy.

Inventory of 1758 — Case V, No. 23

Ref.: K. Feuchtmayr, A. Schädler, Georg Petel 1601/2—1634, Berlin 1973, p. 188 f., no. 157.

116 THE MADONNA WITH THE INFANT JESUS AND THE CHILD JOHN

Adam Lenckhardt (Würzburg 1610—1661 Vienna)
Würzburg (?), c. 1630
Ivory, hardwood overlaid with ebony; signed; 18 cms high (Inv. No. D 211)

In spite of its small format, the convincing statuesque conception of this figure has the same effect as a piece of monumental sculpture. The Madonna holds the infant Jesus on her right arm, and at her feet is John the Baptist as a child, sitting on a lamb, his symbol. Mother and child turn towards the boy, who looks up at the infant Jesus and hands him a grape, a sign of the Passion. The three figures are thus connected with one another through the direction of their gazes. The Mother of God is depicted in mid-stride, her garments billowing out and forming

115 THE RISEN CHRIST

Justus Glesker (?) (Hamelin, c. 1610/1615—1678 Frankfurt am Main)
After a statue by Michelangelo (Caprese 1475—1564 Rome)
Italy, c. 1635/1645 (?)
Ivory, ebonised hardwood; 29 cms high (Inv. No. D 210)

This statuette freely imitates the famous figure of Christ in the Church of Sta. Maria sopra Minerva in Rome made by Michelangelo in 1519/20. However, the piece was probably based on an engraving, since it is a lateral in-

deep folds around the accentuated body, thus adding to its volume. The Würzburg sculptor Adam Lenckhardt presumably executed this piece before he moved to Vienna in 1635/1637. In his conception of the figures he transposes the dominant impulses of Italian Renaissance sculpture, displaying an exceptional sensitivity for surface characterisation.

Inventory of 1758 — Case V, No. 25

Ref.: C. Theuerkauff, Der Elfenbeinbildhauer Adam Lenckhardt, in: Jahrbuch der Hamburger Kunstsammlungen X (1965), p. 38 f.; C. Theuerkauff, Scultura barocca in avorio. Nuove attribuzioni ad Adam Lenckhardt e a Dominicus Steinhart, in: Antichità viva X/2 (1971), p. 40.

117 THE DEATH OF EMPEROR FERDINAND III AS AN ALLEGORY OF TRANSIENCE

Daniel Neuberger (Augsburg 1621—1680 Regensburg)
Vienna, c. 1660
Wax boss, coloured quartz sand, hardwood overlaid with ebony; 26 cms high, 36 cms wide; frame: 36.5 cms high, 46.5 cms wide (Inv. No. Kap. 244)

Emperor Ferdinand III († 11. 3. 1657), clad in black armour, with crown and Imperial mantle, lies on a bier in a rock tomb. The hourglass beside his head is a reminder that even monarchs are subject to the transience of life. Nine skeletons perform a *danse macabre* around him: one of them is bent under the burden of the regal insignia, the others gesture towards the expiration of life, symbolised by the extinguished torch held by the foremost figure. However, a hand appearing from above with a banderole bearing the legend VIVIT (He liveth!) serves as a consolatory reminder of the life eternal. The Imperial wax embosser Neuberger demonstrates his mastery of the medium with the virtuoso execution of the skeletons and the subtle modelling of the Emperor's features; equally im-pressive, however, is the bizarre composition. The background of rocks covered in glittering, dark-red sand forms a subtle contrast to the pallor of the wax figures. Emperor Leopold I commissioned the work around 1660 in memory of his father.

Inventory of 1752 — No. 88 (512)

Ref.: H. Klapsia, Daniel Neuberger, in: Jahrbuch XXXXIII (1935), pp. 223—248, esp. p. 232 ff., illus. 191, 193.

118 DEVOTIONAL BOOK OF EMPRESS CLAUDIA FELICITAS

Constance, 1674, and Augsburg (?), c. 1674
Silver, paper; 12.5 cms high, 7.7 cms wide (Inv. No. Kap. 16)

In this book, entitled "Heiliger Vor-Arlenbergischer Wunder- und Gnaden-quell" (Holy Source of Vor-Arlenberg-ian Miracles and Grace), the Vorarl-berg Capuchin Father Lucianus Monti-fontanus (Lucianus of Montafon) describes the life of the Capuchin Father St. Fidelis of Sigmaringen. The work was published in Constance, in 1674, and was dedicated to the Empress Claudia Felicitas. The silver bind-ing, which probably comes from Augs-

burg, shows the Imperial eagle on the front and a tree decorated with the crown of the House of Habsburg on the back. The book used to be in the Small Privy Treasure Chamber of Emperor Karl VI and was donated to the Capuchin Monastery in 1778 by Empress Maria Theresia († 1780). On the flyleaf, the Empress has noted in her own hand: *"After 104 years, a grandchild of the great Leopold presents this to your monastery and commends herself to God most especially in her prayers for a peaceful hour of death. Maria Theresia."*

Inventory of 1731 — fol. 76, No. 36

119 RELIQUARY OF ST. EUSTACE

Hans Otto († 1678 Augsburg)
Augsburg, c. 1655/1660
Silver, parcel-gilt, diamonds, rubies, onyx, pearls, paste (glass); maker's mark HO, Augsburg hallmark; 41.5 cms high, foot: 11 cms diameter (Inv. No. Kap. 48)

This silver reliquary is formed in the shape of a lofty tree, the crown of which supports a small onyx bowl containing the relics of St. Eustace. A stag bearing a cross between its antlers is said to have appeared to the saint while he was hunting; he is thus revered as one of the patron saints of huntsmen, the other being St. Hubert. The stag is

here standing on a branch of the tree. Opposite it is a small hunting dog made of onyx, its collar set with diamonds and rubies. For the composition of the piece, the Franconian goldsmith Hans Otto has borrowed from the formal repertoire of contemporary Nuremberg embossed goblets, which continued the tradition of older models from the age of Dürer. A number of these goblets displays the same type of foot with a double row of bosses, a concave middle section and similar crowning vases of flowers.

Inventory of 1752 — No. 62 (485)

Ref.: Seling 1980, vol. I, p. 102, III, p. 185, no. 1493 a, illus. 340.

120 RELIQUARY OF THE VIRGIN MARY

Hans Otto († 1678 Augsburg)
Augsburg, c. 1655/1660
Silver, parcel-gilt, shell, mother-of-pearl, pearls, rock crystal; maker's mark HO, Augsburg hallmark; 34.5 cms high, foot: 13 cms diameter (Inv. No. Kap. 50)

Relics of the Virgin Mary are here concealed inside the shell, which is covered by a mother-of-pearl relief showing the Mother of God seated with the child between two angels. The relief was made in the second half of the 16th

century and was probably extant in the Treasury of the Capuchin Monastery as early as the first half of the 17th century. The reliquary was made around 1655—1660, by the Augsburg goldsmith Hans Otto, who has combined oval and rectangular pieces of rock crystal with a silver stand in a composition of subtly matching forms. As with the reliquary of St. Eustace (Cat. No. 119), which is by the same goldsmith, the ornamentation of the foot and the carved silver leafwork employ motifs familiar from embossed goblets produced in Nuremberg in the 17th century.

Inventory of 1626 — No. 0/2 (249)
Inventory of 1752 — No. 63 (486)

Ref.: Seling 1980, vol. I, p. 102, III, p. 185, no. 1493 b, illus. 341.

121 THE SUDARIUM OF ST. VERONICA

Frame: Rome, 1617, and Vienna, c. 1721
Silver, parcel-gilt, ebony, mother-of-pearl, copper-gilt, ivory, onyx cameos; 58.5 cms high, 48.4 cms wide (Inv. No. D 108)

The sudarium of St. Veronica was once regarded as *"one of the most precious relics belonging to the Imperial and Royal Ecclesiastical Treasury and the Imperial Residency of Vienna"* (Catalogue of 1856). The princely family of Savelli had preserved this relic in their palace in Rome for generations and exhibited it annually for veneration during Easter week. According to a tradition, Valusian Savelli, an official at the court of Emperor Tiberius, had been given the sudarium by St. Veronica and brought it from Palestine to Rome. When the dynasty died out with Giulio Savelli, his widow, Princess Catarina Giustiniana Savelli, presented the relic to Emperor Karl VI at a solemn ceremony in 1720. The sudarium was transferred from Rome to Vienna in 1721. As other relics of this kind existed, it was assumed that Veronica had folded the cloth into three and that Christ's blood had soaked into all three layers. The Church had therefore authenticated three Holy Sudaria, among them this one. It is partly covered with gilded copper foil, shaped to accomodate the outline of the facial image. In an inscription dated 1617, Pope Paul V (1605—1621) forbade reproduction of the sudarium upon pain of excommunication. The ebony frame was probably made in Rome in 1617, while the outer silver frame set with cameos was added in Vienna in 1721 to replace a damaged copper frame. The sudarium itself has not yet been subjected to scientific examination.

Inventory of 1758 — Case I, No. 1

122 BOUQUET OF SILVER FLOWERS

Palermo, 1st half of the 18th century
Silver, jasper-agate, copper-gilt; 65.5
cms high (Inv. No. D 52)

This bouquet of silver flowers in a hexagonal jasper-agate vase constitutes a
masterly study of nature. Not only are
the thin silver-foil blooms modelled in
remarkable botanical detail, but all the
concrete characteristics of the leaves
are also captured, down to the exact
reproduction of the web of nervures. In
the 18th century, Sicilian goldsmiths
were renowned for such bouquets of
flowers.

Two pieces closely related to these
Viennese bouquets are to be found in
the Cappella Palatina in Palermo,
another was presented by the Senate of
Palermo to the treasury of S. Petronio
in Bologna. The examples in Vienna
were probably also made in Palermo.
They once stood on the altar of the
chapel of Castle Holics (today in
Czechoslovakia, at that time part of
Hungary), an estate which Emperor
Franz I had acquired in 1736. When the
castle chapel was secularised in 1897,
the two vases of flowers were transferred to the Ecclesiastical Treasury.

123 BOUQUET OF SILVER FLOWERS

Palermo, 1st half of the 18th century
Silver, jasper agate, copper-gilt; 63.5
cms high (Inv. No. D 53)

Apart from insignificant differences in
the leafwork, this flower vase is identical to its companion piece, Cat. No.
122.

124 THE SCOURGING OF CHRIST

Alessandro Algardi (Bologna 1598—
1654 Rome) and Francois Duquesnoy
(Brussels 1597—1643 Livorno)
Rome, c. 1635/1640
Bronze-gilt, hardwood overlaid with
ebony, lapis lazuli; 51.4 cms high;
Christ: 21.6 cms high (Inv. No. D 127)

The two torturers bind Christ with
ropes to a column made of lapis lazuli
and raise their scourges to beat him.
This gilded bronze group is among the
best-known designs of Alessandro Algardi. Not only were several casts of it
made in Algardi's workshop, but it
also had great appeal for other
masters, who made a great many
reproductions of it. While the Treasury
also possesses a second group depicting the scourging (Cat. No. D 187,
Kunstkammer, Kunsthistorische Museum) which is entirely by Algardi,

only the figure of Christ is by him in this group. The two torturers, several examples of which have also survived in other pieces, were made by Francois Duquesnoy, one of the most important contemporaries of Algardi, as a variation on those of the master. The figures by Duquesnoy create a less dynamic effect than Algardi's prototypes, and the softer, less incisive modelling of the body becomes noticeable when compared to the figure of Christ. However, Algardi's masterpiece, which was made in 1635/1640, and which reflects High Renaissance models, is one of the highlights of Italian Baroque sculpture.

Inventory of 1731 — fol. 305, No. 295

Ref: J. Montagu, Alessandro Algardi, New Haven/London 1985, I, p. 197, II, p. 315 ff. and p. 321, no. 9 c 34.

Above a hexagonal pedestal of ajouré embossing, rises a shaft with volutes supporting three glass cylinders which contain the relics of the Three Wise Men: Caspar, Melchior and Balthasar. Statuettes of the kings crown the lids of the receptacles. Between them is a round vessel from which rises the Star of Bethlehem, which forms the crowning element of the reliquary. The highlight of this ingenious piece is represented by the statuettes, which fulfill all the prerequisites for full-sized sculptural figures. The figure of Caspar was replaced in the 19th century.

Inventory of 1758 — Case I, No. 48

Ref.: Seling 1980, vol. I, p. 102, III, p. 124, no. 1138 a

126 OSTENSORY
Naples (?), late 16th century, and Vienna (?), 1st half of the 18th century
Bronze-gilt, jasper-agate, lapis lazuli, quartz, malachite, mother-of-pearl, opal, gold enamel, rubies, 'Klosterarbeit' (pearls, gilded silver wire); 59.5 cms high (Inv. No. Kap. 51)

This reliquary in the form of a monstrance consists of a heavily profiled scrollwork frame made of bronze-gilt, which contrasts with plates of jasper-

125 RELIQUARY WITH RELICS OF THE MAGI
Paulus Baumann (Augsburg, c. 1567—1634 Augsburg)
Augsburg, c. 1630/1635
Silver, gilded and painted, lapis lazuli; maker's mark PB, Augsburg hallmark; 30 cms high (Inv. No. D 38)

magate, quartz and lapis lazuli. A lapis lazuli cross has been inserted into the jasper-agate back plate, and a piece of Christ's shroud can be seen between two shells made of blue glass where the beams of the cross intersect. The relic is flanked by two stones from the Holy Places in Jerusalem, with four relics of various saints occupying the corners of the back plate. It was not until the 18th century that all the relics, together with their mounts and the blossom-shaped appliqués on the frame and the foot, were added to the ostensory, which originally dates from the late 16th century. At one time, a small oval case was probably affixed at the point where the beams of the cross intersect. Comparable pieces of goldsmiths' work, employing similar combinations of materials, derive from Naples.

Inventory of 1752 — No. 53 (476)

127 CHRIST AND THE TWO THIEVES

Leonhard Kern (Forchtenberg 1588—1662 Schwäbisch Hall)
Schwäbisch Hall, c. 1626
Ivory, mahogany; 36.3 cms high (Christ), 33 cms high (repentant thief), 33.5 cms high (unrepentant thief) (Inv. No. E 4 [Thieves], E 45 [Christ])

Christ hangs on the cross, his body outstretched almost exactly along its vertical and horizontal axes. To his right, the repentant sinner seems to strain towards him, gazing at him in expectation, while on his left the unrepentant thief turns away in a contortion of agony. Christ has wrenched his head to the right to announce to the repentant thief: "Today shalt thou be with me in Paradise." It is this moment — an uncommon motif in German art — on which Leonhard Kern bases his composition. He attempts to accentuate the spatiality of the composition by means of the diagonally placed cross-beams of the thieves' crosses. However, it is the figures which form the focus of artistic concentration. They combine technical brilliance in the ivory carving with an extraordinary mastery of anatomy. One of Leonhard Kern's letters reveals that this knowledge was based on an intensive study of live models. However, Kern does not lose himself in details, but works out basic general forms of an almost cubic structure. The sensitive rendering of the facial expressions and use of emphatic gesture establish the relations between the figures. This outstanding achievement of early Baroque German sculpture was made around a decade after the Lamentation reliefs (Cat. Nos. 129, 144) and was one of the most important works of Kern's later years.

Inventory of 1758 — Case VI, No. 30

Ref.: Fillitz 1957, p. 203 ff.; Grünenwald 1969, p. 46, no. 109; Möller 1970, p. 41 ff.

128a

128 FOUR PASSION RELIEFS

Workshop of Dominikus Stainhart (Weilheim 1655—1721 Munich)
Munich, beginning of the 18th century
a) The scourging of Christ
   Ivory, ebonised hardwood; 8.8 cms high, 16.1 cms wide (Inv. No. 3696)
b) Christ falls beneath the weight of the cross
   Ivory, ebonised hardwood; 10.5 cms high, 18.8 cms wide (Inv. No. 4181)
c) The divestment of Christ
   Ivory, ebonised hardwood; 10.6 cms high, 18.7 cms wide (Inv. No. 4187)
d) The lamentation of Christ
   Ivory, ebonised hardwood; 8.6 cms high, 16.1 cms wide (Inv. No. 3691)

These reliefs portray Christ's Passion with extreme violence and brutality. Christ has collapsed during the scourging; one torturer kneels scornfully beside him, while the other rests on a stool after his exertions and jokes with a third man about the scourging. The relief of Christ carrying the cross shows how Christ has fallen under the weight of the cross and is being forced up again with blows, while the gigantic figure of Simon of Cyrene attempts to help him with the cross. The height of cruelty, however, is reached with the profoundly moving scene of the divestment of Christ. A torturer tears the clothes from Christ's body, and at the same time kicks him against the cross. In the last relief, Mary and two angels lament over the corpse.

The composition of these reliefs may have been partly inspired by depictions of the 'Seven Falls of Jesus' by the Munich court painter Christoph Schwarz. All four pieces are related to works by Dominikus Stainhart in their conception of relief technique: figures carved in high relief, with fully-modelled limbs and sharp folds in their garments, arranged in a pictorial frieze-like manner with minimal spatiality. The artist developed his style in Italy, together with his brother Franz Stainhart I, between 1674 and 1682, before settling in Munich in 1690 to be-

128b

128c

come one of the city's leading ivory carvers. For a long time no-one succeeded in clearly differentiating the work of one brother from that of the other, or distinguishing their respective areas of responsibility in the large workshop. Even though both of the reliefs were transferred from the collection in Laxenburg in 1879, they probably did not belong to the same cycle originally. The reliefs of the scourging and the lamentation of Christ correspond in their dimensions and style, as do those of Christ's fall beneath the cross and his divestment.

With their simple composition and less subtle execution, the scourging and the lamentation can almost certainly be attributed either to the workshop or to the successors of Dominikus Stainhart. The fall beneath the cross and the divestment, on the other hand, in which the composition is more complex and the figures are arranged with greater freedom, exhibiting a much

finer, more differentiated execution, bear a strong resemblance to pieces from the master's own hand.

Ref.: C. Theuerkauff, 'Kunststückhe von Helfenbein' — zum Werk der Gebrüder Stainhart, in: Alte und moderne Kunst XVII/H. 124/125 (1972), pp. 22—33.

129 THE LAMENTATION
Leonhard Kern (Forchtenberg 1588—1662 Schwäbisch Hall)
Forchtenberg or Heidelberg, c. 1614/1620
Ivory, hardwood overlaid with ebony; 32.5 cms high, 35 cms wide (Inv. No. D 206)

The body of Christ lies on the anointing slab, the ointment vessel at his feet. Mary Magdalen bends over him, while Mary gazes down at her dead son. The figures have been carved from three

128d

separate pieces of ivory and mounted on an ebony base. They represent a reduced variation of the Lamentation reliefs Cat. No. 144, and were probably executed at the same time as the latter, i.e. shortly after Leonhard Kern's return from Italy. In these early works, the artist demonstrates the knowledge he had recently acquired from his travels in Italy in a virtuoso display of his art as a carver, continually exploiting the fascinating surface properties of the material to their full advantage. This characteristic is revealed both in the soft folds of Christ's shroud and in the superb modelling of the nude.

Inventory of 1758 — Case V (below), No. 1

Ref.: Fillitz 1957, p. 205; Grünenwald 1969, p. 47, no. 112; Möller 1970, p. 41.

130 THE SCOURGING OF CHRIST
Circle of Adam Lenckhardt (?)
Vienna, 3rd quarter of the 17th century
Ivory, ebonised hardwood; 26 cms high, 15.5 cms wide (Inv. No. Kap. 324)

The scourging of Christ is depicted in an extraordinarily realistic way in this relief. Christ has slumped down in front of the short scourging-column. One torturer grasps him by the hair, about to strike at him, a second is still occupied with binding his hands to the post. The rough and distorted faces of the torturers provide a marked contrast to the beautiful figure of Christ (the traditional way of increasing the graphic vividness of the scene from the Gothic age awards). A segmental projection in front of the shallow background architecture makes it possible to develop the figures in high relief. Parallels to the formal language used in this carving, above all in the figural types and the depiction of naked parts of the body, are to be found in the work of Adam Lenckhardt, who was active in Vienna. The relief presumably derives either from his workshops or from his professional circle.

Inventory of 1752 — No. 131 (557)

Refs: C. Theuerkauff, Zum Werk des Monogrammisten B.G., in: Aachener Kunstblätter XLIV (1973), pp. 245—296, p. 285, Cat. No. 51.

131 CHRIST CROWNED WITH THORNS
Circle of Adam Lenckhardt (?)
Vienna, 3rd quarter of the 17th century
Ivory, ebonised hardwood; 26 cms high, 15.5 cms wide (Inv. No. Kap. 325)

In this companion piece to Cat. No. 130, Christ sits on a rock, his hands tied together around a reed which has been mockingly given to him as a sceptre. Two tormentors force the crown of thorns onto his head using sticks, so that he collapses under the pain. The effectiveness of the scene derives from the vehemence of its depiction.

Inventory of 1752 — No. 131 (557)

Ref.: Theuerkauff, cf. Cat. No. 130.

132 RELIQUARY WITH A NAIL FROM THE CROSS

Augsburg, mid-17th century
Gold, silver-gilt, partially enamelled and painted, painted brass, emeralds, sapphires, topazes, amethysts, turqoises, aquamarine, hyacinth, garnets, rock crystal, pearls, glass; 79.6 cms high (Inv. No. D 62)

Two angels, kneeling on clouds, clasp two curved palm trunks which meet to form a wreath composed of enamelled bouqets of flowers and precious and semi-precious stones. Between the trunks is a large emerald, decorated with the initials IHS (Jesus) in rock crystal, and encircled by an aureole of garnets. The reliquary consists of gold, the angels and the palm trunks are silver-gilt, and the angel busts between the semi-precious stones are of brass. The original ebony socle and the copes of the two angels have not survived. This costly setting was made around the middle of the 17th century for what is one of the most famous relics of the Ecclesiastical Treasury. Displayed in the almond-shaped glass receptacle is the nail with which the right hand of Christ was supposedly affixed to the cross. It is accompanied by the seal of Pope Innocence II (1130—1143), who testifies in a document (copy, 17th [?] century) that Emperor Konrad III (1138—1152) had presented it to him for certification. On the basis of other authentications, the Pope confirms that it was one of the nails which Emperor Constantine bore on his helmet. The relic presumably arrived in Vienna as a present to Emperor Ferdinand III, although no relevant sources regarding its provenance are extant. The first report of its presence in the Ecclesiastical Treasury occurs in 1660 (itinerary of J. J. Müller). At that time, visitors would rub their rosaries against the glass receptacle in the hope of receiving the nail's widely extolled healing power by transference. The goldsmiths' work was probably executed in Augsburg; the stones and the enamel flowers of the frame are closely related to pieces from Augsburg (e.g. jewellery caskets, Munich Treasury).

Inventory of 1758 — Case 1, No. 2

Ref.: L. von Wilckens, Kunsthandwerk, in: Erich Hubala, Die Kunst des 17. Jahrhunderts (Propyläen Kunstgeschichte IX), Berlin 1970, p. 332.

this type of ornamentation was widely used in Italy, this particular variation is characteristic of Neapolitan goldsmiths' work. The probability that this piece was in fact made in Naples is strengthened by its close parallels to a reliquary executed by the Neapolitan goldsmith Constanzo Pisa in 1603 (Amalfi Cathedral).

Inventory of 1758 — Case VIII, No. 13

133 ROCK CRYSTAL OSTENSORY WITH MINIATURES OF CHRIST AND THE VIRGIN MARY
Naples (?), c. 1600
Rock crystal, silver-gilt; 39.5 cms high
(Inv. No. D 219)

A parchment miniature with a half-figure of Christ is set into the front of the oval rock crystal capsule, corresponding to a miniature of the Virgin on the back. The possibility should not be ruled out that the capsule, which was actually intended as a pendant (cf. Cat. No. 88), was only mounted on this richly-decorated rock crystal stand and framed with the chased silver-gilt mounts at a later date. The reliquary Cat. No. 126 displays the same exuberant ornamentation and a similarly emphatic plasticity of execution. Although

134 DOUBLE-EAGLE RELIQUARY
Augsburg and Freiburg in Breisgau (?), 1st quarter of the 17th century
Silver-gilt, rock crystal; 18 cms high
(Inv. No. D 69)

Seated on the crystal and silver-gilt stand, which is shaped like a baluster, is a double-eagle bearing the Imperial crown upon its heads. The eagle's trunk is formed by a crystal vase, in which is enclosed a relic of St. Thomas Aquinas (c. 1225—1274). The coats of arms represented on the eagle's wings are those of the donor and recipient. On the left can be seen the arms of Austria *(Bindenschild)* and on the right the arms of the Order of the Dominicans, to which St. Thomas belonged. The goldsmiths' work suggests an

Augsburg workshop of the early 17th century. On the other hand, the crystal elements, which are partially decorated with chip carving, probably derive from the crystal cutting workshop in Freiburg in Breisgau, which what was at that time of great importance, exporting bored and polished crystal elements to all the major trade centres of Europe. The double-eagle reliquary bears close resemblances to similar pieces mounted in Augsburg.

Inventory of 1758 — Case VIII, No. 8

135 THE MONSTRANCE OF THE STAR CROSS ORDER

Augsburg, c. 1668
Silver-gilt, partially enamelled and painted, gold foil, diamonds, garnets, chrysolites, rock crystal, enamel painting; 53.5 cms high (Inv. No. D 25)

Preserved in the niche of the monstrance, in front of a painted miniature of Jerusalem, is a particle of the Cross. The cruciform relic is enclosed in a receptacle of rock crystal and gold, and bears a diamond crown. Around the niche is a wide border of enamelled scrollwork, bands of garnets and large chrysolites. The tall stand, resembling a candlestick in form, is decorated in similar, albeit less ornate fashion. The

particle of the cross had been in the possession of the Habsburgs for generations, and was then entrusted to Empress Eleonora (of the House of Gonzaga), widow of Emperor Ferdinand III, for the duration of her lifetime by her stepson, Emperor Leopold I. In February 1668, parts of the Hofburg were destroyed in a huge fire, and the Empress, who was only rescued with difficulty, was forced to abandon the relic to the flames. Five days afterwards, the particle of the cross was found undamaged in the wreckage of her bedchamber, although its gold receptacle had melted. In devout gratitude, Empress Eleonora founded an order for noblewomen, the aims of which were the veneration of the Cross and the excercise of charity. The Empress awarded the members gold crosses surrounded by four diamond stars with the motto 'Salus et Gloria' (salvation and glory). These crosses were called 'star crosses' and the order the 'Order of the Star Cross', after the Italian name *crociera* for the heavenly constellation of the Southern Cross.

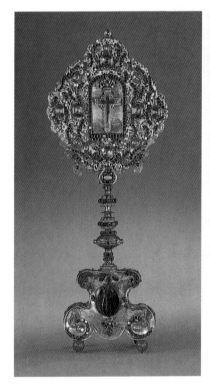

The principal and patroness of this Order — the highest-ranking order for women established by the House of Austria and still in existence today — was always the Empress. Probably made in 1668 by an Augsburg goldsmith (cf. Cat. No. 1), the monstrance was subsequently displayed annually in the chapel of the Hofburg on the feast days of the Order.

Inventory of 1758 — Case I, No. 127

Ref.: Hochadelige und gottselige Versammlung vom Sternkreuze (anonymous), Vienna 1839.

136 RELIQUARY HOUSE ALTAR OF EMPEROR LEOPOLD I

Milan (?), c. 1660/1680

Ebony facings on hardwood, gold enamel, silver-gilt, oil paints, brass-gilt, diamonds, precious stones, semi-precious stones, pearls, pastes (glass), glass beads; 70 cms high (without socle); Socle: 12 cms high (Inv. No. D 59)

The reverse of the flower vase on the broken pediment bears a crowned L and the inscription ERIT UNICA MIHI (This shall belong to me alone). Both monogramme and motto refer to the owner of the piece, Emperor Leopold I. In the rectangular central section, five relics are affixed to red velvet ornamented with pearls in gold settings. The main relic is a thorn from Christ's crown, preserved in the small glass cylinder in the centre and surrounded by four relics of SS. Stephen, Eustace, Andrew and George in the corners. In the form of a small house altar, the reliquary is of the same type as Cat. No. 93, yet it surpasses all previous models by reason of its extended proportions and abundant decoration. For instance, by doubling the traditional predella, a further socle area is added, containing drawers which are lined with red silk. The quality of the decorative work, however, is variable. The pillars, the central section of the socle and the pediment border all display enamelled gold ornamentation, while the volutes and the lateral socle decoration are of silver-gilt painted with oils and the crowning angels made of gilded brass. The individual forms within this ornamentation, which covers the whole altar, coalesce to create an overall impression of unparalleled richness. Although such a design would, of course, have been entirely in accord with the client's wishes, it had nevertheless been a fashionable style of gold work ever since the middle of the 17th century. This piece was possibly made in Milan as a gift for Emperor Leopold I. Similar pieces, exhibiting comparable technical execution, can be found in Upper and Middle Italy (e.g. Bologna, Tesoro di San Petronio).

Inventory of 1758 — Case III, No. 1

137 RELIQUARY HOUSE ALTAR BELONGING TO EMPEROR LEOPOLD I
Milan (?), c. 1660/1680
Hardwood, overlaid with ebony, ebony, gold enamel, silver-gilt, oil paints, gilded brass, iron (feet), diamonds, precious stones, semi-precious stones, pearls, pastes (glass), glass beads; 70 cms high (without socle), socle: 12 cms high (Inv. No. D 63)

This small house altar contains five relics belonging to Christ and the same four saints whose relics are preserved in its companion piece, Cat. No. 136. A putative fragment of Christ's shroud is surrounded by the relics of (from upper left to bottom right) SS. Andrew, George, Stephen and Eustace. On the back of the crowning vase is the same emblem as on that of the altar Cat. No. 136.

Inventory of 1758 — Case III, No. 1

138 IVORY CRUCIFIX
Leonhard Kern (Forchtenberg 1588—1662 Schwäbisch Hall)
Schwäbisch Hall, c. 1626/1630
Ivory, hardwood, painted black; cross: 98.3 cms high, 45 cms wide; corpus: 43.3 cms high, 43.3 cms wide (Inv. No. E 1)

Christ is braced upon the cross, his arms stretched to their utmost extent. His body seems to rise up for the last time, as he looks towards heaven the sky with pain-filled face and asks: "My God, why hast thou forsaken me?" The astonishingly fine detail of the corpus is without doubt one of the most remarkable achievements of German Baroque ivory carving. Nonetheless, the piece used to be regarded as an anonymous mid-17th century work and has received hardly any acclaim at all. There was a certain reluctance to ascribe it to Leonhard Kern, despite the fact that a comparison with his Crucifix (Cat. 127), or the figures of Christ in his Lamentation Reliefs (Cat. Nos. 129 and 144), shows that it must be a work of his own hand. It matches these not only in conceptual type, proportions and motifs, but also in the idiosyncratic style of the carving. Up until now, only two crucifixes by Leonhard Kern were known: that of Cat. No. 127 and the one in the Museum für Kunst und Gewerbe in Hamburg. Together with Cat. No. 4, this crucifix has since been attributed to the master and is now regarded a further example of his work.

Inventory of 1780 — Case VIII, No. 3

Ref.: Fillitz 1957, p. 209 ff.

139 CHRIST AND ST. JOHN THE BAPTIST AS CHILDREN

Leonhard Kern (Forchtenberg 1588—1662 Schwäbisch Hall)
After an etching by Guido Reni (Bologna 1575—1642 Bologna)
Forchtenberg or Heidelberg, 1614/1620
Ivory, hardwood, painted black; 14.5 cms high, 9 cms wide (without frame)
(Inv. No. D 203)

The infant Jesus sits on a rock and embraces John the Baptist, apparently lifting him up towards him. John is represented with his attributes of wooden cross and lamb and also already clothed in the penitential sheepskin he was later to wear as an adult. This relief is based on an etching by the Bolognese Baroque painter, Guido Reni. Like its companion piece, it was until recently stored in the Depot of the Ecclesiastical Treasury, where its existence was first documented in 1758, as an anonymous 16th century German work. The unusually high quality of the carving in both of these works is striking. With their clearly defined contours, the figures stand out against the flat background. The bodies are carefully modelled, with meticulous attention having been paid to the soft gradations of form; the drapery displays swelling folds with shallow hollows and curving hems. These formal features are typical of Leonhard Kern's early work. His other reliefs display not only the same plasticity of conception and identical treatment of the drapery but also the same standard motif of large-sized individual tussocks of grass (cf. Cat No. 144).

Inventory of 1758 — Case I, No. 118

Ref.: Tietze Conrat 1920/21, p. 150 ff.

140 JESUS AND JOHN THE BAPTIST AS CHILDREN

Leonhard Kern (Forchtenberg 1588—1662 Schwäbisch Hall)
Forchtenberg or Heidelberg, 1614/1620
Ivory, hardwood painted black; 14.5

cms high, 9 cms wide (without frame) (Inv. No. D 204)

As in the companion piece, Christ and John the Baptist sit in a field and embrace each other. Yet while the companion piece depicts John the Baptist with his characteristic attributes and Christ without any symbols of majesty, in this piece the relationship is reversed. On the left sits John the Baptist, only the uncut hair indicating the future penitent and hermit, while Christ holds in his left hand the *fasces,* as a symbol of his coming sovereignty. In ancient Rome this bundle of rods bound together with an axe was regarded as a symbol of official power and sovereignty and was carried by lictors and consuls. Leonhard Kern presumably used an earlier model as the basis for both this relief and its companion piece.

Inventory of 1758 — Case I, No. 118

141 THE PERSECUTION OF THE CHRISTIANS

Johann Caspar Schenck (Constance, c. 1630/1640—1674 Vienna)
Vienna, 1665/1674
Ivory, ebonised hardwood; signed ICS (on the helmet of the soldier with the raised sword); 14 cms high, 9 cms wide (Inv. No. D 199)

This relief depicts the massacre of Christian soldiers, probably that of the Theban legion of the Roman army, which converted to Christianity in a body and was put to death on the orders of Emperor Maximilian.

Two cherubs swoop down from above to offer the martyrs a laurel wreath, the symbol of everlasting life.

Johann Caspar Schenck came from a family of sculptors in Constance and in 1665 was appointed 'Painstecher' (engraver) to the court of Emperor Leopold I, at an annual salary of 500 gulden. This work and its companion piece Cat. No. 142 were produced while he was working in Vienna. The delicately modelled figures shrouded in angular folds of drapery occupy the whole expanse of the pyramid which rises to the upper right of the picture. Although the figures are densely set, Schenck succeeds in conveying the impression of a differentiated spatial perspective by endowing the relief with a finely gradated plasticity.

Inventory of 1758 — Case I, No. 119

Ref.: E. von Philippovich, Hauptwerke des Elfenbeinkünstlers Johann Caspar Schenck, in: Kunst in Hessen und am Mittelrhein XIII (1973), pp. 47—51; C. Theuerkauff, Zum Werk des Monogrammisten B. G. in: Aachener Kunstblätter XLIV (1973), p. 250 ff.

142 CHRIST CARRYING THE CROSS

Johann Caspar Schenck (Constance, c. 1630/1640—1674 Vienna)
After an etching by Jacques Callot (Nancy 1592/1593—1635 Nancy)
Vienna, 1665/1674
Ivory, ebonised hardwood; signature ICS (over the city gate); 13.7 cms high, 9 cms wide (Inv. No. D 200)

141

banner rounding off the left side of the relief and providing a counterbalance to the ruined tower on the rock. Johann Caspar Schenck's relief reproduces in lateral inversion an etching by the French graphic artist Jacques Callot. Although the original, which positively luxuriates in perspective, is here condensed to upright background staffage, the impression of spatial gradation is nevertheless retained. With great narrative exuberance, Schenck spreads a densely packed conglomeration of figures across the whole of the foreground.

Inventory of 1758 — Case I, No. 119

Ref.: Tietze Conrat 1920/21, p. 146, 153, 171.

142

143

The procession of people going to the crucifixion pours through the city gate of Jerusalem and winds down the rocky path. Christ has fallen beneath the weight of the cross and is being forced up again with blows. At the front, on the right, a soldier attempts to hold back Veronica, who has kneeled down to give Christ the sudarium. To the left, a captain observes the scene from his horse, his raised Roman

143 THE SCOURGING OF CHRIST

Southern Germany, 1st quarter of the 18th century
After an engraving by Albrecht Dürer (Nuremberg 1471—1528 Nuremberg)
Ivory, hardwood, painted black; 12.1 cms high, 7.1 cms wide (Inv. No. 4183)

The anonymous ivory carver has based his relief on an engraving from Dürer's 'Kleine Passion' of 1512. He has used the main scene and made only small alterations: while omitting Christ's robe on the ground, he has added the capital of the column which is not visible in Dürer's engraving. Although the style of the relief has been considerably influenced by the original, the copyist's own artistic quality is nevertheless also evident. He broadens and shortens the proportions of the figures, which are merely juxtaposed without any real narrative relation to each other: the blows of the torturers seem to be aimed past, not at the figure of Christ. A comparable relief after a model by Dürer (Monastery of Klosterneuburg) has been attributed to the circle of the ivory carver Jakob Dobberman. This piece comes from the collections at Castle Ambras near Innsbruck.

Castle Ambras, Inventory of 1821 — p. 83, No. 17

144 THE LAMENTATION

Leonhard Kern (Forchtenberg 1588—1662 Schwäbisch Hall)
Forchtenberg or Heidelberg, 1614/1620
Ivory, hardwood, ebony facing; 24.5 cms high, 40.2 cms wide (Inv. No. D 198)

After the body of Christ has been taken down from the cross, preparations are made for his embalmment. To the left of Christ, a man — almost certainly Nicodemus — is already reaching into the ointment vessel, while Maria Magdalen continues to kiss the Saviour's hands. Behind her stands Joseph of Arimathea, in whose tomb Christ is to be laid, and to the right of him, in lamentation, are Mary and John. The sculptor and ivory carver Leonhard Kern became familiar with Italian art while travelling in Italy between 1609—1614. The present work, which was probably done immediately after his return, testifies to the knowledge he acquired there. In the composition as a whole, as well as in individual motifs, there are references to reliefs by the sculptor of the Venetian Renaissance, Tullio Lombardo, although it also reveals familiarity with the work of Giambologna (lamentation relief in the Cappella Grimaldi in Genoa). Kern demonstrates his virtuoso mastery of the art of ivory carving as much in the rich folds of antique drapery as in the superbly modelled nude figure of Christ. Although the figures turn towards one another with animated and meaningful gestures, they are not united in a dramatic whole. This impression is strengthened by the lack of spatial effect, with the figures silhouetted against the ebony background, and by the the way in which the relief is composed solely of individual groups of figures. The Ecclesiastical Treasury possesses a total of three lamentation reliefs by Leonhard Kern in which he explores variations on this theme (cf. Cat. No. 129).

Inventory of 1758 — Case I, No. 118 or 119

Ref.: Fillitz 1957, p. 203 ff.; Grünenwald 1969, p. 46 f., no. 110; Möller 1970, p. 32 ff.

145 ST. MARY MAGDALEN
Franz Stainhart I (?) (Weilheim 1651—1695 Weilheim)
After a painting by Guido Reni (Bologna 1575—1642 Bologna)
Weilheim, c. 1680/1690 (?)
Ivory, ebonised hardwood; 21.3 cms high, 11.3 cms wide (Inv. No. 3784)

This ivory relief is closely based on a painting by the great Baroque artist from Bologna, Guido Reni (Galleria Nazionale d'Arte Antica, Palazzo Corsini, Rome). The composition had become well-known through the many engravings made of it. The companion piece of the relief, however, is based on a painting by Annibale Caracci. Thus the two works provide an opportunity of determining the considerable degree to which the original has influenced the style of the relief. The treatment of the relief — a shallow niche, figures in mezzo or alto relievo, modelled with full forms and a markedly offset ground — can be compared to ivories from the workshops of the brothers Dominikus and Franz Stainhart I (cf. Cat. No. 128). It is possible that the artists had seen the original paintings by Reni and Caracci themselves in Rome. It was there that they had executed their main work, the large ivory cabinet in the Palazzo Colonna, to which Franz Stainhart I contributed a number of reliefs, and these correspond stylistically to the Viennese pieces. Both works were transferred to the Treasury from the Imperial collections at Laxenburg in 1879.

Ref.: D. S. Pepper, Guido Reni, Oxford 1984, p. 267, no. 137, pl. 165; Tietze Conrat 1920/21, p. 149, 154, 170, no. 24.

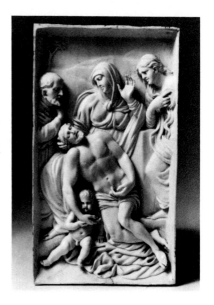

146 PIETÀ
Franz Stainhart I (?) (Weilheim 1651—1695 Weilheim)
After a painting by Annibale Carracci (Bologna 1560—1609 Rome)

Weilheim, c. 1680/1690 (?)
Ivory, ebonised hardwood, 21.3 cms high, 11.3 wide (Inv. No. 3785)

Mary holds the corpse of Christ on her lap, his left hand supported by an angel. On the left is Mary Magdalen, weeping, and on the right St. Francis, his arms crossed, kneeling in worship of the Pietà. The composition of the companion piece (Cat. No. 145) was the work of one of the most important masters of the Roman High Baroque, Annibale Carracci. This piece is a lateral inversion of a painting executed by him in 1603/1604 (Paris, Louvre), which was widely known from an engraving, also laterally inverted, by Pietro Aquila.

Ref.: D. Posner, Annibale Carracci, Vol. II, London 1971, p. 60 f., no. 136; Tietze Conrat 1920/21, p. 170, no. 25, p. 174.

147 MONSTRANCE

Geraardsbergen (Belgium), c. 1670/1676
Silver; Geraardsbergen hallmark, unidentified maker's mark (a crowned P), unidentified mark (male head in right-hand profile); 84.5 cms high (Inv. No. B 9)

This monstrance comes from Geraardsbergen in Belgium, as is indicated by the arms displayed on the foot, which belong to Hubertus Meurant, Abbot of the monastery at Geraardsbergen from 1656 to 1676. However, the inscription below the arms VINCIT QUI PATITUR (that which is here displayed shall prevail), refers to the Host. In addition, a town mark and two unidentified marks are engraved on the edge of the foot. The stand rises in sweeping volutes to support the aureole of the receptacle for the Host, which is flanked by two angels. They support bands of clouds which terminate in a large foliate crown with a cross. Each of the individual elements of the monstrance is emphasised in its intrinsic plastic value. This type of receptacle was frequently used in Flemish monstrances from the second half of the 17th century. Similar works have been preserved in Brussels and Liège (Eglise Saint-Jean), among other places. This monstrance was transferred to the Treasury from the Franzensburg at Laxenburg in 1880.

148 TRAVELLING CHAPEL

Venice (?), c. 1750/1760, and (missal) 1823
Silver, parcel-gilt, glass, velvet; unidentified (Venetian ?) hallmark, three different Venetian hallmarks from the 19th century (Inv. No. H 5)

a) Chalice
   24 cms high
b) Two cruets for mass, with salver
   18.8 cms high
c) Candle salver (Lumen Fidei)
   21.5 cms long
d) Wick trimmers
   13.2 cms long
e) Aspergillum
   13.4 cms long
f) Aspersorium
   18 cms high, no hallmarks
g) Silver relief of the Holy Trinity
   18 cms high
h) Missal, printed in Venice in 1823, cover c. 1750/1760;
   25 cms high, 17 cms wide

In order to be able to hold Mass while making a journey — which was formerly very time-consuming — 'travelling chapels' were used by the Imperial court. Apart from the sacral implements shown here, these chapels also included a portable altar (usually with an altar painting), linen for Mass, a set of liturgical vestments and a case. A wooden case covered with black leather also belongs to the ensemble displayed here.

The decorative motif on the implements are in fully developed Rococco style, the Holy Trinity relief, for example, being framed by alternating concave and convex curves, rocaille and latticework. Although the forms belong to the standard repertoire of Italian goldsmiths' work, they were almost certainly made in Venice. Similar gold work can be seen in the Treasury of San Marco. With the exception of the aspersorium, all the objects display the same selection of 19th century Venetian maker's marks, varying solely according to the size of the object. Furthermore, the missal, which is bound in an older cover, was printed in Venice in 1823. In the 18th century, the Venetian Republic was one of the most important centres of goldsmithery in Europe, and its influence can be discerned not only in the whole of upper Italy, but also in Austria.

149 PRESENTATION SALVER FOR THE FOOT-WASHING CEREMONY

Samuel Schneeweiß (Dresden, c. 1640/1650—1697 Augsburg)
Augsburg, 1670/1675
Silver; maker's mark SS, Augsburg hallmark; 41.5 cms wide, 48 cms long
(Inv. No. XIV/31)

This salver was used for the presentation of the alms distributed to the poor at the Easter foot-washing ceremony. From the Middle Ages onwards, on the Thursday before Easter, Christian monarchs had participated in a foot-washing ceremony in imitation of Christ washing the feet of the Twelve Apostles. At the Imperial court in Vienna, this ceremonial act took place annually in the Hall of Ceremonies at the Hofburg. In a symbolic act of Christian humility, the Emperor and Empress washed the feet of twelve elderly men and women respectively. Each of the old people, who had been chosen from the ranks of the poor and given new clothing beforehand, then

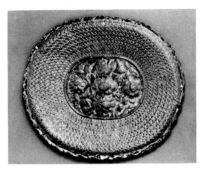

Silver; maker's mark HM, Augsburg hallmark; 42 cms high, 48 cms wide (Inv. No. XIV/32)

The second salver for the foot-washing ceremony is signed by the Augsburg goldsmith Heinrich Mannlich. Its central section displays a couple riding on horses in a landscape, with a framing border of fruit and birds embossed in high relief.

Ref.: Beitl, op. cit. Cat. No. 149.

received a purse containing 30 silver coins. For this purpose, the Imperial Treasurer presented the Emperor and Empress with two silver salvers with red silk covers attached to the edges (cf. the holes at the edge of the salver). Under the cover of each salver lay 12 white leather purses with black and yellow strings, which the Emperor and Empress hung around the necks of the men and women respectively. One of the salvers used was a profane display plate executed by the Augsburg master Samuel Schneeweiss. A central section of chased flowers is surrounded by a wide ornamental border. The convincing impression of a three-dimensional basket weave was achieved by the precise execution of the ornamental motifs.

Ref.: K. Beitl, Die österliche Fußwaschung am Kaiserhofe zu Wien, in: Volkskunde. Fakten und Analysen. Festgabe für Leopold Schmidt, Wien 1972, pp. 275—286.

150 PRESENTATION SALVER FOR THE FOOT-WASHING CEREMONY
Heinrich Mannlich (Troppau, c. 1625/1635—1698 Augsburg)
Augsburg, c. 1670/1675

151 RELIQUARY IN THE FORM OF A SARCOPHAGUS
Vienna (?), c. 1750/1758
Silver-gilt; 23.5 cms high, 15.5 cms wide, 10 cms deep (Inv. No. D 60)

The inscription in the cartouche on the front reveals that this miniature sarcophagus contains the relics of the 'innocent children' (RELIQUIAE SS. INNOCENTIUM): this refers to the children put to death on the orders of King Herod. Glazed cartouches make the relics visible from all four sides. The receptacle is surrounded by four busts of angels, over which rise four martyrs' palms, encircled by a crown. The ornamentation of the cartouches, the shape of the handles and the ingenious voluted feet indicate that the gold work was probably executed between 1750 and 1758.

Inventory of 1758 — Case III, No. 23

mentioned in the 1776 inventory of the Große Galerie, as well as pieces identified as the work of the 'Master of the Fury'.

Ref.: C. Theuerkauff, Die Bildwerke in Elfenbein des 16.—19. Jahrhunderts (Die Bildwerke der Skulpturengalerie Berlin II), Berlin 1986, p. 121 ff.

153 RELIQUARY WITH A RELIC OF ST. CHARLES BORROMEO

Milan, 1st quarter of the 18th century
Gold, silver-gilt, rock crystal; 27.5 cms high (Inv. No. D 46)

The crystal ostensorium of this reliquary displays a relic of St. Charles Borromeo (1538—1584), Archbishop of Milan. The reliquary was probably owned by Karl VI, who dedicated the Karlskirche in Vienna to his patron saint, Charles Borromeo. The foot, the nodus and the broad surround of the niche are embossed in gold, while the back plate is silver-gilt. The richly-decorated volutes which soften the outline of the receptacle are related to the decorational motifs of pieces produced

152 IVORY CRUCIFIX

"The Master of the Fury"
Salzburg (?), 1st quarter of the 17th century
Ivory, walnut; 77.7 cms high, 43.7 cms wide (Inv. No. 3694)

With his knees pointing to the left and his head inclined towards the right, Christ hangs on the cross, looking up to heaven. Distinctive features of the body are the extreme elongation of its proportions and the sinuous structure. Some of the individual motifs, such as the hair, the crown of thorns and the knots of the loincloth are masterly achievements in the art of carving, their detailed execution reminding one of chased gold work. The loincloth, for example, is undercut to such an extent that it seems as if it is slipping from the body like a piece of real cloth. The unknown artist acquired his name from a large statuette of a Fury that he had executed (Kunsthistorische Museum, Vienna). The 'Master of the Fury' achieved similar illusionistic effects in his other works, using a very expressive formal vocubulary. He presumably worked in Salzburg, at certain periods perhaps in Italy. The cross was transferred from the collections in Laxenburg in 1879 and probably derives from Salzburg, where ivory crucifixes are

by Milanese goldsmiths in the early 18th century. Various emblems refer to the saint's archepiscopal rank. The crowning element is formed by an angel's head above which is a bishop's hat; just below this, a bishop's pall (pallium) is entwined around the uppermost volute. A crozier and a staff rise at an oblique angle on either side of the niche. Below the receptacle is the saint's device HUMILITAS (humility), surmounted by a crown signifying the bishop's noble birth. The reliquary was deposited in the Ecclesiastical Treasury on 14. 10. 1766 by Empress Maria Theresia.

Inventory of 1758 — Case V, No. 40 (addendum of 1766)

154 RELIQUARY WITH A PARTICLE OF THE CROSS
Matthias Unverdorben (Piding, c. 1670/1680—1754 Salzburg)
Salzburg, 1721/1727
Silver, parcel-gilt, rock crystal, pastes

(glass); maker's mark MU, Salzburg hallmark; 32.7 cms high (Inv. No. D 220)

A nimbus of green pastes and silver-gilt rays emanates from the supposed particle of the cross in the centre of this reliquary's silver cross. In front of the cross kneels the Virgin Mary in lamentation, her breast pierced by a sword. The design, by the Salzburg goldsmith Matthias Unverdorben, is based on motifs taken from monumental sculpture. As may be inferred from the arms affixed to the socle, the reliquary was made for Franz Anton Count Harrach, Prince Archbishop of Salzburg (1709—1727). The period of its manufacture can be narrowed down further from the authentication, dated 1721, concealed in the socle. In 1910, the piece came into the Treasury's possession from the chapel of the Salzburg Residenz.

Ref.: Catalogue: Gold und Silber. Kostbarkeiten aus Salzburg, Salzburg 1984, p. 130 f., no. K 122.

155 TORTOISESHELL CASKET
Workshop of Johann Heinrich Köhler (?) (Langensalza 1669—1736 Dresden)
Dresden, c. 1700
Tortoiseshell, mother-of-pearl, silver, gilded and painted, gold enamel, bone, diamond, onyx cameo; 15.2 cms high (Inv. No. D 192)

This small, sumptuously decorated casket comprises three receptacles. In addition to the larger octagonal base, there are two further compartments, one above the other, in the tall, graduated lid, which can be opened by means of hinges and diamond knobs. The original purpose of the casket had already become obscure by the middle of the 18th century. A comparable object (from the collections at Castle Moritzburg) was later used to hold a rosary. In view of the ornamental richness and formal wealth displayed by this cabinet-piece, the question of its function came to have little import. Doors of mother-of-pearl adorned with the

figures of various saints are set into the eight sides. Behind these were once scenes from the Passion (?) of Christ; however, only that of the Resurrection has been preserved. Four female figures are seated on the lid and, together with four cherubs, hold a garland set with diamonds. Standing on the lid are two gold enamel figures representing Synagoge and Ecclesia, as symbols of the Old and New Testaments. The crowning element is an onyx cameo showing the penitential St. Jerome, surrounded by an aureole set with diamonds. The casket is also encrusted with ornamental elements: enamelled figures and appliqués, mother-of-pearl plates, mounts of red-dyed bone and diamonds. Small-scale masterpieces of this kind, of incomparable sumptuousness and displaying a supreme refinement of artistic technique, brought great renown to the goldsmith's art at the court of the Saxon Electors in Dresden. The anonymous master of this piece is most likely to have belonged to the circle of artists working for the Dresden court, perhaps in the workshop of Johann Heinrich Köhler, court jeweller to August the Strong. The presence of Dresden court art in the Ecclesiastical Treasury

can be explained by the dynastic connections of the Imperial family: in 1719, Archduchess Maria Josepha, the daughter of Joseph I, married the Saxon Elector, later King August III of Poland.

Inventory of 1758 — Case IX, No. 6

156 PACIFICALE
Dresden (?), c. 1704
Silver-gilt, enamel painting, rock crystal, diamonds, precious stones, semiprecious stones, pearls, lapis lazuli, coral, cornelian and hyacinth cameos, mother-of-pearl, parchment miniatures; 29 cms high (Inv. No. Kap. 45)

A pacificale was sometimes used for the pax at the celebration of High Mass; which is why there is a handle on the back of it. Beneath this is the inscription "von Gebrüder Palm 1704" (by the Palm Brothers 1704). Since the Palm brothers were Viennese bankers

and not goldsmiths, this must be an indication of the provenance of the piece and not a signature. The piece imitates the structure of a large-scale altar, even down to the two miniature candlesticks at the front. The central niche, which is surrounded by garnets, contains an enamel picture of the Virgin Mary, in front of which is a facetted ball of rock crystal with a gilded spike on top. To the side of it are enamel figures of saints in niches made of rock crystal, flanked by a columnar structure housing two further figures and two coral statuettes. Surmounting it is the Holy Trinity, adored by two angels and surrounded by an aureole of diamonds. The luxurious ornamentation of diamonds, precious stones and pearls, together with lapis lazuli columns, coral and cameos, are to be found in similar execution in pieces of Dresden courtly art (an early work of Johann Heinrich Köhler?). In 1758 the pacificale was in the Ecclesiastical Treasury, but was later transferred to the Monastery of the Capuchins and then reincorporated into the Ecclesiastical Treasury in 1922.

Inventory of 1758 — Case I, No. 7

157 ASPERSORIUM

Augsburg (?), 3rd quarter of the 17th century
After a painting by Joseph Heintz the Elder (Basle 1564—1609 Prague)
Silver-gilt, enamel painting, gold enamel, rock crystal. diamonds, precious stones, semi-precious stones, pearls; 20.7 cms high, 14 cms wide (Inv. No. D 188)

As with Cat. No. 67, the division of this piece into a central image surmounted by a round arch, flanking columns and clusters of fruit, as well as a socle and a crowning element, reflects the composition of full-sized altar retables. However, this architectonic structure is merely suggested by the contours of the individual parts, which are covered by ornamental motifs in enamel tendrilling set with precious stones. A small rock crystal vessel in the socle identifies the piece as an aspersorium. In the centre of the composition is an enamel of the Adoration of the Shepherds, which is based on a painting executed over 50 years beforehand (1599 ?) by Joseph Heintz the Elder. The artist himself painted two further versions of this much-copied work (1st version: Národni Gallery, Prague. 2nd and 3rd versions: Kunstmuseum, Basle and the Augustinermuseum in Freiburg in Breisgau). The crowning gold enamel originally depicted a battle scene and was only later reduced to a representation of St. George.

Inventory of 1731 — fol. 159', No. 20
Inventory of 1758 — Case I, No. 45
Inventory of 1780 — Case X, No. 8

158 MONSTRANCE WITH A FIGURE OF THE VIRGIN MARY AS OSTENSORIUM

Zacharias Frill (active in Vienna, c. 1695—1742)
Vienna, 1701
Silver, parcel-gilt, semi-precious stones, rock crystal, one pearl, glass; maker's mark ZF, Vienna hallmark for 1701; 66 cms high (Inv. No. Kap. 88)

In the aureole of the monstrance appears the Virgin Mary, represented in a half-length figure as the Queen of Heaven with crown and sceptre. Above her are suspended God the Father and the Dove of the Holy Spirit. The open body of the Virgin Mary is intended to hold the Host, in which form Christ is present. In this way, the part played by the motherhood of Mary in the salvation of mankind is symbolised in the Eucharist. This representation derives from the Byzantine iconographic image of Maria Platytera (Greek: she who is greater, i.e. than the heavens). In Byzantium, images of the Virgin Mary which contained a round picture of the child Jesus had been current ever since the 11th century. This was a way of venerating the pregnant Virgin as she who had been chosen as the dwelling place of the Lord — he whom the heavens could not otherwise contain. In the High Baroque the traditional form of this type of monstrance was reinterpreted: Christ is no longer represented by a picture, but is present in the form of the Host itself. The goldsmith's work is by Zacharias Frill. In the design of the stand he follows the model for sacral implements which was predominant around 1700 (cf. Cat. Nos. 159 and 160), yet he has found particularly original solutions for

mounting the angels, stones, flowers and grapes (symbols of the Eucharist) on top of the aureole: they are attached to long spirals of wire and are therefore flexible. The monstrance was donated to the Treasury of the Capuchin Monastery by Maria Theresia and remained there, in the tabernacle of the Imperial chapel, until 1921.

159 CHALICE WITH THE ARMS OF EMPEROR KARL VI

Ludwig Schneider (Bachern, c. 1640/ 1650—1729 Augsburg)
Augsburg, c. 1710/1715
Silver-gilt, enamel painting, pastes (glass); maker's mark LS, Augsburg hallmark; 28.5 cms high, 18.5 cms diameter (Inv. No. B 21)

The engraved arms with the accompanying initials C VI on the edge of the bowl indicates that the chalice belonged to Emperor Karl VI. The High Baroque ornamentation of chased strapwork, mounted paste stones and enamel medallions remains strictly subordinate to the clarity of the overall structure. The medallions, three each on the foot, the nodus and the bowl, represent scenes from the life of St. Joseph: the Tree of Jesse, Joseph's rod flowering in the Temple, St. Joseph in his workshop (foot); the Birth of

Christ, the Flight into Egypt, the Return from Egypt (nodus); St. Joseph, his marriage to Mary, and the Dream of St. Joseph (bowl). The choice of scenes from the life of St. Joseph is unusual for a chalice, and might perhaps indicate that it was commissioned by Emperor Joseph I, Karl VI's brother, who died suddenly in 1711. The chalice bears the mark of the Augsburg goldsmith Ludwig Schneider and the Augsburg hallmark used between 1710 and 1715.

Ref.: Seling 1980, vol. III, p. 225, no. 1806 d.

entations of SS. Sebastian, Rocco and Anthony of Padua. Three further enamels of Christ, Mary and Joseph are embedded in the carved silver decoration of the basket of the cuppa. The unmarked goldsmith's work was probably executed for Emperor Karl VI by a Viennese goldsmith.

160 CHALICE WITH THE ARMS OF EMPEROR KARL VI

Vienna (?), 1st quarter of the 18th century (after 1711)
Silver, mostly gilt, enamel painting; 17 cms high, 16.5 cms diameter (Inv. No. B 23)

The trefoliate nodus of the stand bears the arms of Emperor Karl VI and the initials C. VI. With regard to its basic form, the chalice is related to Cat. No. 159, although it is not of the same quality as the latter and not so extensively decorated. On the the six-lobed tracery of the foot are mounted three silver busts of angels and three enamel medallions with half-length repres-

161 ENAMEL CRUCIFIX

Upper/Northern Italy (?), c. 1600
Enamelled silver, root wood, hardwood, ebony veneers; 28.5 cms high (without socle), 12 cms wide (Inv. No. E 44)

This remarkable figure of Christ was cast in silver. Some of the details — such as the crown of thorns, the halo and the nails of the cross — are additionally gilded. The superb enamelling is distinguished by the delicate harmony between the white flesh tints and the blue of the loincloth, and by exquisite nuances of colour. The technical

execution indicates that the crucifix was probably made in an Upper Italian workshop.

162 CROSS FOR THE LAST SACRAMENTS

Vienna, end of the 17th century and c. 1770/1780
Ebony, brass, gold; 16.6 cms high, 10.3 cms wide; (Inv. No. E 5)

This simple ebony cross, which bears a brass figure of Christ, was held in the folded hands of the members of the Imperial family while receiving the last rites at the hour of their death. In 1770/1780 Empress Maria Theresa had the reverse covered with a gold plate which bore the inscription: HAEC MEA SIT HEREDITAS. IN CUJUS AMPLEXU LEOPOLDUS ET ELEONORA DEINDE FILII JOSEPHUS ET CAROLUS TUM HUJUS CONJUX ELISABETHA ANIMAM DEO REDDIDERE FRANCISCUS VERO MORTE IN-OPINATA PROSTATUS QUEM MORIENS NON POTUIT MOR-TUUS EST AMPLEXUS (This is to be my legacy. Holding it, Leopold and Eleonora, further their sons Joseph and Karl, then also the latter's wife Elisabeth, returned their souls to the Lord. Franz, who was struck down by death quite unexpectedly, held it when dead, since he could not as he died). The inscription refers to Emperor Leopold I († 1705), his third wife Empress Eleonora († 1720), Emperor Joseph I († 1711), Emperor Karl VI († 1740), his wife Elisabeth Christine († 1750) and the husband of Maria Theresa, Emperor Franz I († 1765), who died unexpectedly at Innsbruck. The cross was presented to the Ecclesiastical Treasury in 1871.

163 CROSS FOR THE LAST SACRAMENTS

Vienna, 2nd quarter of the 18th century and c. 1770/1780
Wooden foundation overlaid with tortoiseshell, brass, gold; 23.9 cms high, 10.6 cms wide (Inv. No. E 6)

163, 162

This tortoiseshell cross with a cast and engraved figure of Christ was made in the 2nd quarter of the 18th century. It probably belonged to the estate of Emperor Karl VI's sister, Archduchess Maria Magdalena (1689—1743), who held it at her death in 1743. It retained this function right up to the end of the monarchy; virtually all the members of the Imperial family received extreme unction with this cross in their hands. The gold mounts on the ends of the cross were commissioned by Empress Maria Theresia, as was the gold plate on the back, which bears the following inscription: PARS HAEREDITATIS MEAE. IN CUJUS AMPLEXU EX-PIRAVIT MARIA MAGDALENA ARCH: AUST: CAROLI VI SOROR. CHARISSIMA SOROR MEA MAR-IA ANNA BELGII AUSTR: GUBER-NATRIX CAROLINA COMES DE FUCHS MEA ET SORORIS QUON-DAM AJA. CAROLUS DILECTUS FILIUS MEUS. JOANNA ET JOSEPHA DILECTAE FILIAE MEAE ARCHIDD: AUSTR. (Part of my estate. Holding this cross, Maria Magdalena, Archduchess of Austria, sister to Karl VI, passed away, also my beloved sister Maria Anna, Stattholder of the Austrian Netherlands, Karoline, Countess Fuchs, mine and my sister's nurse, my beloved son Karl, my beloved daughters Johanna and Josepha, Archdukes and Archduchesses of Austria.) The names refer to Archduchess Maria Anna († 1744), Archduke Karl († 1761), Archduchess Johanna Gabriela († 1762), Archduchess Maria Josepha († 1767) and the wife of the Grand Comptroller, Countess Fuchs († 1754).

164 THE ENCOUNTER OF POPE LEO THE GREAT WITH ATTILA, KING OF THE HUNS

Ercole Ferrata (Pellio Inferiore 1610—1686 Rome)
After Alessandro Algardi (Bologna 1598—1654 Rome)
Bronze, fire-gilt; frame: bronze, copper, silver; 98 cms high, 59.5 cms wide (Inv. No. D 164)

This relief illustrates the legend according to which Pope Leo the Great came to meet Attila, King of the Huns, when the latter was invading Italy, to try to persuade him to turn back. At this encounter, the two Princes of the Apostles, Peter and Paul, are supposed to have appeared to Attila, hovering in the clouds and hurrying with drawn swords to the aid of the Church in her hour of need. Deeply perturbed by this, Attila is said to have withdrawn from Italy. Alessandro Algardi illustrated this theme in a colossal marble relief, made between 1646 and 1653 for St. Peter's in Rome, a work which established his international reputation. Shortly afterwards, his pupil Ercole Ferrata made a smaller version in terracotta, which was cast as a silver relief and presented to the Spanish king in 1657. The bronze relief in the Treasury seems to have been cast from the same model.   M. L.-J.

Ref.: J. Montagu 1985, I, pp. 135—145, and II, pp. 358—364, Cat. No. 61 (D.1.C.2.)

165 TABERNACLE WITH AN OSTENSORY FOR A PARTICLE OF THE CROSS

Giovanni Giardini da Forlì (Forlì 1646—1721 Rome) and Pietro Paolo Gelpi (Degasco 1664—1751 Rome)
Rome, 1711
Porphyry, gilded bronze, silver-gilt, rock crystal, diamonds, 1 ruby, pastes (glass); signed on the right of the bronze base: GIOVANNI GIARDINI DA FORLÌ FEC: ET INV: ROMAE; 122 cms high, 74 cms wide, 27 cms deep (Inv. No. D 77)

This porphyry tabernacle with ornamental elements of gilded bronze displays in its niche an ostensory containing a particle of the True Cross, flanked by two angels in poses of adoration. The silver-gilt ostensory takes the form of a trophy and is surmounted by a rock crystal crucifix surrounded by an aureole. The heads of the nails are represented by diamonds. With the exception of one diamond and one ruby in older settings dating back to c. 1600, all the other stones are glass pastes. They appear to be replacements for an originally rich covering of precious gems. The piece was a gift from

Pope Clemens XI to King Karl III of Spain, later Emperor Karl VI. It was ceremonially presented to him together with a papal brief by Cardinal Imperiali on 8. 11. 1711 in Milan, where the monarch had interrupted his journey while travelling from Barcelona to his coronation in Germany. On 21. 10. 1711, Giardini received 2,400 scudi for this commission. The rock crystal crucifix used in the ostensory had presumably been executed at an earlier date by Gelpi, as he had already been paid for similar diamond set crosses of rock crystal on 28. 8. 1709. According to an entry in the inventory of the Ecclesiastical Treasury from 1758, the tabernacle had been deposited in the Treasury on 13. 3. 1712.   M. L.-J.

Inventory of 1758 — Case II, No. 1

Ref.: G. Chiapponi 1712; A. Weixlgärtner 1929, p. 64, no. 203 (description incorrect); L. von Pastor, XV, 1930, p. 68; C. G. Bulgari 1958, p. 504 and 529; A. Lipinsky 1971, pp. 18—34; H. Honour 1971, p. 117.

166 MEISSEN ALTAR SET OF THE EMPRESS WILHELMINA AMALIA

Johann Joachim Kaendler (Fischbach near Dresden 1706—1775 Meissen) and his workshop
Meissen, c. 1737/1741
Meissen porcelain, parcel-gilt, muffle paints; candle spike and mounts on the standing cross: bronze-gilt

a) Standing cross
   86.3 cms high (Inv. No. 7078)
b) Six altar candlesticks (Meissen marks)
   54.1, 54.3, 54.4, 54.5, 54.5 and 55.3 cms high (Inv. No. 7079—7084)
c) St. John
   The left hand, and the quill originally held in the left hand, are missing.
   46.6 cms high (Inv. No. 7086)
d) St. Matthew
   47.2 cms high (Inv. No. 7087)
e) St. Andrew
   47.4 cms high (Inv. No. 7090)
f) St. Simon (Meissen marks)
   46.7 cms high (Inv. No. 7091)
g) St. Bartholomew
   47.1 cms high (Inv. No. 7093)
h) St. Philip
   45.8 cms high (Inv. No. 7094)
i) St. James the Less
   46.2 cms high (Inv. No. 7095)
j) St. Thomas
   46.8 cms high (Inv. No. 7096)
k) Three canon panels
   36, 19.2, 19.1 cms high, 28, 23 and 23 cms wide (Inv. No. 7098—7100)
l) Chalice foot and bowl setting. The silver-gilt bowl has been lost.
   22.4 cms high (Inv. No. 7097 and 7102)
m) Bell
   16.5 cms high (Inv. No. 7101)
n) Aspergillum (without arms)
   29 cms long (Inv. No. 7107)

August III (1696—1763), King of Poland and (as Friedrich August II) Prince Elector of Saxony, married the Archduchess Maria Josepha, the daughter of Emperor Joseph, in 1719. In 1737 the king gave his mother-in-law, the widowed Empress Amalia (1673—1742) an expensive present: namely, this altar set, which he com-

missioned from the Meissen porcelain manufacturer's. It originally included twelve statuettes of the apostles, made by Johann Joachim Kaendler, the most important modeller at Meissen porcelain manufactory, after the monumental series of apostles in the Church of S. Giovanni in Laterano in Rome. Eight of the original figures have survived. Of the other pieces in the set, some were transferred to other collections, such as the aspersorium (Meissen porcelain Collection, Lustheim Palace, Munich), the salver with the cruets for mass (Württembergisches Landesmuseum, Stuttgart), the lavabo ewer and basin (Historisches Museum, Bern). Only the salver for the bell, and the bowl of the chalice (silver-gilt) have been lost.

Replacements for some pieces which were damaged (the aspergillum [?], four apostles which are not exhibited, doubles of existing figures) had probably already been ordered from Meißen around the middle of the 18th century.

In the 19th century copies were finally made to replace the missing pieces (Herend?, not exhibited).

After the set for the Empress, King August III commissioned a smaller set (only two apostles) in 1736, as a present for Cardinal Annibale Albani, and this has also survived (Urbino, Duomo, Museo Diocesano Albani).

Both sets exhibit gold ornamentation, although that of the Empress is far more luxuriously decorated and also bears her arms — the many-quartered arms of the Alliance Habsburg-Braunschweig-Lüneberg — in brilliant colours. It was a bold innovation to manufacture an altar set from porcelain; however, since the material was quite inappropriate for such a purpose, the present was certainly intended as a cabinet piece. Nevertheless, Kaendler's High Baroque draped figures constitute one of the most significant achievements in the history of porcelain.

In her testament of 18. 6. 1742, the

widowed Empress left the altar set to another Emperor's widow, the Empress Elisabeth Christine (1691—1750), widow of Emperor Karl VI, from whose estate it was presented to the Ecclesiastical Treasury. The set is already listed in the inventory of 1758.

Inventory of 1758 — Case IX, no. 3 f.

Ref.: R. Rückert, Neue Funde zur Wiener Altargarnitur, in: Keramos no. 50 (1970), pp. 122—129; T. H. Clarke: Die »Römische Bestellung«. Die Meißener Altar-Garnitur, die August III. dem Kardinal Annibale Albani im Jahre 1736 schenkte, in: Keramos no. 86 (1979), pp. 3—52.

167 SILVER FRAME WITH A PAINTING OF ST. ANTHONY OF PADUA

Frame: Joseph Moser (Brünn 1715—1801 Vienna)
Vienna, 1747
Painting: circle of Franciabigio
Florence (?), beginning of the 16th century
Silver on wooden foundation; maker's mark IM, Viennese hallmark for 1747; painting: oil on wood; 100 cms high, 102 cms wide (Inv. No. D 166)

This impressive silver frame is based on a clearly-defined architectural structure. A smooth socle projecting on both sides supports the frame of the painting. To each side volutes reach forward, spilling over the edge of the socle below and supporting the massive segmented pediment above. Mounted leafwork, rocailles and ringed lattice ornamentation enrich the composition without dominating the underlying architectonic framework. The half-length portrait of St. Anthony, a central Italian painting from the early 16th century (circle of Franciabigio), has been adapted to fit the silver frame. The crucifix, which intrudes into the composition, was also added at this time. The saint's head was formerly adorned with a diamond diadem and his breast with a gold heart. These two votive gifts were not removed until 1956, when they were put into storage. Joseph Moser was commissioned to make the silver frame in 1747 for the chapel at the Hofburg.

Ref.: Wild 1982, p. 151 f., no. 31.

trian Netherlands. The sculptor also had connections with the court at Vienna. The statues of St. Francis of Assisi and St. Theresa of Ávila, the patron saints of the Empress and her husband, were commissioned by the Empress. St. Francis of Assisi is seated in meditation on a rock. The type of this figure, and the lively contrapposto it displays, reveal that Delvaux had studied the work of the great sculptor of the Roman Baroque, Gianlorenzo Bernini. On 31. 3. 1766, in gratitude for the exquisite figures, the artist received a medallion and chain from Maria Theresia.

Ref.: G. Willame, Laurent Delvaux, Brussels-Paris 1914, p. 73, nos. 183, 184.

168 ST. FRANCIS OF ASSISI
Laurent Delvaux (Ghent ? 1696—1778 Nivelles)
Nivelles, 1765
Carrara marble; signed; 50.5 cms high
(Inv. No. D 93)

This statue bears the signature L. DELVAUX S(VAE) C(AESAREAE) M(AIESTATIS) SCVLPTOR FECIT. Laurent Delvaux was court sculptor to Empress Maria Theresia's brother-in-law, Duke Karl Alexander of Lorraine, who was Stattholder of the Aus-

169 ST. TERESA OF ÁVILA
Laurent Delvaux (Ghent ? 1696—1778 Nivelles)
Nivelles, 1765
Carrara marble; signed; 50.5 cms high
(Inv. No. D 94)

This companion piece to the figure of St. Francis of Assisi (Cat. No. 168) represents St. Teresa of Ávila. She pauses in her reading, as if inspired by a vision. Delvaux gave the saint the features of the Empress Maria Theresia. This figure, too, is signed : L. DEL-

VAUX S(VUAE) C(AESAREAE) M
(AIESTATIS) SCVLPTOR FECIT.

Ref.: Willame, cf. Cat. No. 168.

170 MONSTRANCE
Zacharias Friedrich Würth (active in
Vienna, c. 1740—1760)
Vienna, 1760
Silver-gilt, partially enamelled, dia-
monds, precious stones, semi-precious
stones, pearls; maker's mark ZW,
Vienna hallmark for 1760; 71.5 cms
high (Inv. No. B 30)

In the centre of the vertical axis of this
monstrance appears the Trinity. In the
zenith of the aureole sits God the
Father enthroned, holding the globe;
below him hovers the dove of the Holy
Spirit, and in the ostensorium Christ
would be present in the form of the
Host. Also symbolic of Christ, and his
sacrificial death on the cross, is the
lamb at the bottom of the aureole. All
the gold work has been overlaid with

the rocaille and voluted arches so typical of the Rococo. The ostensorium is
surrounded by a smaller, inner aureole,
densely set with diamonds, precious
stones, pearls and other ornamentation. On the outside it is enclosed by
monumental voluted arches, and behind these radiates the larger, outer
aureole. Vine leaves and grapes made
of pearls are attached to this as symbols of the Eucharist on the sides and
also rise up on either side of God the
Father. The Viennese goldsmith Friedrich Zacharias Würth has based this
richly decorated monstrance on a successful archetype occuring in southern
German goldmiths' work from around
the middle of the 18th century, of
which several examples still exist
(Church of Maria Plain, Salzburg).
The monstrance comes from the Ursu-
line convent in Vienna.

171 PACIFICALE: CHRIST AS
RULER OF THE UNIVERSE
Johann Baptist Känischbauer von Ho-
henried (Angern 1668—1739 Vienna)
Vienna, 1726
Gold, partially enamelled, rock crys-
tal, rubies, pearls, pastes (glass), silver-
gilt; signed, dated; 25.3 cms high (Inv.
No. D 39)

In 1711, Emperor Karl VI received a
particle of the Cross set with brilliants
as a gift from Pope Clemens IX, and
commissioned a gold pacificale for it
from his court jeweller, Johann Baptist
Känischbauer von Hohenried. In the
form of a triumphal monument, the
piece is intended to evoke the Redemption of the world through Christ's
death on the cross, which simultaneously established his dominion over the
world. The four symbols of the Evangelists provide the basis of the composition, above which, floating on a
cloud, is a globe of rock crystal surrounded by a laurel wreath and the inscription: NASCENDO TULIT, MO-
RIENDO RELIQUIT (he received it at
birth, and relinquished it at death). In-

Inventory of 1758 — Case I, No. 47

Ref.: M. Dreger, Zu Känischbauer und der Ba-
rockplastik in Österreich, in: Kunst und Kunsthandwerk XVIII (1915), pp. 521—543.

172 CHALICE WITH THE ARMS OF THE BISHOP OF GROSS-WARDEIN, PAUL COUNT FORGACH

Vienna, 1747
Siler-gilt, enamel painting, diamonds,
precious stones, semi-precious stones;
Vienna hallmark for 1747; 29.4 cms
high (Inv. No. B 7)

On the underside of the foot of the
chalice are the arms of the Bishop of
Grosswardein, Paul Count Forgach
(Bishop 1747—1757), and an inscription: PAULUS COMES FORGACH
DE GYMES EP(ISCO)P(US) VARA-
DIENSIS CO(MI)T(A)TUS BIHARI-
EN(SIS)   SUPR(EMUS)   COMES
S(UAE)   C(AESAREAE)   R(EGIS)
MA(IES)T(A)TIS INTIMUS CON-
SILIAR(IUS) ANNO 1748. The embossed elements, precious stones and
enamels have been harmonised with
extraordinary   sensitivity   in   this
remarkable composition. The dished
foot is covered with volutes set with
diamonds, precious stones and rocaille
work. On the one hand they follow the

side the sphere is the particle of the
cross as the centre of the world. Above,
on the zenith, appears the Redeemer
bearing the banner of the resurrected,
his   hand   raised   in   benediction.
Represented by the figure of a timeless,
eternal child, he is surrounded by an
aureole of polished glass pastes (formerly diamonds) and gold. The goldsmith probably owed the conception of
this magnificent composition to the
outstanding Baroque architect Johann
Fischer von Erlach, who had already
introduced the central motif of a globe
combined with a cross in the high altar
of the pilgrimage church at Maria Zell
(1693, completed by Känischbauer in
1722). Känischbauer succeeded in re-
taining the basic monumental character of the piece through generous handling of the embossed work, thereby
creating one of the most important
achievements of Baroque goldsmiths'
art. Beneath the moveable bull symbol
is the signature: JO. KÄNISCHBAUR
/ V. HOHEN RIED / R. K. M.
KAMER / KÜNSTLER / 1726.

embossed border, and on the other frame the four cartouche-shaped enamels displaying scenes from the Old Testament. The nodus, which follows the outline of the shaft, takes the form of a capital, supporting the bowl. Although some decorative features have been taken over from the Baroque chalice, the ornamentation already displays signs of Rococo forms (cf. Cat. No. 173). The piece, which is unsigned, is one of the most exquisite examples of 18th century Viennese goldsmiths' work.

Ref.: R. S. Janke, A Rococo Chalice by an unidentified Master IW, in: The Register of the Museum of Art Lawrence III/3—4 (1965), p. 18, illus. 4; Hernmarck 1978, no. 821.

173 CHALICE

Joseph M. Hueber (active in Vienna 1760—1800)
Vienna, 1767
Silver-gilt; maker's mark IMH on the trefoil, Viennese hallmark for 1767; 30 cms high (Inv. No. B 4)

This chalice is a perfect example of Rococo art, the predominant style in the second third of the 18th century. The stand rises sharply from the curved edge of the foot, with its asymmetrical, undulating forms, into the shaft, incorporating the nodus over which the bowl seems to float, veiled in ornamentation which reaches two thirds of the way up its sides. The ornamental motifs contain striking variations based on S and C-scrolls. Veiling the structural elements of the chalice, clusters of grapes and ears of corn — as symbols of the missal sacrifice — are combined with roses and volutes. By avoiding all traces of the abundance so typical of the High Baroque, the artist has created an object of subtle refinement and apparent weightlessness, at first glance seemingly indefinable, as if were in continual transformation. This masterpiece, which was even copied in the 19th century (chalice in the Abbey at Speinshart,

executed by the Prague court jeweller Hieronymus Grohmann in 1845), was made by the Viennese goldsmith Joseph Hueber.

174 CHALICE

Joseph Moser (Brünn 1715—1801 Vienna)
Vienna, 1775
Silver-gilt, enamel, diamonds, precious stones, semi-precious stones; maker's mark IM, Vienna hallmark for 1775, 27.2 cms high (Inv. No. B 8)

This piece, by the Viennese goldsmith Joseph Moser, represents one of the most significant and original contributions to chalice design in 18th century Europe. Moser here presents his own interpretation of the traditional form of the chalice. The three-sided foot serves as the socle for a tripod, and this, in its turn, supports a censer. From the censer, which is also the nodus, rises a cloud of silver incense, and the bowl of the chalice seems to float upon this. Below the tripod is a small

Imperial crown, identifying the piece as an Imperial commission. In the middle of the sides of the foot, oval enamels display scenes from the Old Testament: Abraham and Melchisedek, the erection of the brazen serpent, Jonah and the whale. These correspond typologically to three scenes from the New Testament on the bowl: the Last supper, the erection of the Cross and the Resurrection. The decorative motifs of the chalice, which is dated 1775, no longer take the form of rocaille ornamentation but of laurel garlands. This change in the formal vocabulary indicates the emergent influence of early Neo-Classicism.

Ref.: Wild 1982, p. 214 ff., No. 75.

175 RELIQUARY BUSTS OF THE TWELVE APOSTLES, JOHN THE BAPTIST AND ST. PAUL

Joseph Moser (Brünn 1715—1801 Vienna) and workshops
Vienna, before 1758
Busts: silver/bronze gilt; socle: bronze-gilt; no marks

Silver busts:
a) St. Peter
   33 cms high (Inv. No. D 98)
b) St. Matthew
   33 cms high (Inv. No. D 101)
c) St. Paul
   32.8 cms high (Inv. No. D 121)
d) St. Andrew
   33 cms high (Inv. No. D 99)
e) St. John the Evangelist
   33 cms high (Inv. No. D 87)
f) St. Thomas
   33 cms high (Inv. No. D 1)
g) St. John the Baptist
   31 cms high (Inv. No. D 3)
h) St. Judas Thaddeus
   31 cms high (Inv. No. D 133)

Bronze busts:
i) St. Phillip
   31 cms high (Inv. No. D 86)
j) St. Simon
   32 cms high (Inv. No. D 135)
k) St. Matthew
   35 cms high (Inv. No. D 120)
l) St. James the Great
   32,5 cms high (Inv. No. D 117)
m) St. James the Less
   33 cms high (Inv. No. D 100)
n) St. Bartholomew
   33 cms high (Inv. No. D 84)

This unique set of reliquary busts was probably commissioned for the Ecclesiastical Treasury by the Empress Maria Theresia. The series of 14 busts appears for the first time in the inventory of 1758. Eight of the busts are cast silver and six cast and gilded bronze; all the socles are bronze-gilt. The division into silver and bronze busts seems arbitrary and was perhaps caused by financial considerations. As was often the case with Imperial commissions, they bear neither a maker's mark nor a hallmark. However, stylistic similarities with the works of Joseph Moser indicate that the busts were executed in the latter's workshop, and thus around the middle of the 18th century. The

uniformly ornamented socles with their delicately curving forms and framing foliate motifs are typical of the Rococo at its height. In the fronts of the socles are oval receptacles for the relics with a cartouche bearing the name of the saint underneath. The busts themselves are based on models dating from the beginning of the 18th century: Moser modelled his work on the busts of the choir stalls in the monastery church of Heiligenkreuz. Some of his busts are almost identical to those on the choirstalls, although they do not attain the same intensity of expression. For the series in the Treasury, only a comparatively small number of basic types was used for several heads, with superficial variations. Thus the busts of St. Judas Thaddeus and St. John the Baptist are based on the same model, and all six of the bronze busts derive from one single model. These six busts are not as convincing as those in silver, due to the schematic repetition of the motifs, and were perhaps executed by assistants. It is also possible that Joseph Moser ordered the models for the heads from a model-carver and that the latter came from the workshop of Giovanni Giuliani.

Inventory of 1758 — Case IV, No. 6

Ref.: Wild 1982, p. 157 ff., nos. 35—48.

176 FIVE SILVER BUSTS OF PATRON SAINTS OF THE HOUSE OF HABSBURG

Joseph Moser (Brünn 1715—1801 Vienna)
Vienna, c. 1760/1779
Busts: silver; socle: bronze-gilt

a) St. Francis Xavier
   35 cms high (Inv. No. D 85)
b) St. Anthony of Padua
   35 cms high (Inv. No. D 118)

176 d

c) St. Donatus, 1766
   34.5 cms high (Inv. No. D 20)
d) St. John of Nepomuk, 1778
   35 cms high (Inv. No. D 65)
e) St. Anne, 1779; maker's mark IM
   33.7 cms high (Inv. No. D 136)

This group of reliquary busts depicts saints who were especially venerated as the patron saints of the House of Habsburg. The busts of St. Francis Xavier and St. Anthony of Padua were probably made subsequently to the Apostle series. The bust of St. Donatus was made in 1779. The present bust of St. John of Nepomuk was made in 1778, as a replacement for a bust which had been given away as a gift. The last bust, that of St. Anne, was added in 1779. These reliquaries differ from the Apostle series in certain common features: on the one hand, the receptacles for the relics are not situated in the socle but in the busts themselves; on the other, the proportions are more slender, the smooth forms more rigid, and the lineaments more accentuated — details which, in the final analysis, are due to the stylistic developments of the period. According to the entry in the inventory, all these busts were made by Joseph Moser, although only the bust of St. Anne bears a maker's mark.

Inventory of 1758 — Case V, No. 41 (addenda)

Ref.: Wild 1982, p. 167 ff., nos. 49—53.

177 b

177 THREE RELIQUARY BUSTS OF SS. WENCESLAS, LEOPOLD AND MAXIMILIAN

Workshop of Joseph Moser (Brünn 1715—1801 Vienna)
Vienna, c. 1760/1770, 1776 and c. 1775/1780 (?)

a) St. Wenceslas
   Bust: silvered bronze; socle: bronze-gilt; 40.5 cms high (Inv. No. D 54)
b) St. Leopold
   Bust: silvered bronze; socle: bronze-gilt; 42.5 cms high (Inv. No. D 134)
c) St. Maximilian
   Bust: silver; socle: bronze-gilt; 35.5 cms high (Inv. No. D 30)

The busts of SS. Leopold and Wenceslas belonged to a portrait series of canonised and crowned heads. This set formerly included another three busts, those of the Hungarian saints Stephen, Emmerich and Ladislaus, which were handed over to Hungary in 1933 (today in the National Museum of Hungary). Since the group is listed as an addendum to the inventory of 1758, it must have been executed around 1760/70. However, in 1771 Empress Maria Theresia donated the original bust of St. Leopold to the Monastery of St. Blasien (today in the collections of the Monastery of St. Paul in the Lavant valley), and had it replaced by the busts extant today. The more schematic modelling of the heads in comparison to those of the other groups would seem to indicate that these busts were mainly executed by assistants and probably at a considerable time after the apostle series. This is also true of the bust of St. Maximilian, which was added to the apostle series at a later date (around 1775/80?).

Inventory of 1758 — Case V, Nos. 41 and 42 (addendum)
Case IX, No. 26

Ref.: Wild 1982, p. 176 ff.

178 IVORY CRUCIFIX

Gabriel Grupello (Geraardbergen/ Belgium 1644—1730 Ehrenstein near Kerkrade)
Düsseldorf, c. 1700
Ivory, pastes (glass), ebonised hardwood; 87.5 cms high, 31.5 cms wide (Inv. No. E 46)

As Christ raises his eyes plaintively to heaven, his body seems to rear up in a convulsive movement. The death agony on the cross is thus conveyed in a particularly moving way in this crucifix. The anatomy of the hanging body is depicted with numerous details, such as the plexus of veins on the upper belly, or the muscles on the breastbone. These are combined with the masterly carving of the hair, the crown of thorns and the loincloth, which enrich the figure without presupposing or pre-

tip of its loincloth, too, resembles *"the leaf of a thistle abruptly withered in the sun"* (L. L. Möller, Catalogue, Hamburg).

Inventory 1780 — Case VIII, No. 3?

judicing the success of the composition as a whole. This masterpiece is attributed to the Flemish sculptor Gabriel Gruppello (cf. Secular Treasury, Cat. No. 103), who enjoyed great esteem even in his own time. After 1695, he worked in Düsseldorf as the 'Kabinettstatuarius' of the Prince Elector Johann Wilhelm of the Palatinate. This is probably the crucifix which Gruppello presented to the future Emperor Karl VI, when the latter paid a visit to the artist's workshop while in Düsseldorf in 1703. The Museum für Kunst und Gewerbe in Hamburg is in possession of a wooden variation of this successful piece, and the

179 THE DENIAL OF PETER

Magnus Berg (Romedal in Hedemark/ Norway 1666—1739 Copenhagen)
Copenhagen, 1721 (?)
Ivory; 13.6 cms high, 26.1 cms wide
(Inv. No. D 202)

"Before the cock crow, thou shalt deny me thrice." This relief depicts the fulfillment of the prophecy made to Peter by Christ. On the left in the background, Christ is brought before the High Priest, while the soldiers outside warm themselves by the fire. On the right, Peter weeps over his betrayal, which is depicted in the centre of the relief. The "damsel that kept the door" recognises him but he denies that he has anything to do with Jesus of Nazareth. Behind him sits the cock. Berg's composition is full of references to Roman art of the High Renaissance; the seated soldiers in the foreground, for instance, are clearly based on Michelangelo's figures of youths on the ceiling of the Sistine Chapel.

Inventory of 1758 — Case I, No. 119

Ref.: Paulsen 1989, no. I/22.

179

180 ECCE HOMO

Magnus Berg (Romedal in Hedemark/
Norway 1666—1739 Copenhagen)
Copenhagen, 1721 (?)
Ivory; 13.6 cms high, 26 cms wide (Inv.
No. D 201)

Pilate presents Christ to the people
with the words: "Ecce homo!" (Behold the man!). Magnus Berg conveys
the drama of the scene by means of the
pronounced, frenzied gestures of his
figures. On the right, the cross has already been erected, on the left are
gathered the scribes and pharisees. The
artist makes no attempt to conceal the
fact that he spent the years between
1695 and 1699 in Rome, and the composition in fact borrows from Raphael's
famous fresco 'The School of Athens'
in the rooms of the Vatican. The
figures, too, are taken from Raphael's
frescoes and Michelangelo's ceiling in
the Sistine Chapel. On the other hand,
the masterful manipulation of the subject matter is quite individual and
unique, guaranteeing Berg a special
place in the history of European ivory
carving. His reliefs are carved from
thin plates which in places attain a
bluish translucency, displaying the
most exquisite details merging in an
almost painterly manner.

Inventory 1758 — Case I, No. 118

Ref.: Paulsen 1989, no. 1/21.

181 THE ENTOMBMENT OF CHRIST

Magnus Berg (Romedal in Hede-
mark/Norway 1666—1739 Copenhagen)
Copenhagen, 1710
Ivory; signed, dated; 16 cms high, 17.6
cms wide (Inv. No. 3611)

In the background loom the three
empty crosses; in the foreground, the
dead body of Christ is being carried to
the sepulchre by the disciples. The
scene is loosely based on Raphael's
'Entombment' in the Galleria Borghese in Rome. Further references to
Raphael's work — the kneeling female
figure in the lower right-hand corner is
taken from the 'Transfiguration' in the
Vatican, a work completed by Raphael's
pupils — are intended to display the
master's learning. Among the three
reliefs on display, the Entombment
represents the peak of Magnus Berg's
delicate style of carving. With the ex-

ception of a few parts of the main figures, the relief is almost completely flat and in its soft, flowing transitions approaches the quality of a painting. The artist had in fact trained as a painter before he turned to the art of ivory carving. On the back of the relief is a small piece of paper with the almost completely faded signature MAGNUS BERG INV. ET FEC. 1710. The artist was resident in Vienna in 1722/23 and — according to historical sources — sold two ivory reliefs to Emperor Karl VI. These were probably two of the four reliefs extant in the collections of the Kunsthistorische Museum.

Castle Ambras, Inventory of 1788 — Case X, No. 119

Ref.: Paulsen 1989, no. I/9

182 FRAGMENT OF A CRUCIFIXION GROUP

Matthias Steinl (Mattsee/Salzburg ? 1643/44—1727 Vienna)
Breslau (?), c.1685/1687
Ivory, ebonised hardwood; signed; 45 cms high, socle: 23 cms high (Inv. No. E 45)

These three ivory figures once surrounded a cross bearing the figure of Christ. Mary Magdalen kneels at its foot, Mary the mother of Jesus looks up at her son and John the Baptist directs the spectator's attention to the event. One further figure — like the cross, now lost — once stood behind Mary Magdalen and supported her. In the centre of the curved socle, an ivory appliqué showing the sudarium of St. Veronica, provides a reminder of the Passion.

Little of the ivory work by Matthias Steinl has survived; even though, as a sculptor and architect, he was one of the most outstanding personalities of the Austrian Baroque. This piece, which is signed STEINLE, is imposing despite its fragmentary form. It is worth bearing in mind that the height of the socle has been calculated for the missing crucifix. Steinl probably made it in Breslau, that is, before coming to Vienna in 1688 to enter the service of

Emperor Leopold I as court ivory carver with an annuity of 500 gulden. The statuettes, whose gestures express a certain measured pathos, reveal the master's familiarity with classical monumental sculpture.

The differentiation of the standing and trailing legs reinforces the accentuated contrapposto, as a result of which the drapery is wrapped around the bodies in deeply incised folds, thus creating a lively zone of light and shadow.

Inventory of 1758 — Case IV, No. 13

Ref.: L. Pühringer-Zwanowetz, Matthias Steinl, Vienna 1966, p. 62 f., p. 207 f., no. 1.

183 CHRIST AS THE MAN OF SORROWS

Paul Egell (1691—1752 Mannheim)
Mannheim, c. 1730/1735
Ivory, carved hardwood frame, 17.7 cms high, 13.7 cms wide (Inv. No. 3660)

This small ivory medallion depicts Christ as the Man of Sorrows with the crown of thorns, chain and the reed which was thrust into his hands in mockery as a sceptre. Under the robe, the body appears to have no volume, as in a portrait bust, this space being occupied instead by a head of a putto and

the reed poking loosely from the material of the robe. This prototype of Christ in agony, his eyes turned upward in a soulful gaze, derives from compositions of the Bolognese Baroque painter Guido Reni (1575—1642), which had become widely disseminated by the 18th century. In this work, Paul Egell, one of the most important and influential sculptors of the Rococo, exhausts all the possibilities of ivory carving. Heightened formal refinement and a soft surface effect intent on conveying the nuances of half-shade are combined with an exceptional sensitivity of expression. Typical of the Rococo style is the blurring of the distinction between the genres of art: the frame encroaches on the relief, while the end of the robe hangs over the edge of the frame; the reed, the chain and the individual thorns in the crown are fragile, fully elaborated sculptural forms. The piece was acquired as a "work of Albrecht Dürer" in 1825.

Ref.: P. Volk, Zwei kleinplastische Arbeiten von Paul Egell, in: PANTHEON XLI (1983/2), pp. 104—108.

184 RELIQUARY WITH A RELIC OF ST. FELIX OF CANTALICE

Joseph Moser (Brünn 1715—1801 Vienna)
Vienna, 1758
Silver; maker's mark IM, Vienna hallmark for 1758; 28.8 cms high (Inv. No. Kap. 14)

There is an entry in the codex of the Capuchin Monastery, the so-called 'Protocollum', regarding the donation of this reliquary by Maria Theresia. In folio 276, dating from 1758, is noted (in Latin!): *"The present year, like the year before, was no less dangerous on account of the pox from which Archduke Joseph and the Archduchess Maria Anna, Christina, Carolina and Maria Antonia"* (and Archduke Karl) *"became ill. (. . .) Her Majesty the Empress (. . .) let it be known that she felt herself indebted to St. Felix on account of his help in restoring the health of her children, who had become quite dangerously sick from the pox. Her Majesty the Empress commissioned Herr Moser, the goldsmith, to make a silver bust of St. Felix, complete with socle. In the centre of the latter is to be enclosed the relic of the saint, in the pedestal of the statuette the authentication. On the reverse are engraved the names of the children who were happily freed from the power of the pox: Archduke Joseph, Archduchess Maria Carolina, Archduchess Maria Antonia"* (and Archduke Karl). St. Felix of Cantalice († 1587) was widely venerated as a saint who protected against the plague.

Ref.: Wild 1982, p. 180 ff., no. 154.

mounted on the trunk describes the Holy Kinship as S. ANNAE FAMILIAE. The curving trunk of the tree and its circular, stylised crown reflect the dynamic movement of contemporary Rococo ornamentation, also displayed in the cartouche. Although the naturalistic representation of a tree was of secondary importance, the impression of organic growth is nevertheless conveyed.

Inventory of 1758 — Case V, No. 39 (addendum)

Ref.: Wild, 1982, p. 127 ff., no. 12.

185 RELIQUARY OF ST. ANNE
Joseph Moser (Brünn 1715—1801 Vienna)
Vienna, 1760
Silver; maker's mark IM, Viennese hallmark for 1760; 28.3 cms high (Inv. No. D 24)

This small, silver tree represents the family tree of the Holy Kinship, here with St. Anne at its centre, as she was the object of especial veneration in Vienna. A round receptacle with a relic of the saint forms the centre of the crown of the tree. Arranged around it are medallions with the names of *Joachim, Joseph, Zacharias, Joannes Bapt., Elisabeth* and *Maria,* and, as the crowning element, the name of JESUS surrounded by an aureole. A cartouche

186 FOUR SETS OF CRUETS WITH SALVERS

Cruets are the containers which hold, on the one hand, the wine required for the Eucharist, on the other, the water to be admixed with the wine. The cruets are distinguished from each other in various ways. The lid hinges of inventory numbers H 2, C 29 and C 300 are soldered with the initials V(inum) for wine and A(qua) for water, while Inv. No. H 6 has grapes on the knob of the lid of one cruet (to indicate wine) and a fish on that of the other (to indicate water). Furthermore, the water cruet was used by the priest during Mass for the ritual hand-washing. During the first hand-washing, before the consecration, the water is collected in the salver; during the second hand-washing, however, it is collected in the chalice. Cruets were either made together with the chalice and decorated to match it, or else as a separate set. These sets were made in the first half of the 18th century, two of them in Vienna and two in Augsburg. Simply intended as functional objects, they were either decorated solely with strapwork or else left unadorned.

a) Johann David Saler (Augsburg 1665—1724 Augsburg)
   Augsburg, c. 1708/1710
   Silver, parcel-gilt; maker's mark IDS, Augsburg hallmark; 12 cms high; salver: 27.2 cms long, 21.9 cms wide (Inv. No. H 2)
   Ref.: Seling 1980, Vol. III, p. 277, no. 1877 b.

b) Franz Ignaz Berchtold (Augsburg, c. 1670/80—1762 Augsburg)
Augsburg, c. 1712/1715
Silver; maker's mark IFB, Augsburg hallmark; 13.5 cms high; salver: 30 cms long, 24.1 cms wide (Inv. No. C 300)

c) Andreas Joseph Rath (active in Vienna, 1710—1762, court goldsmith)
Vienna, 1737
Silver-gilt; maker's mark AIR, Vienna hallmark for 1737; 14 and 13.5 cms high; salver: 34 cms long, 23.5 cms wide (Inv. No. C 29)

189, 187, 188

186 d

d) Fabian Sebastian Feywary (active in Vienna, 1740—1766)
Vienna, 1747
Silver; maker's mark FSF, Vienna hallmark for 1747; 14.3 cms high; salver: 27 cms long, 17.4 cms wide (Inv. No. H 6)

The two cruets of Inv. No. H 6 originally formed part of what was once the field chapel of the Imperial-Royal Infantry Regiment No. 31. The regiment was founded by the Hungarian estates in 1741 and received the field chapel as a donation from its first commander, Count Samuel Haller von Hallerstein, in 1747. Both the cruets bear the arms of Count Haller von Hallerstein, which are those of the Hungarian line of this Nuremberg patrician family. The set was later placed at the disposal of Field-Marshal Count Josef Radetzky (1766—1858), and they were used to administer the last rites to him in 1858, in Milan. The field chapel was acquired for the Ecclesiastical Treasury by Emperor Franz Joseph I in 1886, on account of its historical significance.

187 RELIQUARY FRAME WITH A RELIC OF ST. DONATUS
Joseph Moser (Brünn 1715—1801 Vienna)
Vienna, c. 1760
Silver, parcel-gilt; 24 cms high (Inv. No. D 42)

The oval capsule of this upright frame contains a relic of St. Donatus, as is indicated by both the inscription S: DONATI M: on the cartouche, and the bolts of lightning, an attribute of the saint, which are attached to it. The composition of the frame follows works which are with certainty by Moser, such as Cat. No. 188. Here, however, the front is formed by crossed palm branches and crowned by a laurel wreath.

Ref.: Wild, 1982, p. 147, no. 26.

188 FOUR RELIQUARY FRAMES
Joseph Moser (Brünn 1715—1801 Vienna)
Vienna, 1759
Silver; parchment miniatures, gold embroidery; maker's mark IM, Vienna hallmark for 1759; 37 cms high (Inv. No. Kap. 17, 18, 19, 20)

The relics of the various saints, designated by banderoles, have been placed under the window-openings of the silver frames. On three sides of each of the principal relics are three smaller relics (two in the case of Inv. No. Kap. 17), and above each is a half-length picture of the respective saint painted on parchment. The pictures depict the saints Vincent, Laurence, Thomas of Canterbury and Peter of Verona. On the backs of all the frames, which take the form of cartouches and have voluted feet, are stands which serve as handles. The decoration, composed of rocaille work, C-shaped curves and a fan of leaves, is in Rococo style. As is typical for the work of Joseph Moser, the symmetrical arrangement of the decoration does not detract from the clarity of the basic form. The frames were made for the Imperial treasury in the Capuchin Monastery.

Ref.: Wild 1982, p. 148 ff., no. 27—30.

189 TWO RELIQUARY FRAMES
Monogrammist IS (Court silversmith Joseph Schneider ?)
Vienna, 1780
Silver, gold embroidery, pearls; maker's mark IS, Viennese hallmark for 1780; 34 cms high, 21 cms wide (Inv. No. Kap. 23, 24)

The niches of the two frames contain relics of St. Stephen and St. Martin respectively. The artistic composition of the receptacle is modelled on the reliquary frames executed by Joseph Moser (cf. Cat. No. 188). The latter's formal vocabulary is retained, only the proportions being reversed and a number of small motifs replaced. The goldsmith cannot be identified with certainty due to the ambiguousness of the mark; it could perhaps have been the court silversmith, Joseph Schneider.

190 STANDING CROSS
Johann Baptist Hagenauer (Strass/ Upper Bavaria 1732—1810 Vienna)
Salzburg, 1759
Lead, marble, wood; signed, dated; 71 cms high, 20 cms wide; corpus: 22 cms high (Inv. No. E 50)

The subtly matching grey tones of the various materials lend an elegant note to this standing cross. The forms of the grey marble socle, which arise from the counter-movement of the curves, display the same High Baroque design as the lead corpus. On the cross, Christ twists in painful contrapposto. Although the figure conveys a powerfully expressive desire for articulation, the clarity of the form is nonetheless preserved — a combination which only became current some decades later, with Neo-Classicism. This superbly modelled early work of Hagenauer's was made in Salzburg in 1759 and transferred to the Treasury from the private chapel of the Salzburg Residenz in 1910. It bears the signature I. HAGENAUER INV(ENIT) ET FEC(IT) 1759. As director of the sculpture class at the Vienna Academy, the master later made some of the figures for the park of Schönbrunn Palace.

191 MONSTRANCE
Joseph Moser (Brünn 1705—1801 Vienna)
Vienna, 1746
Silver-gilt, pearls, translucent enamel; maker's mark CIT, Viennese hallmark for 1746; 56 cms high (Inv. No. B 18)

The small wooden cross in the centre of this ostensorium is supposed to be a particle of the cross of Christ. A broad frame of rocaille decoration and flowers surrounds the relic, combining with the aureole to complete the lozenge shape of the cross. The nodus and the foot are similarly covered with rocaille decoration. Made in the mid-18th century, this piece of gold work is typical of the Rococo style at its height.

This monstrance bears the maker's mark belonging to Conrad Joseph Thomsin († 1742), but was in fact made after his death. Thomsin's workshop had been taken over by the goldsmith Joseph Moser, who married Thomsin's widow in 1745. However, Moser was only permitted his own maker's mark from 21. 6. 1746 and was thus still using the mark of the former owner of the workshop when he finished this piece. A monstrance signed by Moser in the provostry church at Staatz (Lower Austria) closely resembles the Treasury monstrance. The extended aureole is decorated with restrained overlying ornamentation. Green-enamelled vine leaves with grapes of pearls rise from the stem and frame the receptacle for the Host. The crowning element is a baldachin with outspread wings on either side.

Ref.: Wild 1982, p. 103 f., no. 2.

192 RELIQUARY OSTENSORIUM
Vienna (?), c. 1750/1760
Bronze-gilt; 31.5 cms high (Inv. No. Kap. 57)

193 OSTENSORY
Vienna (?), c. 1770/1780
Silver-gilt; 29 cms high (Inv. No. D 47)

This ostensory is supposed to contain a particle of the true cross. The receptacle for the relic is inserted into a cartouche with a frame in the form of a crown. The cartouche is enclosed above by two sprigs of laurel tied together, and below by upright palm branches. This is backed by a silver-gilt aureole. Comparison with the ostensory Cat. No. 192, which was made some years earlier, reveals a change in the conception of the receptacle. The clear contours and the predominant ornamental motifs follow early Neo-Classicistic ideas, Rococo ornamentation

At the front, through an opening in the upright beam, can be seen a piece of wood supposed to derive from the cross of Christ. The reliquary cross itself is made of gold, the foot of gilded silver. To judge from the accompanying authentication, this piece of early Neo-Classicistic goldsmiths' work may well have been made in Vienna in 1777.

195 RELIQUARY WITH A TOOTH OF ST. PETER

Rome, 1st half of the 19th century
Silver, parcel-gilt, bronze, lapis lazuli, diamonds, precious stones, semi-precious stones; 78.5 cms high (Inv. No. D 45)

On 19. 2. 1853, Emperor Franz Joseph I narrowly escaped an assassination attempt. In thanksgiving for the Emperor's life having been saved, a new church (the Votivkirche) was built and consecrated in Vienna in 1856. To mark the Emperor's happy escape, Pope Pius IX (1846—1878) sent this precious reliquary, which was presented to Emperor Franz Joseph I by a papal nuncio in Vienna on 17. 3. 1853. It contains within an aureole a molar which had been taken from the tomb of St. Peter in St. Peter's in Rome. The relic has been inserted into a diamond flower in such a way that the roots of the tooth form the petals of the flower. The receptacle for the relic is surrounded by three angels and the attributes of St. Peter. The form of the reliquary takes up the motif from the famous altar ciborium erected by Gianlorenzo Bernini above the high altar of St. Peter's, between the columns of which can be seen the aureole, surrounded by hovering angels, in the main apse. Roman goldsmiths' art of the 19th century produced a series of reliquaries which reflect this architectonic model even more clearly, for instance the so-called 'ostensorio Berniniano' in the Treasury of St. Peter's. As the reliquary was presented to the Emperor only one month after the assassination attempt, it must have already been in papal pos-

having been relegated to a merely subordinate role.

194 PACIFICALE

Vienna (?), 1777
Gold, silver-gilt; 21.6 cms high (Inv. No. D 102)

In the centre of this cross, the arms of which have trefoil ends, is a seal authenticating the relic preserved inside.

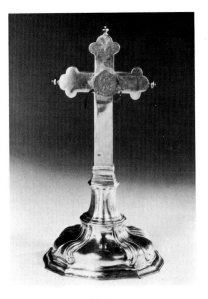

session. The piece, which is unsigned, was probably executed in the first half of the 19th century.

196 PICTORIAL RELIQUARY WITH A RELIC OF ST. FRANCIS OF PAOLA

Pietro de Rossi (St. Petersburg 1761—1831 St. Petersburg)
Rome, 1794
Watercolours, bronze, silver; signed; 27.5 cms high, 14.4 cms wide (Inv. No. D 132)

St. Francis of Paola (1416—1507) is seen summoning John Colomy, the military commander of King Ferdinand I of Naples and Sicily, to do battle against the Turks, promising him victory. On the pedestal beneath the feet of the saint is the signature of the artist who painted this watercolour, the miniaturist Pietro de Rossi: PET(RU)S DE RUBEIS INV(ENIT) ET FECIT ROM(AE) 1794. The Neo-Classicistic bronze frame with silver facings is surmounted by a medallion containing a relic of the saint's garment. The arms

of the secundogeniture of the House of Habsburg-Lorraine are attached to the lower moulding of the frame as the arms of Emperor Franz II. According to an inscription panel in Latin on the reverse, Emperor Franz II received the picture as a gift from Cesare Brancadoro, the Archbishop of Nisibis (Anatolia) and apostolic legate in Belgium, with the wish that the Emperor might triumph over his enemies, just as King Ferdinand I, aided by the intercession of St. Franz of Paola, had triumphed over his. Emperor Franz II presented the picture to the Ecclesiastical Treasury in 1805.

197 RELIQUARY WITH A RELIC OF ST. FRANCIS OF ASSISI

Pietro de Rossi (St. Petersburg 1761—1831 St. Petersburg)
Rome, 1793
Silver, bronze-gilt, green marble, porphyry, miniature on ivory; signed; 29.5 cms high (Inv. No. D 73)

With its emphatically cubic forms and

restrained decorational motives, this reliquary conforms to a type of monument widespread in the age of Neo-Classicism. On a porphyry base rests a socle of green marble, the front of which bears a receptacle containing a piece of the thorn belt (cilicium) of St. Francis of Assisi (1182—1226). The bronze-gilt superstructure frames an ivory miniature with a half-length depiction of the saint. It is signed DE ROSSI FEC(IT) and was most likely executed at the same time as its companion piece, which bears the date 1793. Emperor Franz I presented the reliquary to the Ecclesiastical Treasury in 1826 as a gift.

198 RELIQUARY WITH A RELIC OF ST. TERESA OF ÁVILA

Pietro de Rossi (St. Petersburg 1761—1831 St. Petersburg)
Rome, 1793
Silver, bronze-gilt, green marble, porphyry, miniature on ivory; signed, dated; 29.5 cms high (Inv. No. D 74)

The companion piece to Cat. No. 197, this reliquary was donated to the Ecclesiastical Treasury by the second wife of Emperor Franz I, the Empress Maria Theresia (of Sicily), as early as 1795. It contains a relic of St. Theresa of Ávila (1515—1582). The miniature on ivory, showing a half-length representation of the saint, is signed P. DE ROSSIS F(ECIT) 1793.

199 RELIQUARY WITH A RELIC OF ST. CLEMENS MARIA HOFBAUER

Vienna, beginning of the 20th century (before 1909)
Silver, parcel-gilt, pastes (glass); 20 cms high, 15.5 cms wide (Inv. No. D 228)

Clemens Maria Hofbauer (1751—1820) was canonised on 20. 5. 1909 and declared patron saint of Vienna in 1914. Active as pastor and preacher, the Redemptorist priest became the focus of Catholic reform in Vienna. He received permission to establish his order in Austria from Emperor Franz I and the transferral of the church of Maria am Gestade in Vienna to this order. To mark his canonisation, Emperor Franz Joseph I was presented with this silver reliquary containing a relic of the saint. It is covered with symmetrical floral and foliate motifs,

set into which is a relief bust of St. Clemens Maria Hofbauer above the custodia; the arms of the Redemptorist order are displayed on the foot. The reliquary was probably made in Vienna in or shortly before 1909.

The chalice bears the maker's mark of the Roman goldsmith Giovanni Felice Sanini, as well as an unidentified Roman hallmark.

200 CHALICE
Giovanni Felice Sanini (Lucca 1727—1787 Rome)
Rome, c. 1770/1787
Silver-gilt; maker's mark G. F. Sanini, Roman hallmark; 33 cms high (Inv. No. B 16)

The underside of the foot of this chalice bears the arms of the primogeniture of the House of Habsburg-Lorraine, crowned by an archducal coronet. One quarter shows the arms of Tuscany. These were borne by both Emperor Leopold II or his son Emperor Franz II. The chalice was presumably a gift received by one of these two archdukes, possibly by Archduke Leopold during his sojourn in Rome in 1769. The richly decorated piece already shows signs of early Neo-Classicism. At that time, antiquity had again become the dominating influence, and classical vessel-forms and decorative motifs were being adopted once more.

201 CHALICE WITH THE ARMS OF EMPEROR FERDINAND I OF AUSTRIA
Heinrich Kern (active in Vienna, 1st half of the 19th century)
Vienna, 1840
Silver-gilt; maker's mark Heinrich Kern, Viennese hallmark for 1840; 28.4 cms high (Inv. No. B 24)

With its clear, sober composition, this chalice is a representative example of the style of the early 19th century. The steep foot seems to merge into the baluster-like nodus, separated from it only by a wide enclosing ring. The circular foot is squared off with straight edges, from which the smooth fluting rises to the edge of the nodus. Above the narrow shaft-ring is a cylindrical bowl. The chalice was made by Heinrich Kern in 1840 for Emperor Ferdinand I of Austria.

202 CENSER AND INCENSE BOAT
Heinrich Kern (working in Vienna, 1st half of the 19th century)
Vienna, 1824
Silver, maker's mark Heinrich Kern,

Vienna hallmark for 1824; 34 cms high (censer) and 22.5 cms high (incense boat) (Inv. No. C 35)

The use of incense — resinous seeds, which give off scented smoke when burnt — can be traced back as far as early Christian times.
In this way, the experience of the ceremony of the missal sacrifice was heightened by an additional sensual dimension. The censer consists of a basin for the coals with three chains fastened to it and an ajouré lid which is lifted by another chain. The name given to the receptacle in which the incense was kept derives from its shape, which resembles that of a small boat (Lat. *navicula*). Nevertheless, in this set, the 'boat' is a variation on an oil lamp, with the knob on the lid taking the form of a flame. Both of the vessels are in Neo-Classicistic style and are characterised by their clear, elegant lines, arranged in sparingly used decoration and adopting ornamental forms typical of antiquity, such as the acanthus leaf. These silver pieces were executed by the Viennese goldsmith Heinrich Kern in 1824.

hallmark for 1835; 12.5 cms high; salver: 25.8 cms long, 16.5 cms wide (Inv. No. C 200)

These two cruets for mass were modelled on the forms of ancient jugs. Their functions are distinguished by their differing ornamentation. The belly of the wine cruet is decorated with vine leaves and grapes, the handle consisting of a vine stem crowned with an angel's head. The water cruet displays fish and sea-shells with a handle in the shape of a sea-snake, also crowned with an angel's head. The cruets and the decagonal salver bear the signature I. Kern, which probably stands for the goldsmith Heinrich Kern.

203 TWO CRUETS WITH SALVER
Heinrich Kern (?) (active in Vienna, 1st half of the 19th century)
Vienna, 1835
Silver; signed *I. Kern,* Viennese

204 RELIQUARY CROSS
Pietro Paolo Spagna (Rome 1793—1861 Rome)
Rome, 1817—1823
Steel, bronze, wood, silver-gilt; maker's mark PPSI, Roman hallmark (on the casket); 48 cms high; socle: 29.6 cms long, 18 cms wide (Inv. No. E 11)

This reliquary was a present from Pope Pius VII (1800—1823) to Emperor Franz I of Austria. The cross bearing the dead saviour rises from the base of a column enwreathed by a serpent.

Wingless angels kneel on either side of the cross, with the implements of the Passion in front of them. The socle, which is in the form of a classical sarcophagus, contains a silver and gilt casket enclosing a particle of the cross and relics of St. Peter and St. Paul. On the outer walls of the sarcophagus are reliefs: on the front the resurrection of Christ, on the back the burial, and on the ends a lamenting woman and an angel respectively. In this representation, Christianity triumphs over a declining ancient world. The cross of Christ rising above the ruined column, which is enwreathed by the serpent, can be understood as a symbol of antiquity. While the cross is in Neo-Classicistic style, the Roman goldsmith Pietro Paolo Spagna also makes use of traditional motifs from antiquity, although for the execution he uses the modern material, steel, which corresponds better to his own formal conception. His maker's mark is, however, only to be found on the reliquary casket. The origin of the piece can be dated between 1817, when Spagna was awarded the title of master, and 1823, the year in which Pope Pius VII died. This master also collaborated on the Golden Rose (Secular Treasury, Cat. No. 136).

205 THREE ROSARIES

a) Rosary belonging to Empress Carolina Augusta
   Rome, c. 1816/1823
   Emerald, lapis lazuli, gold, gold enamel; 66 cms long (Inv. No. D 221)

This rosary was a gift from Pope Pius VII (1800—1823) to Empress Carolina Augusta, who became the fourth wife of Emperor Franz I in 1816. The beads are spheres of lapis lazuli mounted in gold settings. Suspended from the lower end is a small ajouré gold enamel frame containing a remarkable oval emerald cameo of the Mother of God. The lapidary work was probably executed in Rome between 1816 and 1823.

b) Rosary
   Rome, 1st quarter of the 19th century
   Lapis lazuli, agate, gold, gold enamel; 40 cms long (Inv. No. D 9)

Ending in a ring like a decade, this rosary divides into two after the fifth bead. The beads are made of lapis lazuli, with a translucent agate cameo (depicting an angel appearing to St. Francis in a dream) as the pendant. The piece probably came from the same workshop as Cat. No. 205a).

c) Rosary
   Rome, 1st quarter of the 19th century
   Heliotrope, gold; 58.5 cms long (Inv. No. D 10)

The beads and pendant of this rosary are made of heliotrope and mounted in gold settings. On the front of the medallion is an intaglio of the Mother of God; the reverse depicts the Baptism of Christ.

206 EPISCOPAL CROSSES AND RINGS

Vienna, last quarter of the 19th century

a) Pectoral cross with chain
   Amethysts, brilliants, gold; maker's mark FF (indistinct), gold hallmark; 13.5 cms high, 7.5 cms wide (Inv. No. C 304)

b) Pectoral cross
   Amethysts, gold; gold hallmark; 10.5 cms high, 6 cms wide (Inv. No. C 317)

c) Pectoral cross with chain
   Burnt amethysts, brilliants, gold; no maker's mark or gold hallmark; 16.3 cms high, 9.4 cms (Inv. No. C 303)

d) Episcopal ring (court jeweller Josef Matzenauer)
   Amethyst, brilliants, gold (Inv. No. C 318)

e) Episcopal ring (court jeweller Vincenz Mayer & Sons), 1891
   Topaz, brilliants, gold; gold hallmark (Inv. No. C 320)

f) Bishop's ring
   Burnt amethyst, brilliants, gold (Inv. No. C 308)

These episcopal crosses and rings are from the estate of Dr. Laurence Mayer, Court Bishop 1876—1912, who donated them to the Ecclesiastical Treasury. The Bishop received some of these pieces of pontifical jewellery from the Imperial family, as a gift for his ecclesiastical officiation at family ceremonies such as baptisms and marriages.

THE MOST IMPORTANT INVENTORIES OF THE VIENNA TREASURY

Inventory 1626 Stefan Krenn, Der ehemals im Wr. Kapuzinerkloster deponierte kaiserliche Schatz und seine Inventare von 1626 und 1752, in: Jahrbuch der kunsthistorischen Sammlungen in Wien, vol. 83, 1987.

Inventory 1731 Inventar der kaiserlichen geheimen kleinen Schatzkammer von 1731, herausgegeben von Heinrich Zimmermann in: Jahrbuch der kunsthistorischen Sammlungen des a.h. Kaiserhauses, vol. 10, 1889, Reg. Nr. 6241, pp. 202—243.

Inventory 1750 Inventar der kaiserlichen Weltlichen Schatzkammer von 1750, edited and published as above, Reg. Nr. 6253, pp. 251—324.

Inventory 1752 see Inventory 1626

Inventory 1758 Inventar der k. k. Geistlichen Schatzkammer vom 23. 2. 1758, herausgeben von Heinrich Zimmermann in: Jahrbuch der kunsthistorischen Sammlungen des a.h. Kaiserhauses, vol. 16/2, 1895, Reg. Nr. 12623, pp. 6—28.

Inventory 1773 Inventar über die k. k. Schatzkammer, edited and published as above, Reg. Nr. 12641, pp. 34—49.

Inventory 1780 Inventar der Geistlichen Schatzkammer nach ihrer Neuorganisation, vom 3. 4. 1780, edited and published as above, Reg. Nr. 12648, pp. 50—56.

TREASURY CATALOGUES

Die k. k. geistliche Schatzkammer. Für Besucher derselben beschrieben von Ferdinand Zenner, Vienna 1856; 1869.

Übersicht der Sammlungen der k. k. Schatzkammer, Vienna 1869.

Übersicht der Sammlungen der Schatzkammer des österreichischen Kaiserhauses in der k. k. Hofburg in Vienna, 1870 bis 1873.

Catalogue des Collections du Trésor de la Maison impériale et royale d'Autriche, par Quirin de Leitner, Vienna 1873.

Die Schatzkammer des allerhöchsten Kaiserhauses, von Quirin v. Leitner, Vienna 1878; 1880; 1882; 1887.

Le Trésor de la Maison impériale d'Autriche au Palais I. R. de la Bourg à Vienne, Vienna 1882.

Führer durch die Schatzkammer des a.h. Kaiserhauses, Vienna 1891—1918.

Guide to the Treasury of the Imperial House of Austria, Vienna 1896.

Guide to the Treasury of the Imperial House of Austria in the Imperial and Royal Palace in Vienna, Vienna 1900—1918.

Guide à travers le Trésor de la Maison Impériale, Vienna 1903; 1912.

Führer durch die Geistliche Schatzkammer, von Hermine Bach und Moritz Dreger, Vienna 1910; 1913.

Führer durch die Geistliche Schatzkammer, Vienna 1923—1928.

Führer durch die Weltliche Schatzkammer. Revised by Arpad Weixlgärtner, Vienna 1926—1937.

Guide to the Weltliche Schatzkammer (Treasury of the Former Imperial House of Austria), Vienna 1929; 1933.

Führer durch die Geistliche Schatzkammer. Revised by Arpad Weixlgärtner, Vienna 1929; 1932.

Guide to the Geistliche Schatzkammer (Ecclesiastical Treasury), Vienna 1930.

Katalog der Weltlichen und der Geistlichen Schatzkammer, von Hermann Fillitz, Vienna 1954; 1956; 1961.

Schatzkammer. Trésor sacré et profane, établi par Hermann Fillitz, Vienna 1956; 1963.

Schatzkammer. The crown jewels and the ecclesiastical treasure chamber, by Hermann Fillitz, Vienna 1956; 1963.

Katalog der Weltlichen und der Geistlichen Schatzkammer, the 4th and 5th editions revised by Erwin Neumann, Vienna 1968; 1971.

PUBLICATIONS ON THE TREASURY

Franz Bock, Die Kleinodien des Heiligen Römischen Reiches Deutscher Nation, Vienna 1864.

Quirin v. Leitner, Die hervorragendsten Kunstwerke der Schatzkammer des österreichischen Kaiserhauses, Vienna 1870; 1871; 1873.

Adolf Sitte, Die kaiserlich-geistliche Schatzkammer in Wien, in: Mittheilungen der k. k. Central-Commission für Erforschung und Erhaltung der Kunst- u. Historischen Denkmale XXVII, Vienna 1901.

Julius v. Schlosser, Die Schatzkammer des allerhöchsten Kaiserhauses in Wien. Dargestellt in ihren vornehmsten Denkmälern, Vienna 1918.

Julius v. Schlosser, Die deutschen Reichskleinodien, Vienna 1920.

Arpad Weixlgärtner, Die Weltliche Schatzkammer in Wien. Neue Funde und Forschungen, Jahrbuch der kunsthistorischen Sammlungen in Wien (vol. 37), new series I, Vienna 1926.

Arpad Weixlgärtner, Die Weltliche Schatzkammer in Wien. Neue Funde und Forschungen II, Jahrbuch der kunsthistorischen Sammlungen in Wien (vol. 38), new series II, Vienna 1928.

Arpad Weixlgärtner, Geschichte im Widerschein der Reichskleinodien, Baden bei Wien/ Leipzig 1938.

Georg Haupt, Die Reichsinsignien. Ihre Geschichte und Bedeutung, Leipzig (1939).

Hermann Fillitz, Die Insignien und Kleinodien des Heiligen Römischen Reiches, Vienna/ Munich 1954.

Hermann Fillitz, Die Weltliche Schatzkammer in Wien. Wandel und Gestalt einer fürstlichen Kunstsammlung. Ein Brevier, Braunschweig 1959.

Hermann Fillitz, Die Schatzkammer in Wien, Vienna/Munich 1964.

Hermann Fillitz, Die Schatzkammer in Wien. Symbole abendländischen Kaisertums, Salzburg/Vienna 1986.

BIBLIOGRAPHICAL REFERENCES

AN DER HEIDEN 1970 = R. an der Heiden, Die Porträtmalerei des Hans von Aachen, Jahrbuch 66, 1970

ANZELEWSKY 1971 = F. Anzelewsky, Albrecht Dürer. Das malerische Werk, Berlin 1971

AUER 1949 = E. M. Auer, Rudolfs-Orden, Franzens-Orden, Leopolds-Orden, in: Numismatische Zeitschrift, vol. 73, Vienna 1949

AUER 1951 = E. M. Auer, Die Ordensgarderobe. Ein Beitrag zur Geschichte der kleinen Wiener Hofdienste, in: Festschrift zur Feier des 200jährigen Bestandes des Haus-, Hof- und Staatsarchives, vol. II, Vienna 1951

AXEL-NIELSSON 1977 = G. Axel-Nielsson, Om Guldsmederna Kring Napoleon och ett arbete av Jean Baptiste Claude Odiot, in: Rösska konstslöjd museets arsbok, 1974—1976, Göteborg 1977

BAUER UND HAUPT 1976 = R. Bauer und H. Haupt, Das Kunstkammerinventar Kaiser Rudolfs II., 1607—1611, in: Jahrbuch 72 (new ser. XXXVI), 1976

BAULEZ 1977 = Ch. Baulez, La Toilette de l'impératrice Marie Louis, le Berceau du Roi de Rome et Henri Victor Roguier, in: Antologia di Belle Arti, 2, 1977

BLAUENSTEINER 1940 = K. Blauensteiner, Gérards Bildnis des Reichsgrafen Fries, in: Jahrbuch des Vereines für Geschichte der Stadt Wien 2, 1940

BULGARI 1958—1959 = C. G. Bulgari, Argentieri, Gemmari e Orafi Italiani — Parte prima, 2 vols., Rome 1958—1959

CASTELLI 1837 = L. F. Castelli, Ausführliche Beschreibung der Erbhuldigung welche dem Allerdurchlauchtigsten Großmächtigsten Herrn Herrn Ferdinand dem Ersten, Kaiser von Österreich, König von Ungarn, Böhmen, Galizien und Lodomerien, Erzherzog zu Oesterreich, von den Staenden des Erzherzogtumes Oesterreich unter der Enns am 14. Juny 1835 geleistet wird, Vienna 1837

CATALOGUE, DÜRERS VERWANDLUNG 1981/82 = Dürers Verwandlung in der Skulptur zwischen Renaissance und Barock, exhibition in the Liebighaus, Frankfurt am Main, 1981/1982

CATALOGUE, GIAMBOLOGNA 1978/79 = Giambologna 1529—1608, Ein Wendepunkt der Europäischen Plastik, exhibition in Vienna 1978/1979

CATALOGUE, MARIA THERESIA 1980 = Maria Theresia und ihre Zeit, exhibition in Vienna 1980 (G. Kugler)

CATALOGUE, MAXIMILIAN VON MEXIKO 1974 = Maximilian von Mexiko, 1832—1867, exhibition at Burg Hardegg 1974 (with bibliography)

CATALOGUE, NAPOLEON 1969 = Napoleon, exhibition in Paris 1969

CATALOGUE, NUREMBERG 1986 = Nürnberg 1300—1550, Kunst der Gotik und Renaissance, exhibition in Nuremberg and New York 1986

CATALOGUE, PORTRÄTGALERIE 1976 = Porträtgalerie zur Geschichte Österreichs von 1400 bis 1800, Vienna 1976, 2nd ed. 1982

CATALOGUE, UNIFORM UND MODE 1983 = Uniform und Mode am Kaiserhof, exhibition in Halbturn 1983

CHIAPPONI 1712 = G. Chiapponi, Legazione del Card. Gius. Renato Imperiali alla S.R.M^{ta} di Carlo III Re della Spagna l'a. 1711 descritta, Roma 1712

COHEN 1986 = D. H. Cohen, Pierre Philippe Thomire — Unternehmer und Künstler, in: H. Ottomeyer und P. Pröschel, Vergoldete Bronzen. — Die Bronzearbeiten des Spätbarock und des Klassizismus, vol. II, Munich 1986

CORNIDES 1967 = E. Cornides, Rose und Schwert im päpstlichen Zeremoniell. Wiener Dissertationen aus dem Gebiete der Geschichte, herausgegeben von Heinrich Fichtenau, Alphons Lhotsky und Erich Zöllner, No. 9, Vienna 1967

DA COSTA KAUFMANN 1985 = Th. da Costa Kaufmann, L'école de Prague, Paris 1985

DEÉR 1952 = J. Deér, Der Kaiserornat Friedrichs II., Dissertationes Bernenses II, 2, Bern 1952

DEÉR 1977 = J. Deér, Byzanz und die Herrschaftszeichen des Abendlandes, Sigmaringen 1977

DISTELBERGER 1985 = R. Distelberger, Gold und Silber, Edelsteine und Elfenbein, in: Ferdinand Seibt (ed.), Renaissance in Böhmen, Munich 1985

DISTELBERGER, The Habsburg Collection, 1985 = R. Distelberger, The Habsburg Collection in Vienna during the seventeenth Century, in: The Origins of Museums — The Cabinets of Curiosities in sixteenth and seventeenth century Europe, Oxford 1985

DREGER 1914 = M. Dreger, Baugeschichte der k. k. Hofburg in Wien bis zum XIX. Jahrhundert. Österreichische Kunsttopographie, vol. XIV, Vienna 1914

DUERLOO 1986 = L. Duerloo, Privilegies uitbeelden de Zuidnederlandse wapenkonigen en wapenkunde in de eeuw van de verlichting, Dissertation, Kathol. Universität Löwen, 1986. (On the heralds' tabards and staffs see esp. pp. 137—153).

EICHLER und KRIS 1927 = F. Eichler und E. Kris, Die Kameen im Kunsthistorischen Museum, Vienna 1927

FILLITZ 1956 = H. Fillitz, Die Insignien und Ornate des Kaisertums Österreich, in: Jahrbuch 52, 1956

FILLITZ 1957 = H. Fillitz, Zu Leonhard Kern, Neu gefundene Werke seiner Hand, in: Jahrbuch 53, 1957

FILLITZ 1969 = H. Fillitz, Ein Szepter Karls IV. Ein Beitrag zur Prager Goldschmiedekunst des 14. Jahrhunderts, in: Gotik in Böhmen, ed. by K. M. Swoboda, Munich 1969

FILLITZ 1986 = H. Fillitz, Die Schatzkammer in Wien. Symbole abendländischen Kaisertums, Salzburg/Vienna 1986

FRITZ 1966 = J. M. Fritz, Gestochene Bilder, Cologne/Graz 1966

FRITZ 1982 = J. M. Fritz, Goldschmiedekunst der Gotik in Mitteleuropa, Munich 1982

GABRIELI/SCERRATO 1979 = F. Gabrieli und U. Scerrato, Gli arabi in Italia, Milan 1979

GALL 1965 = G. Gall, Leder im Europäischen Kunsthandwerk, Braunschweig 1965

GONZALEZ-PALACIOS 1970 = A. Gonzalez-Palacios, Il Mobile Lombardo; parte seconda, in: Arte Illustrata, 3rd ann. vol. No. 25/26, Jan./Feb. 1970

GRAMBERG 1981 = W. Gramberg, Notizen zu den Kruzifixen des Guglielmo della Porta und zur Entstehungsgeschichte des Hochaltarkreuzes in S. Pietro in Vaticano, in: Münchner Jahrb. der bildenden Kunst, 3rd ser., vol. XXXII, 1981

GRIMME 1972 = E. G. Grimme, Der Aachener Domschatz, in: Aachener Kunstblätter vol. 42, 1972

GRIMSCHITZ 1926 = B. Grimschitz, François Gérards Bildnis der Kaiserin Maria Luise, in: Amicis, Jahrbuch der Österreichischen Galerie 1926

GRÖNWOLDT 1977, 1979 = R. Grönwoldt, in: Ausstellungskatalog: Die Zeit der Staufer, Stuttgart 1977, vol. 1; vol. 5, 1979

GRÜNENWALD 1969 = E. Grünenwald, Leonhard Kern, Schwäbisch-Hall 1969

HARTMANN-FRANZENSHULD 1883 = E. von Hartmann-Franzenshuld, Die Potence des Toison d'Or und ein Wappenbuch des Ordens vom Goldenen Vließe, in: Jahrbuch der k. k. Heraldischen Gesellschaft »Adler«, X, Vienna 1883

HAUCK 1974 = K. Hauck, Versuch einer Gesamtdeutung des Einhard-Kreuzes, in: Das Einhardkreuz. Vorträge und Studien der Münsteraner Diskussion zum arcus Einhardi, Göttingen 1974

HERNMARCK 1978 = C. Hernmarck, Die Kunst der europäischen Gold- und Silberschmiede von 1450—1830, Munich 1978

HONOUR 1971 = H. Honour, Goldsmiths & Silversmiths, London 1971

JAHRBUCH = Jahrbuch der kunsthistorischen Sammlungen in Wien

KÁBDEBO 1880 = H. Kábdebo, Matthäus Donner und die Geschichte der Wiener Graveur-Akademie in der ersten Periode ihres Bestandes, Vienna 1880

KARAJAN 1863 = T. G. von Karajan, Die alte Kaiserburg zu Wien von dem Jahre MD nach den Aufnahmen der k. k. Burghauptmannschaft Ludwig Montoyer, in: Berichte und Mitteilungen des Altertums-Vereines zu Wien, VI, 1863

KOHLHAUSSEN 1968 = H. Kohlhaussen, Nürnberger Goldschmiedekunst des Mittelalters und der Dürerzeit 1240 — 1540, Berlin 1968

KUGLER 1986 = G. Kugler, Die Reichskrone, 2nd ed., Vienna 1986

KÜHNEL 1956 = H. Kühnel, Forschungsergebnisse zur Geschichte der Wiener Hofburg im 16. Jahrhundert, in: Anzeiger der österreichischen Akademie der Wissenschaften — Philosophisch-Historische Klasse, 93rd ann. vol. 1956

KÜHNEL 1964 = H. Kühnel, Die Hofburg zu Wien, Vienna 1964

LARSSON 1967 = L. O. Larsson, Adrian de Vries — Adrianus Fries Hagiensis Batavus 1545—1626, Vienna/Munich 1967

LHOTSKY 1939 = A. Lhotsky, Führer durch die Burg zu Wien, I. Die Gebäude, Vienna 1939

LHOTSKY 1941—1945 = A. Lhotsky, Festschrift des Kunsthistorischen Museums zur Feier des fünfzigjährigen Bestandes. Zweiter Teil: Die Geschichte der Sammlungen, Vienna 1941—1945

LIPINSKY 1971 = A. Lipinsky, Arte Orafa a Roma: Giovanni Giardini da Forlì, in: Arte Illustrata, No. 45—46, Nov./Dec. 1971

LÖWE 1975 = R. Löwe, Die Augsburger Goldschmiedewerkstatt des Matthias Walbaum, Berlin 1975

LULLIES 1974 = R. Lullies, Zur Victoria aus Fossombrone und zu den Bienen Napoleons I., in: Mélanges Mansel, Ankara 1974

LUSCHIN VON EBENGREUTH 1899 = A. Luschin von Ebengreuth, Die ältesten Beschreibungen der kaiserlichen Schatzkammer zu Wien, in: Jahrbuch XX/2, 1899

MEISS 1967 = M. Meiss, French Painting in the time of Jean de Berry, London/New York 1967

MĚŘIČKA 1966 = V. Měřička, Orden und Auszeichnungen, Prague 1966

MĚŘIČKA 1974 = V. Měřička, Orden und Ehrenzeichen der öster.-ungar. Monarchie, Vienna/Munich 1974

MIÖG = Mitteilungen des Instituts für Österreichische Geschichtsforschung

MÖLLER 1970 = L. L. Möller, Zur Frühzeit Leonhard Kerns, in: Pantheon 28/1, 1970

NICLAUSSE 1947 = J. Niclausse, Thomire Fondeur — Ciseleur (1751—1843). Sa vie — son oeuvre, Paris 1947

OTAVSKY 1978 = K. Otavsky, in: Ausstellungskatalog: Die Parler und der schöne Stil 1350—1400. Europäische Kunst unter den Luxemburgern, vol. II, Cologne 1978

OTTOMEYER/PRÖSCHEL = H. Ottomeyer / P. Pröschel, Vergoldete Bronzen. Die Bronzearbeiten des Spätbarock und Klassizismus, 2 vols., Munich 1986

PASTOR 1930 = L. Frh. von Pastor, Geschichte der Päpste seit dem Ausgang des Mittelalters, Bd. XV, Freiburg i. Brg. 1930

PAULSEN 1989 = Å. Paulsen, Magnus Berg, Oslo 1989

PICKL v. WITKENBERG 1903 = W. Pickl von Witkenberg, Kämmerer-Almanach. Historischer Rückblick auf die Entwicklung der Kämmerer-Würde. Zusammenstellung seit Carl V. bis zur Gegenwart. Die Geschichte der Landeserbkämmerer, Vienna 1903

PLANISCIG 1924 = L. Planiscig, Die Bronzeplastiken-Statuetten, Reliefs, Geräte und Plaketten. Kunsthistorisches Museum Wien — Publikationen aus der Sammlung für Plastik und Kunstgewerbe, vol. IV, Vienna 1924

PROBSZT 1927 = G. Probszt, Friedrich von Amerling, der Altmeister der Wiener Porträtmalerei, Zurich/Leipzig/Vienna 1927

PÜCHL 1954 = A. Püchl, Die Erbhuldigungen der niederländischen Stände im 17., 18. und 19. Jahrhundert, Dissertation Vienna 1954

SCHLAGER 1850 = J. E. Schlager, Materialien zur österreichischen Kunstgeschichte (über die alten Kunstsammlungen des Kaiserlichen Hofes), in: Archiv für Kunde österreichischer Geschichtsquellen, vol. V, Vienna 1850

SCHÖNBERGER 1935/36 = G. Schönberger, Narwal-Einhorn. Studien über einen seltenen Werkstoff, in: Städel-Jahrbuch IX, 1935/36

SCHRAMM-FILLITZ 1978 = P. E.
Schramm und H. Fillitz, Denkmale der
deutschen Könige und Kaiser, Bd. II. Ein
Beitrag zur Herrschergeschichte von
Rudolf I. bis Maximilian I. 1273—1519,
Munich 1978

SCHRAMM-MÜTHERICH 1962 = P. E.
Schramm und F. Mütherich, Denkmale
der deutschen Könige und Kaiser. Ein
Beitrag zur Herrschergeschichte von Karl
dem Großen bis Friedrich II. 768—1250,
Munich 1962 (2nd ext. ed. 1981)

SCHWINEKÖPER 1981 = B. Schwineköper, Christus-Reliquien-Verehrung und
Politik, in: Blätter für Deutsche Landes-
geschichte vol. 117, 1981

SCOTT 1981 = B. Scott, An Imperial
Trousseau. The marriage of Marie-Louise
and Napoleon I., in: Country Life, 24. 12.
1981

SELING 1980 = H. Seling, Die Kunst der
Augsburger Goldschmiede 1529—1868, 3
vols., Munich 1980

SITTE 1901 = A. Sitte, Die kaiserlich geistliche Schatzkammer in Wien I—IV, in:
Mitteilungen der k. k. Central-Commission für Erforschung und Erhaltungen
der Kunst- und historischen Denkmale.
ann. vol. XXVII, new ser., Vienna 1901

SITTE 1909 = Zur Baugeschichte der kaiserlichen Hofburg in Wien, in: Berichte
und Mitteilungen des Altertums-Vereins
zu Wien, 42, 1909

STEINGRÄBER 1972 = E. Steingräber,
in: Spätmittelalter und beginnende Neuzeit, Propyläen-Kunstgeschichte vol. 7,
Berlin 1972

STRIEDER 1981 = P. Strieder, Dürer,
Königstein im T. 1981

THOMAS 1963 = Chr. Thomas, Die Wiener Weltliche Schatzkammer. Verwaltung
und Funktion: 1800—1870, diss. Vienna
1963

TIETZE CONRAT 1920/21 = E. Tietze
Conrat, Die Erfindung im Relief, in: Jahrbuch XXXV, 1920/21

WARDWELL 1988—1989 = A. E. Ward-
well, Panni tartarici: Eastern islamic silks
woven with gold and silver (13th and 14th
centuries), in: Islamic Art III 1988—1989,
pp. 95—173.

WEBER 1975 = I. Weber, Deutsche,
Niederländische und Französische Ren-
naissanceplaketten 1500—1650, Munich
1975.

WEIXLGÄRTNER 1910/11 = A. Weixlgärtner, Ungedruckte Stiche, in: Jahrbuch
XXIX, 1910/11

WEIXLGÄRTNER 1916 = A. Weixlgärtner, Anmerkungen zu drei Napoleoni-
schen Gegenständen in der Wiener Kaiserlichen Schatzkammer, in: Kunst und
Kunsthandwerk XIX, 1916

WEIXLGÄRTNER 1926 = A. Weixlgärt-
ner, Die Weltliche Schatzkammer in
Wien. Neue Funde und Forschungen, in:
Jahrbuch, new ser. I, 1926

WEIXLGÄRTNER 1928 = A. Weixlgärtner, Die Weltliche Schatzkammer in
Wien. Neue Funde und Forschungen II,
in: Jahrbuch, new ser. II, 1928

WEIXLGÄRTNER 1938 = A. Weixlgärtner, Geschichte im Widerschein der
Reichskleinodien, Baden bei Wien/Leip-
zig 1938

WILCKENS 1987 = L. v. Wilckens, Zur
kunstgeschichtlichen Einordnung der
Bamberger Textilfunde, in: Textile Grab-
funde zur Sepultur des Bamberger Dom-
kapitels, Intern. Kolloquium, Schloß
Seehof 1985, Arbeitsheft 33, Bavar.
Regional office for the Preservation of
Historical Monuments, 1987, pp. 62—79.

WILD 1982 = B. Wild, Der Goldschmied
Joseph Moser und die Wiener Goldschmiedekunst des 18. Jahrhunderts,
typescr. diss. Vienna 1982

ZENNER 1856 = F. Zenner, Die k. k.
geistliche Schatzkammer, Vienna 1856

ZIMMERMANN 1883 = H. Zimmermann, Urkunden und Regesten aus dem
k. u. k. Haus-, Hof- und Staatsarchiv in
Wien, in: Jahrbuch I/2, 1883

ZIMMERMANN 1889 = H. Zimmer-
mann, Inventare, Acten und Regesten aus
der Schatzkammer des Allerhöchsten
Kaiserhauses, in: Jahrbuch X/2, 1889

ZOLGER 1917 = J. von Zolger, Der
Hofstaat des Hauses Österreich. Wiener
Staatswissenschaftliche Studien, Vienna/
Leipzig 1917